THE VEGAN
TRAVEL
GUIDE

UK AND
SOUTHERN
IRELAND

First published May 1998

© The Vegan Society

ISBN 0 907337 22 8

Design by Taylor McKenzie
58 Charlotte Road, London

Printed on recycled paper by
Litho Techniques (Kenley) Ltd
46–50 Godstone Road
Whyteleafe, Surrey

Published by The Vegan Society
Donald Watson House
7 Battle Road
St Leonards-on-Sea
East Sussex TN37 7AA
United Kingdom
(Tel 01424 427393)

EXCLUSIVELY VEGAN QUICK REFERENCE GUIDE

ENGLAND

Places to Stay

CORNWALL Bodmin Middle Rylands *17*

CORNWALL St Ives Making Waves Vegan Guest House *20*

CUMBRIA Kendal Fox Cottage/ (Fox Hall) *25*

DEVON Lydford The Sanctuary *38*

NORFOLK Worstead Barwick, Dick *111*

SOMERSET Chard Ashanika Sanctuary *131*

SOMERSET Glastonbury Arcturus B&B *132*

Places to Eat

AVON Bristol Kebele Community Project *11*

LONDON N22 Popcorn in the Park *88*

LONDON NW1 & SW3 VEG *88, 92*

MANCHESTER Unicorn Grocery *103*

NOTTINGHAM Rainbow Centre Canteen *125*

NOTTINGHAM Salamander Restaurant *125*

WEST MIDLANDS Birmingham One Earth Shop *148*

WEST YORKSHIRE Bradford Cocobana Restaurant & Club *155*

WALES

Places to Stay

CLWYD Mold Bron Afon *164*

Places to Eat

GWYNEDD Porthmadog Vegonia Wholefoods *168*

SCOTLAND

Places to Stay

HIGHLANDS Wester Ross Taigh na Mara *193*

Places to Eat

ABERDEENSHIRE Huntly Borve Brewery *181*

SOUTHERN IRELAND

Places to Stay

COUNTY CORK Bantry Trawnamadree *211*

SPECIAL INTEREST

Bicycle Beano *231*
Vegan Camp *234*
Vegan Summer Gathering *234*

🐕	animals welcome
♀	bar
Beds	bedrooms
🏃	children welcome
Cc	credit cards accepted
✗	children's portions available
♿	disabled access
🚭	non smoking
P	vegans catered for with prior notice only
pp	per person
V	vegetarian business
VEGAN	vegan business
VS	Vegan Society

Business addresses and contact details are followed by the type of business (**bold**) and then types of cuisine.

Unless marked with **P**, all businesses listed have stated that they are able to cater for vegans *without* prior notice.

To qualify for a Vegan Society members' discount at participating businesses (any restrictions appear in *italics*), you will need to produce your Vegan Society membership card. (Note: *To join the Vegan Society, simply complete the **MEMBERSHIP APPLICATION** form on page 256.*)

GUIDELINES

• Although, as far as is practical, the publisher has taken care to ensure the accuracy and reliability of information supplied to it, the reader should bear in mind that the facilities and services described may vary according to demand, and the understanding and diligence of the businesses' staff. The vigilant reader always confirms the accuracy of the information provided before making a booking or placing an order. (Note: *A current errata slip for this publication may be obtained by sending an SAE marked 'VTG Errata' to:* The Vegan Society, Donald Watson House, 7 Battle Road, St Leonards-on-Sea, East Sussex TN37 7AA.)

• The absence of an (apparently) vegan-friendly business does not necessarily mean it does not meet the Vegan Society's **VEGAN FOOD CRITERIA** *(page 237)* or does not adhere to the **GUIDELINES FOR FEEDING AND ACCOMMODATING VEGANS** *(page 240)*. Despite a reminder, some businesses known to cater for, or accommodate vegans failed to supply the information requested.

• In order to make effective use of this *guide*, it is suggested that the new reader familiarises him/herself with the location of the **KEY** *(page iii)* and **CONTENTS** *(page i)* — and, at least initially, regularly consults the **INDEX** *(page 244)*.

• The publisher may have edited (for brevity or clarity) the descriptions accompanying the businesses listed.

• If you do not wish to patronise businesses with either domestic and/or farm animals, you are advised to check with your chosen business before visiting or making a booking. (Note: *Future editions of the* **Vegan Travel Guide** *will contain this information.*)

• The inclusion of businesses providing accommodation and/or food should not be construed as constituting official Vegan Society approval for the businesses listed. The sole requirement for inclusion in the *Vegan Travel Guide* is a signed declaration that the business is able to accommodate, or cater for vegans, and that the information supplied to the Society is correct.

Photos From 4

A Vegan Travel Guide? Brilliant idea! Hands up those of you who have wearily trod the streets in a hunger-induced daze, praying that a vegan-friendly eaterie lies just around the next corner, only to find yourself, two hours later, back at the less-than-inviting chippie? Or perhaps you've been forced to alter your dream holiday plans because that Area of Outstanding Natural Beauty you always wanted to visit doubles up as an AALVA — Area Apparently Lacking Vegan Accommodation?

It's not fair is it? All we want to do is get out and eat a bit, drink a bit (OK, perhaps a lot!), holiday a bit, and kip a bit — in the knowledge that none of our animal chums has given up its life, secretions or body parts to help us do it. Yet, more often than not when away from home, we find ourselves struggling to maintain our animal-free credentials. Lucky for us then, that those nice Vegan Society people have, once again, come to our rescue with this, the very first (and *very* welcome) edition of the **Vegan Travel Guide (UK & Southern Ireland)**.

So, arm yourself with this useful little book and, with a new-found confidence and sense of optimism, go forth and sample all the vegan eats, treats, adventures and springy mattresses the businesses listed in the following pages have to offer. Who knows? Perhaps I'll see you there!

Wendy Turner

Wendy Turner

Presenter of *Absolutely Animals* and *Pet Rescue*

INTRODUCTION

Welcome to the first edition of the *Vegan Travel Guide* — intended to be a regularly-published *guide* to businesses in the UK and Southern Ireland able to accommodate, or cater for vegans. Its publisher, the Vegan Society — an educational charity — has encouraged the provision of animal-free services and products to vegans, and others, since its inception in 1944. The Society's last travel guide was published way back in 1988 — so some of you have been exceptionally patient!

There is no doubt it *is* becoming easier to eat out as a vegan, but the less-than-adequate provision in much of the geographical area covered by this guide means that many of us are constantly struggling to maintain a 'normal' social life and not feel marginalised from mainstream society. Not that it is just vegans who suffer similar dietary limitations — to a lesser degree, vegetarians and the dairy-intolerant will benefit from the information contained within the following pages.

But, as the song goes, 'Things can only get better'. In the last few decades the Society has seen a dramatic growth of interest in the animal rights, vegetarian/vegan and green movements — as well as health, diet, nutrition and food safety issues. As the accommodation and catering industries respond to this increasing demand for animal-free food and services, it *will* continue to get less problematic to practise one's lifestyle preferences outside the home — and it shouldn't prove too difficult to force the pace. The 1997 Realeat/Gallup survey into Meat-Eating and Vegetarianism puts the number of vegans in the UK at around 224 000 — nearly $\frac{1}{4}$ million. Just think of the 'vegan food maximising potential' of each vegan popping into their nearest eateries or guest houses to ask if the establishment obliges vegans! If they show interest, leave photocopies of **VEGAN FOOD CRITERIA** *(see page 237)* or **GUIDELINES FOR FEEDING AND ACCOMMODATING VEGANS** *(see page 240)*, or simply put them in touch with the Vegan Society.

And don't forget: if a business is currently vegan-unfriendly, point out the economic sense of catering for vegans — that they'll automatically be meeting the needs of vegetarians at the same time!

ACKNOWLEDGEMENTS

This first edition of the *Vegan Travel Guide* would not have been possible without the leads provided by readers of *The Vegan* magazine, and the substantial and invaluable contributions given, on a voluntary basis, by Amanda Rofe and Eileen Hardy.

LOOKING AHEAD . . .

Research for the *Vegan Travel Guide* is an ongoing process and the Vegan Society needs your involvement! If you discover a business able to accommodate, or cater for vegans, and you cannot find it in this edition, please share your finding by contacting us at: *The Vegan Society, Donald Watson House, 7 Battle Road, St Leonards-on-Sea, East Sussex TN37 7AA* Tel 01424 427393; Fax 01424 717064; e-mail **info@vegansociety.com**.

To keep up-to-date with new businesses accommodating, or catering for vegans why not subscribe to *The Vegan* magazine? Each issue contains display and classified advertisements placed by such businesses. Contact the address above for details.

AND FINALLY . . .

When contacting any of the businesses appearing in the *Vegan Travel Guide*, please take a moment to mention where you saw their details. This will help ensure their continued co-operation with us for future editions. Thank you!

Travel well. Eat well. Sleep well.

3

4

England

AVON

Places to Stay

BATH

ALBANY GUEST HOUSE, THE
24 Crescent Gardens, Bath, Avon
BA1 2NB
Tel 01225 313339
Guesthouse
Traditional British
*A cheerful Victorian home offering
first class friendly service. Comfortable
well decorated rooms and a homely
unpretentious atmosphere. Very oblig-
ing and keen to cater to guests'
requirements. Vegan margarine and
soya milk always available. Private
parking.*
P 医 ⊁
Typical tariff single/double room
£19.22/£32 Beds 4 Open all year
except Xmas

APSLEY HOUSE HOTEL
Newbridge Hill, Bath, Avon BA1 3PT
Tel 01225 336966 Fax 01225 425462
Email apsleyhouse@easynet.co.uk
Website
http://www.gratton.co.uk/apsley
B&B Hotel
Traditional British
*An elegant Georgian country house
built for the Duke of Wellington in
1830 and set in its own charming gar-
den. The interior includes many period
features including original oil paint-
ings. Guests are offered a very warm*
welcome and personal care.
♀ 医 (5 yrs+) Cc ⊁ (areas)
Typical tariff single/double room
£45/£55 Beds 9 Open all year except
Xmas
VS members' discount 10% except
Bank Hols

BATH SPA HOTEL
Sydney Road, Bath, Avon BA2 6JF
Tel 01225 444424 Fax 01225 444006
Email fivestar@bathspa.u-net.com
Website
http://www.bathspahotel.com
Hotel Restaurant
A la Carte French Italian/Mediter-
ranean
Traditional British
*Past winner of The Caterer and Hotel-
keeper and the RAC Hotel of the Year
awards. A range of meeting and conference rooms, indoor pool, jacuzzi,
saunas, gymnasium, solarium and tennis court. Only 10 minutes from the
city centre.*
🐕 ♀ 医 Cc ✗ ⊁ ઠ (Public
entrance/designated parking
area/one bedroom, bathroom & WC
on same level/dining room/restau-
rant/bar/TV lounge)
Typical tariff single/double room
£129/£159 Beds 98 Open 24 hours
Typical tariff 3 course meal £35 Seats
140 Open: Alresco Restaurant
12pm–2pm & 6.30pm–10pm; Vellore
Restaurant 12pm–2pm & 7pm–10pm
Sun

PLAINE GUEST HOUSE, THE
Norton St Philip, nr Bath, Avon
BA3 6LE

Tel 01373 834723 Fax 01373 834101
Guesthouse
Traditional British
圭 Cc ᵇ⊁ ᵹ (public entrance/one
bedroom, bathroom & WC on same
level/dining room/TV lounge)
Typical tariff single/double room
£40/£55 Beds 3 Open all year *except
Xmas & Boxing Day*

SERENDIPITY
19f Bradford Road, Winsley, nr Bath,
Avon BA15 2HW
Tel 01225 722380
B&B
*A beautiful bungalow set in its own
grounds with lovely gardens and near
a river/canal. Only 5 miles from Bath
and 2 miles from Bradford on Avon. A
charming peaceful village, good for
walking and cycling. Luxury bedrooms. Plenty of parking. Friendly
hosts.*
P 圭 ᵇ⊁ ᵹ (public entrance/desig-
nated parking area/one bedroom,
bathroom & WC on same level/dining
room/restaurant)
Typical tariff single/double room
£29/£39 Beds 3 Open all year
VS members' discount 10% *Oct–Apr*

WELLSGATE
131 Wells Road, Bath, Avon BA2 3AN
Tel 01225 310688 Fax 01225 310143
Guesthouse
*Only 10 minutes from the centre of
Bath. Well appointed rooms, welcome
tray, garage at rear and garden.
Panoramic views. Warm welcome. ETB
3 crowns.*
P 圭 Cc ᵇ⊁

Typical tariff single/double room
£28/£47 Beds 3 Open all year *except
Xmas*
VS members' discount 5%

BRISTOL

BASCA HOUSE
19 Broadway Road, Bishopston,
Bristol, Avon BS7 8ES
Tel 0117 942 2182
B&B
*Elegant Victorian home restored to a
high standard and offering a warm
and friendly atmosphere. Quiet residential area adjacent to the A38. Only
1 mile from the city centre. Easy parking. Facilities include central heating
throughout plus colour TVs, tea/cof-
fee making and ironing facilities. ETB
1 crown commended.*
P 圭 ᵇ⊁
Typical tariff single/double room
from £19/£38 Beds 4 Open all year
except Xmas & New Year

Places to Eat

BATH

BATH SPA HOTEL
See page 6.

BATHTUB BISTRO
2 Grove Street, Bath, Avon, BA2 6PJ
Tel 01225 460599
Bistro
Chinese French
Italian/Mediterranean Mexican
Spanish Thai Traditional British
A relaxed and informal bistro with

seating in three rooms, serving high quality food at good prices. Food for carnivores is given equal billing but scrupulous hygiene adhered to in preparing and serving dishes for vegans and vegetarians.
🏠 Cc ♿ (public entrance/dining area)
Typical 3 course meal £13 Seats 65
Open 6pm–11pm Mon–Fri;
12pm–2.30pm Tues–Fri; 12pm–11pm
Sat & Sun

CAFFE UNO
The Empire, Grand Parade, Bath,
Avon BA2 4DF
Tel 01225 461140 Fax 01225 462912
Cafe Restaurant Take away
A la Carte Fast Food
Italian/Mediterranean
One of 40 restaurants in a chain owned by City Centre and offering an extensive menu of high quality food freshly prepared each day. The menu includes a wide range of vegetarian and some vegan dishes. High chairs available for children.
🏠 Cc ⛽ ♿ (public entrance/dining area)
Typical 3 course meal £12 Seats 84
Open 10am–11pm

CIRCUS
34 Brock Street, Bath, Avon BA1 2LN
Tel 01225 318918 Fax 01225 318918
Restaurant
A la Carte French Traditional British
An intimate stylish restaurant amidst Georgian splendour with classical music and candles. Excellent cuisine from a varied menu. Special set priced dinners from Monday to Thursday.

Traditional Sunday lunch. "The Circus — always a good choice."
Cc ♿ (public entrance/designated parking area/dining area/bar)
Typical 3 course meal £20 Seats 70
Open Mon–Sun for lunch & dinner

DEMUTH'S
2 North Parade Passage, Bath, Avon
Tel 01225 446059
Website
http://www.gold.net/users/amo3/demuth.html
Restaurant
International Organic Snacks/Drinks
Bath's only licensed vegetarian eating place with a great choice of vegan dishes. Organic wines suitable for vegans available.
V Cc ✗ ⛽
Typical 3 course meal £12–£15 Seats 40 Open 10am–10pm Sun–Fri;
9am–11pm Sat
VS members' discount 10%

GREEN PARK BRASSERIE
Green Park Station, Green Park, Bath,
Avon BA1 2JB
Tel 01225 338565 Fax 01225 460675
Cafe Restaurant
A la Carte French Snacks/Drinks
Quality fresh food prepared on the premises and served informally in a friendly ambience. Live jazz at a reasonable volume Wednesday to Saturday evenings. Free parking under the old station roof. Egon Ronay recommended 1992–7.
🏠 Cc ⛽ ♿ (public entrance/designated parking area/dining area/bar/not toilets)

Typical 3 course meal £13.50 Seats 100 Open 10am–11pm Tues–Sat

PORTER, THE

2 Miles Buildings, Bath, Avon
BA1 2QS
Tel 01225 424104
Fax 01225 404447
Email moles@moles.co.uk
Website
http://www.moles.co.uk/moles/
Public House
Fast Food French
Italian/Mediterranean Snacks/Drinks
*A busy pub in Bath city centre.
Open all day serving a vegetarian
menu at lunch times. A wide range
of customers from tourists to
students.*
V (menu) 🍺 🏛 ✗
Seats 36 Open 11am–11pm Mon–Fri;
12pm–10.30pm Sun

PUPPET THEATRE CAFE

Riverside Walk, 17 Argyle Street,
Bath, Avon BA2 4AY
Tel 01225 480532
Cafe
Snacks/Drinks
*Situated by the river overlooking the
weir. Serving a wide variety of vege-
tarian food with fresh fruity salads.
Vegetarian breakfasts are available
until midday. A combination of rea-
sonably priced fresh food in beautiful
surroundings.*
V Cc ✗
Typical 3 course meal £7.50 Seats 57
Open 8.30am–5.30pm Mon–Fri;
8am–5.30pm Sat–Sun; *later opening
in summer*

RASCALS BISTRO

8 Pierrepont Place, Bath, Avon
BA1 1JA
Tel 01225 330201 Fax 01225 330201
Bistro Restaurant
A la Carte Chinese French Indian
Italian/Mediterranean Mexican
Snacks/Drinks Spanish Thai
Traditional British
*Situated in the converted cellars of
two town houses. A cool, laid back
atmosphere to accompany award win-
ning cuisine. "Brilliant. Highly recom-
mended."*
🏛 **Cc** (not American Express/Diners)
🍴 (areas)
Typical 3 course meal £6.95–£15
Seats 70 Open 11.30am–2.30pm
Mon–Sat; 6pm–10.30pm Mon–Fri &
Sun; 6pm–11pm Sat

SALLY LUNN'S REFRESHMENT HOUSE

6 North Parade Passage, Bath, Avon
BA1 1NX
Tel 01225 461634 Fax 01225 447090
Restaurant Take Away Tea Rooms
Traditional British
*Relax in the homely atmosphere of
the oldest house in Bath where Sally
Lunn came in the 1680s and estab-
lished her baking as a favourite of
fashionable society. Coffee, tea and
light meals are served during the day.
In the evening the restaurant provides
a delightful candlelit atmosphere.
Booking advised.*
P Cc ✗
Typical 3 course meal £8.50–£12
Seats 60 Open 10am–6pm Mon–Sat;
12pm–6pm Sun; 6pm–11pm Mon–Sun

SCOFFS WHOLEFOOD CAFE
19–20 Kingsmede Square, Bath, Avon
Tel 01225 462483
Bakery Cafe Take Away
Fast Food Organic Snacks/Drinks
Wholefood
A wholefood cafe with a bakery stocking a wide range of organic and non-organic breads. Offers freshly prepared dishes on a daily basis. Selection of vegan foods always available.
V ₪✖
Typical 1 course meal £2.90 Seats 30
Open 8am–8pm

BRISTOL

ARCHES HOTEL
123 Cotham Brow, Cotham, Bristol,
Avon BS6 6AE
Tel 0117 924 7398 Fax 0117 924
7398
B&B
A small, friendly, private hotel close to central stations and 100 yds from the A38. Tariff includes 5 choices of vegetarian and vegan cooked breakfasts. Evening meals are not served but there are several good vegetarian restaurants in the area.
🐾 🏛 ₪✖
Typical tariff single/double room
£22.50/£39.50 Beds 9 Open all year
except Xmas & New Year

BOUBOULINA'S RESTAURANT
9 Portland Street, Clifton, Bristol,
Avon BS8 4LY
Tel 0117 973 1192/742833
Fax 0117 973 8387

Email kerry@saqnet.co.uk
Restaurant
Greek/Mediterranean
A family-run Greek restaurant specialising in Mezedes. Organic pulses and vegetables used when available. Set meals plus a la carte menu. Bring your own wine or use the fully licensed bar. Emphasis on good healthy Mediterranean-style cooking. Lively atmosphere. Plate smashing and Greek dancing optional!
Cc ✖ ₪✖ ♿ (public entrance/dining area/bar)
Typical 3 course meal £12.95 Seats
100 Open 12pm–11pm Tues–Sat;
5pm–11.30pm Sun–Mon

BRISTOLIAN CAFE, THE
2 Picton Street, Montpelier, Bristol,
Avon BS18 9LE
Tel 01179 422233
Cafe
American French Indian
Italian/Mediterranean
Cobbled courtyard, indoor garden and fountain. Large choice of vegetarian and vegan breakfasts. Soya milk cappuchino, hot chocolate, etc. Homemade humous, baked potatoes, cakes, salads, fruit juices, soups and herb teas. Spiritual books, incense and tapes for sale. Waitress service.
V ₪✖
Typical 3 course meal £7 Seats 35
Open 8.15am–6pm Mon–Fri;
10am–6pm Sat–Sun

CAFE TASCA
12 York Road, Montpelier, Bristol,
Avon BS6 5QE

Tel 0117 942 6799
Cafe Restaurant
Portuguese Traditional British
A very busy lively cafe in the heart of Montpelier serving a wide variety of food from breakfasts to crepes or Portguese specialities. Two to three vegan choices always available.
🏛 ✕
Typical 3 course meal £8 Seats 36
Open 9.15am–4.30pm Mon–Thurs & Sun; 9.15am–9.30pm Fri & Sat

FRIARY CAFE
9 Cotham Hill, Bristol, Avon BS6 6LD
Tel 0117 973 3664
Cafe
Fast Food Snacks/Drinks
Traditional British
A traditional cafe with liquor licence. Serving a wide range of homemade dinners including vegetarian and vegan dishes. Child friendly. No smoking in basement.
🏛 ✕ ⤬
Typical 3 course meal £7 Seats 52
Open 9am–8pm Mon–Sat; 10am–8pm Sun & Bank Hols

GLASNOST
1 William Street, Totterdown, Bristol, Avon BS3 4TU
Tel 0117 972 0938 Fax 0117 972 0938
Restaurant
Continental French
Italian/Mediterranean Spanish
Busy residential restaurant close to the City with ample parking. 40% of food is vegetarian. Vegans and special diets are catered for with 24 hours notice.

P Cc ✕ ♿ (public entrance/dining area)
Typical 3 course meal £12.99 Seats 60
Open 6.30pm–10pm Tues–Sat
VS members' discount 10%
Tues–Thurs nights

KEBELE COMMUNITY PROJECT
14 Robertson Road, Bristol, Avon BS5
Tel 0117 939 9469
Squat Cafe
International Organic
Began as a meeting point for different activists and campaigners. Exhibitions, talks, bike workshops, alternative library, children's workshop as well as a vegan cafe. Non-profit making.
After 2 years and a threat of eviction from Lloyds Bank, considering setting up a co-op to carry on.
🐕 🏛 ✕ ♿
Typical 3 course meal £donations only
Seats 25–30
VEGAN

PUSHPANJLI VEGETARIAN RESTAURANT
217a Gloucester Road, Horfield, Bristol, Avon BS7 8NN
Tel 0117 924 0493 Fax 0117 924 0493
Restaurant Take Away
Indian
Family-owned and run during the last 15 years, serving vegetarian Gujarati Indian food. Great value 'eat as much as you like' for £6.95. Some take away food.
V Cc ⤬
Typical 3 course meal £10.15 Seats 60

Open 12pm–2pm & 6pm–10pm
Mon–Sat

ROYCE ROLLS WHOLEFOOD
Corn Exchange, St Nicholas Market,
Bristol, Avon BS1 1JQ
Tel 0117 982 4228 Fax 0117 982
4228
Cafe Take Away
Fast Food Snacks/Drinks
*Bristol's oldest vegetarian take away
and cafe. Own special recipe rolls
voted best rolls in town with vast
choice for fillings. Huge range of
savoury foods each day eg fresh
samosas. Lots of cakes and flapjacks.
Own blend coffee and range of tea
infusions. Wide range of music.
Relaxed atmosphere.*
V ✳
Seats 20 Open 7.30am–4pm
Mon–Fri; 9.30am–4pm Sat

WILD OATS
9–11 Lower Redland Road, Bristol,
Avon BS6 6TB
Tel 0117 973 1967 Fax 0117 973 1967
Email wild_oats@compuserve.com
Health Food Shop Take Away
*Natural foods shop featuring a wide
range of vegan take away foods,
ready meals, books, supplements and
dairy alternatives.*
V

BEDFORDSHIRE
Places to Stay

SILSOE

OLD GEORGE HOTEL, THE
High Street, Silsoe, Bedfordshire
MK45 4EP
Tel 01525 860218
Hotel Public House Restaurant
A la Carte
*Originally an old coaching inn. Full a la
carte menu in the restaurant. Bar
snacks also available. A large garden
with children's area. Peaceful area
near to Wrest Park.*
*Note: Garden contains a "small ani-
mal zoo".*
⏛ 🛏 Cc ✗
Typical tariff single/double room
£32/£48 Beds 7 Open 11am–11pm
Typical 3 course meal £15 Seats 60
Open 12pm–2.30pm & 7pm–9.30pm

Places to Eat

SILSOE

OLD GEORGE HOTEL, THE
See above.

BERKSHIRE
Places to Stay

MAIDENHEAD

**LIONEL BRADFORD TENNIS &
SWIMMING ACADEMY**
See **SPECIAL INTEREST**, page 228.

Places to Eat

READING

CAFE IGUANA
11 St Mary's Butts,
Reading, Berkshire RG1 2LN
Tel 01734 581357
Cafe Cocktail Bar Restaurant
Italian/Mediterranean
Japanese Lebanese
Mexican Organic
Spanish Thai
*Chill out at the Cafe Iguana and enjoy
fair-traded tea, coffee, fruit teas,
organic expresso coffee, etc. All wine
is organic and some are specifically
suitable for vegans.*
V Cc ♿ (public entrance/dining area)
Typical 3 course meal £10 Seats 40
Open 11am–11pm Mon–Sat

CAMBRIDGESHIRE
Places to Stay

CAMBRIDGE

EAGLE, DILYS
87 Mawson Road, Cambridge CB1 2DZ
Tel 01223 367399
B&B
*A small, elegant establishment situ-
ated in a quiet road about 15 minutes
walk from Cambridge town centre.
Good quality food including many
homemade breads, jams, etc.*
P 🍽
Typical tariff single/double room
£25/£48 Beds 2

DYKELANDS GUEST HOUSE
157 Mowbray Road, Cambridge
CB1 4SP
Tel 01223 244300 Fax 01223 566746
Guesthouse
*Homely guesthouse only 1.75 miles
from historic city centre. Spacious
rooms, most with showers and toilets.
Lounge and garden for use by guests.
Parking available.*
P 🐎 📺 **Cc** ♿ (public entrance/one
bedroom, bathroom & WC on same
level/dining room)
Typical tariff single/double room
£23.50/£39.50 Beds 9 Open all year

ELY

CATHEDRAL HOUSE
17 St Mary's Street, Ely,
Cambridgeshire CB7 4ER

Tel 01353 662124
B&B
Traditional British
Mid 1800s Georgian style house. All rooms furnished individually with period look and well equipped with tea/coffee making facilities, TV, own luxury bathroom and cast iron bath. Delightful walled garden viewed from all rooms — including dining room where guests breakfast around a farmhouse table.
P ⌕✖
Typical tariff single/double room from £33/£50 Beds 3

Places to Eat

CAMBRIDGE

RAINBOW VEGETARIAN BISTRO
9a Kings Parade, Cambridge CB2 1SJ
Tel 01223 321551
Bistro Cafe Restaurant
International
All food made on the premises. Vegan organic wine and beer available. Specialises in food allergies. Many regular vegan customers.
V ✖ ⌕✖ ර (public entrance, dining area)
Typical 3 course meal £10 Seats 52
Open 9am–9pm Mon–Sun

CHESHIRE
Places to Stay

CHESTER

GREEN BOUGH HOTEL, THE
60 Hoole Road, Chester Cheshire
CH2 3NL
Tel 01244 326241 Fax 01244 326265
Hotel
Chinese French Indian
Traditional British
Impeccably maintained Victorian hotel furnished with antiques on Victoriana. Individually designed ensuite bedrooms. Hospitality and quality to the highest order. Fleur de Lys Restaurant produces excellent cuisine.
♀ 氡 Cc ✖ ⌕✖ ර (public entrance/designated parking area/one bedroom, bathroom & WC on same level/dining room/restaurant/bar/TV lounge)
Typical tariff single/double room £35/£60 Beds 20
Typical 3 course meal £12.75 Seats 36
Open 7pm–9pm Mon–Sat

NANTWICH

RED COW, THE
Beam Street, Nantwich, Cheshire
CW5 5NF
Tel 01270 628581 Fax 01270 628581
B&B Public House
A la Carte Snacks/Drinks
Traditional British
A grade I listed farmhouse which

Rainbow Vegetarian Bistro

9A KINGS PARADE, CAMBRIDGE

(Opposite Kings College Gates)

Tel: 01223 321551

RAINBOW is unique in Cambridge serving only vegetarian, vegan and gluten free food. Everything is freshly made daily on the premises, from natural ingredients without additives, colourings or flavourings. For those with food intolerances we can state every ingredient and our famous home-made soups are made without added stock. A non-dairy spread is used for herb and garlic 'butter' and sandwiches and as much of our supplies as is possible are organic.

Swedish Glace Ice Cream is made from soy and is therefore vegan as well as being low cholesterol and low in fat. All wines, beers, and ciders are vegan, and ecologically produced without the usual additives which can cause allergy and intolerance problems.

Children and babies are made welcome and we can provide highchairs and other baby items, half portions are available on request. The dressing on the tables is vegan, made with grain mustard.

The menu is marked throughout with symbols:
V = Vegan, G = Gluten free, N = Nuts are included with this item

Throughout the menu when butter is included, we can substitute non-dairy spread or soya milk for drinks, and substitutes are available for gluten free diets, please ask if you require special assistance!

Daily "Specials" are displayed on the boards throughout the Restaurant and under the table top. We endeavour to produce something different at lunchtime and in the evening.

became a public house in the 17th century. Log fires plus vegetarian and vegan food. Run by Nick & Libby Casson who were featured in the Sunday Observer for their vegetarian food.

🐾 ♀ 🏛 🐾 (areas) ♿ (public entrance/designated parking area/dining room/bar/TV lounge)
Typical tariff single/double room £19.50/£38 Beds 3 Open 11.30am–3pm & 5pm–11pm Mon–Thurs; 11.30am–11pm Fri–Sat; 12pm–3pm & 7pm–10.30pm Sun
Typical 3 course meal £9.75 Seats 48

ROOKERY HALL HOTEL & RESTAURANT
nr Worleston, Nantwich, Cheshire CW5 6DQ
Tel 01270 610016
Fax 01270 626027
Hotel Restaurant
French Italian/Mediterranean Organic Snacks/Drinks Traditional British
Built in 1816 and later modified by Baron von Schroder. Many guest rooms overlook the gardens and all rooms are ensuite and opulently furnished with generous sized beds. Splendid staircase and dining room. Within easy reach of the M6 and major airports.
♀ 🏛 Cc 🐾 ♿ (public entrance/designated parking area/one bedroom, bathroom & WC on same level/dining room/restaurant/bar/TV lounge)
Typical tariff single/double room £120/£165 Beds 45 Open all year
VS members' discount 10%

Places to Eat

NANTWICH

RED COW, THE
See page 14.

STOCKPORT

LOWRY'S
15 Lower Hillgate, Stockport, Cheshire SK1 1JO
Tel 0161 474 7770
Bistro Cafe Restaurant Sandwich Bar Take Away
International
A small family-run restaurant in the historic port of Stockport.
♀ 🏛 Cc ♿ (public entrance/designated parking area/dining area/bar)
Typical 3 course meal £8.10 Seats 36 Open 9am–4pm Mon–Sat

WILMSLOW

ALCAZAR RESTAURANT
102 Waterlane, Wilmslow, Cheshire SK9 5DB
Tel 01625 526855
Restaurant
Armenian Middle Eastern
A friendly welcoming family-run business offering authentic Middle Eastern cuisine. Excellent selection of vegan and vegetarian dishes available. Ideal for romantic dinners through to business parties. Fixed price menu for group bookings of parties larger than 8.
Cc ✗ ♿ (public entrance/dining

area/bar)
Typical 3 course meal £16 Seats 50
Open Mon–Fri 12pm–2.30pm &
6.30pm–10.30pm; Sat
6.30pm–10.30pm

CLEVELAND
Places to Eat

MIDDLESBROUGH

ELIANO'S BRASSERIE
20–22 Fairbridge Street,
Middlesbrough, Cleveland TS1 5DJ
Tel 01642 868566/868568 Fax 01642
220484
Bistro
A la Carte French
Italian/Mediterranean
*A warm, friendly, family-run bistro
specialising in Italian and French cui-
sine. Menu changes daily. "Good
food, great place and fine people."*
P Cc ✕ ⊭ ⅍ (public entrance/desig-
nated parking area/dining area/bar)
Typical 3 course meal £18 Seats 60
Open Mon–Thurs 12pm–2pm & 5pm–
–10pm; Fri–Sat 12pm–2pm &
5pm–11pm
VS members' discount 5%

COUNTY DURHAM
Places to Eat

BARNARD CASTLE

33 NEWCATE GUEST HOUSE
33 Newcate, Barnard Castle, County
Durham DL12 8NJ
Tel 01833 690208
Email peter.whittaker@indirect.co.uk
B&B Guesthouse
Organic Traditional British
*A warm welcome to a lovely old
house in peaceful surroundings with
large beautiful garden. Children's
play facilities in garden. Food is
always prepared from locally sourced
ingredients. When in season, fruit
and vegetables from own garden.
Happy to respond to individual
requirements.*
P ⊡ ✕ ⊭
Typical tariff single/double room
£18/£36 Beds 1 Open all year
Typical 3 course meal £10.50 Seats
2–5 Open evening meal to suit
guests

CORNWALL
Places to Stay

BODMIN

MIDDLE RYLANDS
Redmoor, nr Bodmin, Cornwall,
PL30 5AR

Tel 01208 872316 Fax 01208 872316
B&B
*A cottage situated near Bodmin.
Charming wildlife garden with pond,
ducks and geese. Quiet country loca-
tion central to all coasts and moors.
Near Red Moor, Plyn and Breney
Nature Reserves. Ensuite facilities,
colour TV and 'kettle'. Substantial
cooked breakfast.*
VEGAN 🐾 ᵇ✖
Typical tariff double room £18pp
Beds 2

HELSTON

LANHERNE VEGETARIAN
& VEGAN B&B
Meaver Road, Mullion, Helston,
Cornwall TR12 7DN
Tel 01326 241381
Fax 01326 240662
B&B
*Situated close to the village and only
5 minutes from picturesque Mullion
Cove. Explore the beautiful Lizard
Peninsular, an Area of Outstanding
Natural Beauty or visit the beautiful
beaches. Plenty of attractions for rainy
days. Delicious breakfasts. Family
atmosphere.*
V 🏛 ᵇ✖
Typical tariff double room £17.50pp
Beds 2 Open all year

ISLES OF SCILLY

GLANDORE GUEST HOUSE
Porthloo, St Mary's, Isles of Scilly,
Cornwall TR21 0NE
Tel 01720 422535

Guesthouse
Traditional British
*A small relaxed family-run seashore
guesthouse with peaceful private
garden. Superb varied home cooking
and catering for vegetarian and
special diets. Comfortable ensuite
rooms with sea or country views.
Enjoy the open fire in the lounge on
cooler evenings. Come as guests,
leave as friends.*
P ✖ 🏛 (over 7 yrs) ᵇ✖ (public rooms)
Typical tariff single/double room
£25.25/£50.50 Beds 7 Open
April–Oct
Typical 3 course meal £10 *(residents
only)* Open breakfast
8.15am–8.45am; dinner 6.15pm

LAUNCESTON

OLD VICARAGE, THE
Treneglos, Launceston, Cornwall
PL15 8UQ
Tel 01566 781351
B&B
Imaginative
*An elegant grade II listed Georgian
vicarage in idyllic rural setting near
spectacular North Cornwall coast.
Ideal touring base. Guesthouse
renowned for its hospitality, excel-
lent food and high standards.
Superb food with imaginative cuisine
using produce from own organic
garden.*
P 🏛 ᵇ✖
Typical tariff double room £46–£48
Beds 2 Open all year *except Xmas &
New Year*
Typical 3 course meal £15

MAWNAN SMITH

TRENEERE
Penwarne, Mawnan Smith, Cornwall
TR11 5PG
Tel 01326 250297
B&B Private House
*A quiet private house catering
thoughtfully for vegans. High quality,
comfortable ensuite accommodation.
Hot drinks facilities. Excellent break-
fasts plus dinner if required. Good
walks locally. Close to Helford River
and coastal path. Easy access to Truro,
Falmouth and The Lizard. Always a
warm welcome.*
V ⊁
Typical tariff double room £40 Beds 1
Open Mar–Oct

NEWQUAY

TREISAAC FARM VEGETARIAN GUEST HOUSE
St Columb Minor, Newquay, Cornwall
TR8 4DX
Tel 01637 880326
Email stuart.thomson@virgin.net
Guesthouse
*Situated in a 300-year-old farmhouse
only 4 miles from the coast of North
Cornwall and 3 miles from Newquay.
Cooking based around produce from
own organic vegetable garden. All
rooms ensuite. No single supplement.*
V 🐾 ⍜ Cc
Typical tariff double room £42 Beds 3

> **Please mention the** Vegan
> **Travel Guide when contacting a list-**
> **ed business or advertiser**

PENZANCE

WOODSTOCK GUEST HOUSE
29 Morrab Road, Penzance, Cornwall
TR18 4EZ
Tel 01736 369049 Fax 01736 369049
Email woodstocp@aol.com
B&B Guesthouse
*A family-run guesthouse in central
Penzance. Ideally situated for walking
and touring the Land's End Peninsula
and visiting the Isles of Scilly. Most
rooms are equipped with ensuite facilities and all have radio, TV, hairdryer
and tea/coffee making
facilities.*
🐾 ⍜ Cc
Typical tariff single/double room from
£12/£24 Beds 8 Open all year

ST AGNES

PORTHVEAN HOTEL & FRINS RESTAURANT
Churchtown, St Agnes, Cornwall
TR5 0QP
Tel 01872 552581 Fax 01872 553773
Hotel Restaurant
A la Carte Italian/Mediterranean Tra-
ditional British
*A small, cosy hotel with an enormous
log fire in the bar. All bedrooms fur-
nished with antiques and the
hospitality is warm and friendly. Will
happily cater for all tastes and diets.*
⍩ ⍜ Cc ✗ ⊁ *(restaurant)*
Typical tariff single/double room from
£32.50/£45 Beds 7 Open 3rd week
Jan–mid Dec
Seats 28 Open 7pm–9pm *(last
orders); closed to non-residents Sun*

when set dinner is at 7pm

ST AUSTELL

MOUNT PLEASANT FARM
Gorran High Lanes, St Austell,
Cornwall PL26 6LR
Tel 01726 843918
B&B
*Organic smallholding offering
vegetarian and vegan B&B. Set in a
very peaceful location in typical rural
Cornish countryside. Evening meals
are vegetarian and vegan only. Bike
hire and alternative therapies also
available.*
🏠 ♿✖
Typical tariff per person £14–£20
Beds 3 Open April–Oct
VS members' discount 10% *except
child tariff & evening meals*

ST IVES

BOSWEDNACK MANOR
Zennor, St Ives, Cornwall TR26 3DD
Tel 01736 794183
B&B Guesthouse Self Catering
Organic *(when available)*
*Situated in the wildest part of
Cornwall. Mainly vegetarian.
Meditation barn, Mindlab machine,
free walk sheets and guided wildlife
walks by arrangement. Views of
moorland, fields and sea. Secret coves
and stone circles nearby.*
🏠 ♿✖
Typical tariff single/double room
£16/£32 Beds 5 Open all year *except
Xmas*

**MAKING WAVES VEGAN
GUEST HOUSE**
3 Richmond Place, St Ives, Cornwall
TR26 1JN
Tel 01736 793895
B&B Guesthouse
Indian Italian/Mediterranean
Lebanese Macrobiotic Mexican
Organic Spanish Thai
*A delightful Victorian house with
stunning views of St Ives Bay and
tropical gardens. Sunny patio and
wild garden. 2 minutes stroll to
harbour and shops; 10 minutes to
beaches and Tate Gallery. Relaxed
friendly atmosphere. Small 'green'
library, musical instruments, surf
boards and essential oils available.
Special diets catered for.*
VEGAN ✖ ♿✖
Typical single/double room
£20/£16pp Beds 3 Open Mar–Nov
Typical 3 course meal £11.50 Seats 8
Open by arrangement with guests
VS members' discount 10%

ST JUDES GUEST HOUSE
St Ives Road, Carbis Bay, St Ives,
Cornwall TR26 2SF
Tel 01736 795255
B&B Guesthouse Self Catering
*A family-run guesthouse overlooking
St Ives Bay and minutes from Carbis
Bay. Beautiful sandy beach and scenic
coastal paths. A self catering apart-
ment is also available in St Ives. It is a
modern, attractive flat with ensuite
bedrooms, central to St Ives town har-
bour, beaches and Tate Gallery. Sleeps
2–6.*
V 🏠 ♿✖

Typical tariff single/double room
£15.75/£31.50 Beds 5 Open all year

WOODCOTE HOTEL

The Saltings, Lelant, St Ives, Cornwall
TR26 3DL
Tel 01736 753147
Hotel
Eastern European Traditional British
*Established in the 1920s to cater
exclusively for vegetarians. UK's oldest
vegetarian hotel. Situated in own
grounds with a small secluded wood
to the rear and overlooking a tidal
estuary and bird sanctuary. Fresh local
produce prepared in own kitchen to
the highest standards of quality and
originality.*
V ⊯✕
Typical tariff single/double room
£22/£44 Beds 6 Open Mar–Oct
Typical 3 course meal £13 Seats 14

TINTAGEL

MICHAEL HOUSE

Trelake Lane, Treknow, Tintagel,
Cornwall PL34 0EW
Tel 01840 770592
Email michaelhse@aol.co
Website
http://www.members.aol.com/micha
elhse
Guesthouse
Macrobiotic Organic
*Situated on the wild and beautiful
north coast of Cornwall. Comfortable
rooms with sea views and gourmet
vegan and vegetarian meals. A relaxing retreat or a centre for touring and
walking. Guests are collected from*

*local station. Bike hire and musical
instruments available.*
V ⊛ ✕ ⊯✕
Typical tariff double room from
£15.50 Beds 4 Open all year *except
Xmas*
Typical 3 course meal £10 Seats 8
Open for eve meals all year *except
Xmas*
VS members' discount 10% *5 nights +*

TREVELYAN HOUSE

Trewarmett, Tintagel, Cornwall
PL34 0ES
Tel 01840 770486 Fax 01840 770486
B&B
*A family-run B&B situated approxi-
mately 1.5 miles from Tintagel.
Panoramic sea views across Port Isaac
Bay. Nearby coastal path with easy
access to most of Cornwall. Own
preserves, marmalade and sugar-free
spreads are available in retail outlets
across Cornwall.*
V ⋔ ⊛ Cc
Typical tariff single/double room
£14.50/£28 Beds 3
VS members' discount 10%

TORPOINT

BLUE HAVEN HOTEL

Looe Hill, Seaton, Torpoint, Cornwall
PL11 3JQ
Tel 01503 250310
Website
http://www.visitus.co.uk/cornwall/bl
uehaven.htm
B&B Guesthouse Hotel
Italian/Mediterranean Traditional
British

Well situated in an Area of Outstanding Natural Beauty. Magnificent panoramic views from most rooms and sun terraces. Adjacent to coastal footpath. 3 minutes from the beach. 4 miles to Looe; 15 miles to Plymouth. Easy access to Dartmoor, Bodmin and various National Trust properties.
P ⚑ ♀ 🏠 Cc ⋡ (dining room)
Typical tariff single/double room £17/£35 Beds 5 Open all year *except Xmas*
Typical 3 course meal £8 Seats 10 Open all year *residents only*

Places to Eat

COVERACK

CROFT, THE
Coverack, Cornwall TR12 6TF
Tel 01326 280387 Fax 01326 280387
B&B
In an Area of Outstanding Natural Beauty. Uninterrupted sea views from every room and terraced garden, bordered by cliff edge. Ensuite facilities. Private parking and lift. Private stream and coastal footpath.
V ⚑ 🏠 ⋡ ♿ (public entrance/designated parking area/one bedroom, bathroom & WC on same level/dining room/restaurant/bar/TV lounge)
Typical single/twin room £19/£36
Beds 3 Open Feb–Dec & Jan *if in residence*

Please mention the Vegan Travel Guide **when contacting a listed business or advertiser**

ST AGNES

PORTHVEAN HOTEL & FRINS RESTAURANT
See page 19.

TRURO

FEAST, THE
15 Kenwyn Street, Truro, Cornwall TR1 3BU
Tel 01872 272546
Restaurant Take Away
A friendly atmosphere with a Mediterranean feel. Lush green plants, marble tables and terracotta tiles.
V 🏠 ✕ ⋡ ♿ (public entrance/dining area/bar)
Typical 3 course meal £8 Seats 40 Open 10am–5pm Mon–Sat; last weekend of every month

CUMBRIA
Places to Stay

AMBLESIDE

BEECHMOUNT
nr Sawrey, Hawkshead, Ambleside, Cumbria LA22 0TZ
Tel 015394 36356
B&B Guesthouse
Traditional British
A charming, spacious country house, ideally situated in Beatrix Potter's picturesque village with its delightful Olde Worlde Inne. 2 miles from Lake Windermere and Hawkshead. All

modern comforts including ensuite rooms. Country views and delightful walks. Proprietors are vegan and vegetarian.

🐕 ⛯ ↳✻ (areas)

Typical tariff single/double room £29.40/£42 Beds 3 Open all year

APPLEBY IN WESTMORLAND

BONGATE HOUSE
Appleby in Westmorland, Cumbria
CA16 6UE
Tel 017683 51245
Guesthouse
Traditional British
A large Georgian guesthouse situated in an acre of secluded gardens. All rooms have TV and beverage making facilities. Ideal situation for touring the Lakes, Dales and Borders. The famous Settle Carlisle line runs through Appleby. Relaxed Cumbrian hospitality.
P ⴲ ⛯

Typical tariff single/double room £17.50/£40 Beds 8 Open all year except Xmas & New Year
VS members' discount 5% except Bank Hols

CALDBECK

WATERMILL RESTAURANT, THE

See page 30.

CARLISLE

WARREN GUEST HOUSE, THE
368 Warwick Road, Carlisle, Cumbria

CA1 2RU
Tel 01228 533663/512916 Fax 01228 533663/512916
Guesthouse
A cosy family-run guesthouse. Ground floor access, CTV, telephone, bathrooms, hairdryers, coffee/tea making facilities and all the comforts of home. Conservatory and patio area. A good base for touring the Lake District and Scotland. The first guesthouse off junction 43 of the M6.
P 🐕 ⛯ ↳✻

Typical tariff single/double room from £16/£38 Beds 7 Open all year

GRANGE OVER SANDS

HAVEN, THE
10 Birch Street, Windermere, Cumbria
LA23 1EG
Tel 015394 44017
B&B Guesthouse
Traditional British
A small friendly Victorian guesthouse situated in a quiet road just yards from the town centre. The bedrooms are large and the ensuite has an original brass bed. All rooms have coffee/tea making facilities and CTV.
P 🐕 (guide dogs only) ⛯ ↳✻

Typical tariff single/double room from £16/16pp Beds 3 Open all year

GRASMERE

LANCRIGG VEGETARIAN COUNTRY HOUSE HOTEL
Easedale, Grasmere, Cumbria
LA22 9QN

FOX HALL
VEGAN B&B

Sedgwick, Near Kendal, Cumbria LA8 0JP
tel/fax: (015395) 61241

Plus!! Fox Cottage
Vegetarian self-catering
Opening August 1998

Tel 015394 35317 Fax 015394 35058
Hotel
An old country house with timeless charm built in 1840 and set in 30 acres of woodlands. Mountains, a waterfall and a lake on the doorstep. All rooms have TV, tea/coffee making facilities, cassette player and ensuite facilities. Wordsworth, Tennyson and Charles Dickens have all stayed here. Vegan dishes are available at each course in the restaurant. Inform staff of dietary requirements on arrival.
V 🐾 (dogs) 🏛 Cc 🎋 (public rooms)
Typical tariff double room from £45pp Beds 14 Open all year
Typical 3 course meal £20 Seats 30
Open to residents all year *and non-residents for evening meal 6.30pm–8pm with advance notice*

GREENHEAD

HOLMHEAD GUEST HOUSE
Hadrian's Wall, Greenhead, via Carlisle, Cumbria CA6 7HY
Tel 016977 47402 Fax 016977 47402
B&B Guesthouse Self Catering
Tea Rooms
Snacks/Drinks Traditional British
Lovely old farmhouse built with stones from Hadrian's Wall. Quality home cooking with vegetarian and vegan wines. Bike hire, garden games, table tennis, golf 500 yards and tours. Host was former tour guide and is expert on Hadrian's Wall and local history. Healthy Heartbeat award.
P ♀ 🏛 Cc ✕ 🎋 ๕ (public entrance, designated parking area/one bed-

room, bathroom & WC on same level/dining room/restaurant/bar/TV lounge)
Typical tariff double room from £24
Beds 4 Open 18 Jan–18 Dec
Typical 3 course meal £16.95 *(evening meal at set time & for residents only)*

KENDAL

FOX COTTAGE
Sedgwick, Kendal, Cumbria LA8 0JP
Tel 015395 61241 Fax 015395 61241
Self Catering
Holiday style cottage adjoining Fox Hall (vegan B&B) in attractive village of Sedgwick. 4 miles south of Kendal and the South Lakes. Sleeps 4 plus baby. Sitting room, kitchen, bathroom, garage, colour TV, high chair, cot and bedding available. Vegan bedding and cleaning equipment used.
VEGAN 🏛 🎋
Typical tariff £150–£260 per week
Beds 2 Open all year *from August 1998*

LAKELAND NATURAL VEGETARIAN GUEST HOUSE
Low Slack, Queens Road, Kendal, Cumbria LA9 4PH
Tel 01539 733011 Fax 01539 733011
Guesthouse
Wholefood
Situated in a stunning location overlooking Kendal. Luxury, comfort and a friendly service in a warm, welcoming atmosphere. All rooms have ensuite facilities. Drying room, satellite TV, hairdryers, laundry facilities and

evening meals available.
V 🐕 ♀ ⚥ Cc ❄
Typical tariff single/double room
£27/£54 Beds 3 Open all year
VS members' discount 2 nights +

SUNDIAL GUEST HOUSE
51 Milnthorpe Road, Kendal, Cumbria
LA9 5QG
Tel 01539 724468
Fax 01539 736900
B&B Guesthouse
A large Victorian house only 5 minutes walk from Kendal. Good access to M6 and main line station at Oxenholme. Parking for 7 cars. Ideal for visiting the Lake District and Yorkshire. Ensuite and family rooms. Excellent vegan breakfast.
⚥ ❄ (rooms)
Typical tariff single/double room
£15.17/£15.18pp Beds 5 Open all year

KESWICK

BOWFELL
Chestnut Hill, Keswick, Cumbria
CA12 4LR
Tel 017687 74859
B&B
Located in a Victorian house only 1 mile from Keswick town centre. Small family-run B&B where "muddy boots and bikes are welcome". Private parking, BBQ/patio area, cycle store and drying room. Lovely views from all rooms. Evening meals at reasonable rates.
🐕 ⚥ ❄
Typical tariff single/double room

£17.50/£18.50pp Beds 3

DALKEITH GUEST HOUSE
1 Leonard Street, Keswick, Cumbria
CA12 4EJ
Tel 017687 72696 Fax 017687 72696
Email f.marsden@aoi.com
Guesthouse
Traditional British Organic *(on request)*
Less than 5 minutes walk from the popular market town of Keswick and only 10 minutes from the shores of Derwent Water. A warm, friendly welcome and excellent home cooked food. Will happily cater for any diet — eg gluten-free, fat-free, diabetic, vegetarian, vegan, or for people with religious requirements.
P ⚥ ✗ ❄
Typical tariff single/double room
£16/£36 Beds 7 Open all year *except Xmas & New Year*
Typical 3 course meal £10 Seats 14

EDEN GREEN VEGETARIAN GUEST HOUSE
20 Blencathra Street, Keswick, Cumbria CA12 4HP
Tel 017687 72077 Fax 017687 71331
Email 106143.1772@compuserve.com
Guesthouse
Highly recommended, comfortable and relaxing Victorian guesthouse. Central for town, lake and fells. Extensive and delicious breakfasts with menu choice. Ensuite and standard rooms available, some with fell views. Families and groups welcome. Safe cycle storage and drying room.
V 🐕 ⚥ ❄

Typical tariff single/double room
£17.50/£18–£23pp Beds 5
VS members' discount 5% up to 6
nights; **10%** 7 nights +

GREENSIDE
48 Saint John Street, Keswick on
Derwentwater, Cumbria CA12 5AG
Tel 017687 74491
B&B Self Catering
*B&B and mini break self-catering
holidays for couples.*
V ⤸✦
Typical tariff double room £15pp
Beds 3 Open all year

KENDOON B&B
Kendoon, Braithwaite, Keswick,
Cumbria CA12 5RY
Tel 017687 78430
B&B Private House
*Friendly welcome for wet walkers
and cyclists. Good drying facilities.
Lockable bike shed. Featured on*
Coast to Coast *and* Himalyan
Challenge. *Proud pioneer of non-
smoking establishment since 1973.
Views of Skiddaw, Blencathra and
Helvellyn.*
�)(🏛 ⤸✦
Typical tariff single/double room
£15/£29 Beds 3 Open all year *Ring
to confirm*
**VS members' discount £1 off first
night's stay**

TARN HOWS
3–5 Eskin Street, Keswick, Cumbria
CA12 4DH
Guesthouse
Centrally located in a quiet location a
*few minutes walk from all amenities.
All rooms have colour TV, radio,
tea/coffee making facilities, central
heating, hair dryer and iron. Private
car park, secure cycle store and drying
facilities for outdoor clothes. Friendly
welcome assured.*
P ⤸✦
Typical tariff single/double room
£21.50/£43 Beds 8 Open all year

WILLOW COTTAGE
Bassenthwaite, nr Keswick, Cumbria
CA12 4QP
Tel 017687 76440
Private House Self Catering
Traditional British
*A charming converted stonebuilt barn
with ensuite rooms, tea & coffee mak-
ing facilities and radios in rooms. Ideal
for walking, cycling or just relaxing.
Self-catering cottage also available
with many features including cast iron
bath.*
P ⤸✦ 🏛 (self-catering)
Typical tariff double room £20 Beds 2
Open all year *except last 2 weeks Dec*

KIRKBY STEPHEN

CHESTNUT HOUSE
Crosby Garrett, Kirkby Stephen,
Cumbria CA17 4PR
Tel 017683 71230
Guesthouse
*Traditional cottage in a quiet village
situated amid the hills of Cumbria's
Upper Eden Valley. Excellent walking
and cycling country. Comfortable
accommodation, books, CDs and log
fires. Home grown produce when*

A ROOM WITH A VIEW
VEGETARIAN RESTAURANT

Serving imaginative home cooked cuisine
on a vegetarian & vegan theme, Jim &
Isobel welcome you to Room with a View.

You can now enjoy our delicious range of
organic wines and beers with your meal.

Open seven days a week in summer,
weekends in winter.

Open for—

Dinner 6pm – 9pm
Brunch 10.30am – 2.30pm

Reservations advisable.
Tel. (015394) 36751
The Square, Hawkshead, Cumbria.

available.
V 🐴 🏊 🍽️
Typical single/double room
£16.50/£33 Beds 2 Open all year

WASDALE

SCREES HOTEL, THE
Nether Wasdale, Wasdale, Cumbria
CA20 1ET
Tel 019467 26262 Fax 019467 26262
Hotel Public House
French Indian Italian/Mediterranean
Mexican Spanish Thai
Traditional British
*Situated in Wasdale, the home of the
highest mountain, the deepest lake,
the smallest church and the biggest
liar in England. The Inn is 300 years
old with stunning views from the
beer garden. The staff are friendly,
vegetarian, and knowledgeable
about the local area. Regular live
music.*
🐴 ♀ 🏊 Cc ✕
Typical single/double room £28/£42
Beds 5 Open 12pm–3pm &
6.30pm–late
Typical 3 course meal £12.95 Seats 40
Open 12pm–2.30pm &
6.30pm–9.30pm
VS members' discount 10%

WINDERMERE

KIRKWOOD GUEST HOUSE
Princes Road, Windermere, Cumbria
LA23 2DD
Tel 015394 43907
Fax 015394 43907
B&B

*A warm and tastefully decorated
house with ensuite, TV and tea/coffee
making facilities in all rooms. Ideally
positioned for exploring the Lakeland
area. Situated in a quiet corner
between Windermere and Bowness.
Owners are keen walkers.*
P 🐴 Cc 🍽️ (except lounge)
Typical tariff double room £22–£30
Beds 7 Open all year

Places to Eat

AMBLESIDE

ROOM WITH A VIEW
Laburnam House, The Square,
Hawkshead, Ambleside, Cumbria
LA22 0NZ
Tel 015394 36751
Cafe Restaurant
A la Carte Snacks/Drinks
*Overlooking the picturesque square in
the village of Hawkshead, this fully
licensed restaurant offers high class
home-cooked vegetarian cuisine.
Open in the day for brunch which
consists of light meals and snacks, and
in the evening for high class home
cooked cuisine.*
V Cc ✕ (on request)
Typical 3 course meal £13 Seats 30
Open Mon–Fri 10.30am–2.30pm &
6pm–9pm; 10.30am–2.30pm hols &
weekends; *booking advised*

ZEFFIRELLIS
Compston Road, Ambleside, Cumbria
LA22 9AD
Tel 015394 33845 Fax 015394 31771

Email zeffirellis@btinternet.com
Restaurant
Italian/Mediterranean
A lively and stylish wholefood pizzeria alongside two cinemas, shopping gallery and garden room cafe. Situated in the heart of the English Lake District.
V Cc ✗ ⭐

Typical 3 course meal £11 Seats 84
Open 6pm–9.45pm Mon–Fri;
12pm–2pm & 5pm–9.45pm Sat–Sun;
closed Mon–Tues Jan & early Feb

CALDBECK

WATERMILL RESTAURANT, THE
Priests Mill, Caldbeck, Cumbria
CA7 8DR
Tel 016974 78267
Bistro Cafe Caravan Restaurant Sandwich Bar Take Away
Tea Rooms
Organic
Food is made on the premises each day from the best quality produce. Light refreshments or full meals available. Some tables overlook the river or customers may sit outside on the grassy terrace next to the village cricket pitch. During the winter the restaurant is warm and inviting with a cosy log stove and candles on the tables.
V ⚲ ⭐ ⭐

Typical tariff £185 (weekly let 2/4 berth caravan) Open Mar–Aug
Typical 3 course meal £15 Seats 50
Open 10am–5pm Mon–Fri Mar–Sept;
11am–4pm Mon Oct–Jan; *closed Xmas Day & Boxing Day*

COCKERMOUTH

COCKATOO RESTAURANT, THE
16 Market Place, Cockermouth,
Cumbria CA13 9NQ
Tel 01900 826205
Restaurant
A la Carte Italian/Mediterranean
Round the World Thai Traditional
British
Run by mother and daughter, this is a relaxed and friendly restaurant serving vegetarian and vegan food. Food is homemade using seasonal fruit and vegetables. All ingredients are fresh daily and served with an individual touch. Vegetarian Society Cordon Vert Certificate (Merit) plus Food & Drink Guild Award.
⭐ Cc ⭐

Typical 3 course meal £14 Seats
30–36 Open until 7pm *except Tues*

QUINCE & MEDLAR
13 Castlegate, Cockermouth, Cumbria
CA13 9EU
Tel 01900 823579
Restaurant
A la Carte
A licensed fine food restaurant with a candlelit wood panelled dining room. Carefully prepared and creatively presented food in friendly and intimate surroundings. Twice winner of Vegetarian Restaurant of the Year. Booking advisable.
V ⭐

Typical 3 course meal £15 Seats 26
Open 7pm onwards Tues–Sun; *closed Sun in winter*

GRANGE OVER SANDS

**FERNHILL VEGETARIAN
COUNTRY HOUSE**
See **SPECIAL INTEREST** page 228.

GRASMERE

**DOVE COTTAGE TEAROOMS &
RESTAURANT**
The Wordsworth Trust, Town End,
Grasmere, Cumbria LA22 9SH
Tel 015394 35268 **Fax** 015394 35268
Cafe Restaurant Tea Rooms
*Adjacent to Wordsworth's famous
home at Grasmere in the heart of the
English Lake District. Always some
vegan options on the menu and
happy to provide more choice with
prior notice. Occasionally features live
music, poetry readings and vegetarian
cookery demonstrations in the
evenings.*
V Cc ✗ ➽
Typical 3 course meal £5–£10 Seats
60 Open 10am–5pm Mon–Sun;
6.30pm onwards Thurs–Sat

**LANCRIGG VEGETARIAN COUNTRY
HOUSE HOTEL**
See page 23.

ROWAN TREE, THE
Church Bridge, Stock Lane, Grasmere,
Cumbria LA22 9RS
Tel 015394 35528
Cafe Restaurant
*Set in a quiet location by the side of
the River Rothay. Offers light snacks,
lunches and refreshments throughout
the day. Evening meals at the restaurant are imaginative and complemented by organically produced
wines and beers.*
V Cc ✗ ➽ ♿ (public entrance/
dining area)
Typical 3 course meal £12 Seats 70
Open: cafe 10am–5pm; restaurant
6pm–9pm

GREENHEAD

HOLMHEAD GUEST HOUSE
See page 25.

KENDAL

**LAKELAND NATURAL WATERSIDE
WHOLEFOODS**
Kent View, Waterside, Kendal,
Cumbria LA9 4PH
Tel 01539 729743 **Fax** 01539 733011
Cafe Restaurant Shop Take Away
Wholefood
*Attractive riverside location. All food
freshly prepared on the premises and
menu changes daily using seasonal
produce. Special vegetarian/vegan
evenings are arranged for which
booking is essential. Outside catering
also available.*
V ✗
Typical 3 course meal £7.85 Seats 40
inside; 18 outside Open 9am–4pm
Mon–Sun

KESWICK

**LAKELAND PEDLAR WHOLEFOOD
CAFE, THE**
Hendersons Yard, Bell Close Car Park,
Keswick, Cumbria

Tel 017687 74492 Fax 017687 75752

Cafe Restaurant

Italian/Mediterranean Mexican
Snacks/Drinks

*The food is totally natural and
vegetarian/vegan, prepared with
unrefined ingredients. When combined with the finest, freshest fruits
and vegetables, delicious vegetarian
and vegan meals are created.*

V ✗ ﷽ ♿ (public entrance/desig-
nated parking area/dining area/bar)
Typical 3 course meal £7.50
day/£10.50 eves Seats 30 Open
9am–5pm Mon–Sun; 9am–8pm sum-
mer & school hols — *ring for confirma-
tion*

KIRBY LONSDALE

TEA ROOMS
39 Main Street, Kirby Lonsdale,
Cumbria LA6 2AH
Tel 015242 72133
Cafe
Italian/Mediterranean Snacks/Drinks
*A Georgian fronted building situated
in a Cumbrian market town. Serving
morning coffee, light lunches and
snacks all day. Always something suitable for vegans on the menu. Owner
is vegetarian.*
✗ ﷽ ♿ (public entrance/dining
area/bar)
Typical 3 course meal £7–£8 Seats 40
Open 9am–5pm Mon–Sun
VS members' discount 10%

Please mention the Vegan
Travel Guide **when contacting a
listed business or advertiser**

KIRKBY STEPHEN

OLD FORGE BISTRO
39 North Road, Kirkby Stephen,
Cumbria CA17 4RE
Tel 017683 71832
Bistro
Italian/Mediterranean Mexican
Traditional British
*A small busy bistro with an informal
atmosphere. Situated on the famous
'Coast to Coast' walking route. Vegan
dishes always comprise half the menu.
Booking advised.*
♀ Cc ﷽ (area) ♿ (public
entrance/designated parking
area/dining area/bar) Seats 28 Open
6pm–10pm Tues-Sun

PENRITH

WATERMILL, THE
Little Salkeld, Penrith, Cumbria
CA10 1NN
Tel 01768 881523
Email njbj@aol.com
Website
http://www.cumbria.com/watermil/
Tearooms Mail Order Mill Shop
Organic
*Peaceful tearooms overlooking
Sunnygill Beck. Vegan food usually
available but check first. Guided tours
available around traditional country
corn mill which produces stoneground
organic flour using water power.*
V Cc ✗ ﷽ ♿ (public entance/desig-
nated parking area/dining area/dis-
abled toilet/access to ground floors
of tearooms and mill)
Typical 3 course meal £4 Seats 70

Open 10.30am–5pm Mon–Tues & Fri
Mar–Oct

WASDALE

SCREES HOTEL, THE
See page 29.

DERBYSHIRE

Places to Stay

BUXTON

BUXTONS VICTORIAN GUEST HOUSE
5 Wye Grove, off Macclesfield Road,
Buxton, Derbyshire SK17 9AJ
Tel 01298 78759
B&B Guesthouse
Traditional British
A Victorian guesthouse tastefully furnished with conservatory, antiques, festoon blinds, matching curtains and pretty linen. Situated in a quiet cul-de-sac in a nice residential area near the Pavilion gardens and town centre. All rooms have colour TV and tea/coffee facilities. Two ensuite rooms and one with own bathroom.
恚 ⠜⠭
Typical tariff single/double room
£19.50–£24pp Beds 4

**GLENWOOD VEGETARIAN
& VEGAN GUESTHOUSE**
134 Lightwood Road, Buxton,
Derbyshire SK17 6RW
Tel 01298 77690

Guesthouse
A large 1920s house situated close to the centre of the spa town of Buxton with its opera house and festivals. Surrounded by the Peak National Park. Spacious and comfortable rooms, Cordon Vert catering and off street parking.
V ⠹ 恚 ⠜⠭
Typical tariff single/double room
£16/£17.50 per person Beds 3 Open all year
Typical 3 course meal £9.50 Seats 87
Open all year *residents & their guests only*

HOPE VALLEY

APPLE CROFT B&B
Fidler's Well, Bamford, Hope Valley,
Derbyshire S33 0AR
Tel 01433 651495
B&B
A friendly Victorian family house in the centre of Bamford village. Good base for walkers exploring the rugged beauty of the Peak District. Specialises in hearty breakfasts with vegetarian options always available and vegan alternatives by prior arrangement. Off road parking.
P 恚 ⠜⠭
Typical tariff single/double room
£15/£34 Beds 3 Open all year *except Xmas*

ROUND MEADOW BARN
Parsons Lane, Hope, Hope Valley,
Derbyshire S33 6RA
Tel 01433 621347
B&B

Traditional British
Two family rooms available with a shared bathroom.
P ♈ 主 ♀
Typical tariff single/double room
£25/£36 Beds 2 Open all year

STONECROFT
Edale, Hope Valley, Derbyshire
Tel 01433 670262
Guesthouse
Luxury country house accommodation in the heart of the beautiful Peak District at the start of the Pennine Way. Friendly homely welcome. Caters for all diets but vegetarian and vegan dishes are a speciality. Owner vegetarian with Cordon Vert Diploma. 7.5% discount for B&B (3 nights +).
♀ 主 (12 yrs+) Cc ✕ ♀
Typical tariff double room £23pp
Beds 2 Open all year *except Xmas*
Typical 5 course meal + coffee £20
Seats 4 *Open for residents by prior arrangement*

WOODBINE CAFE & B&B
18 Castleton Road, Hope, Hope Valley, Derbyshire S33 6RD
Tel 01433 621407
B&B Cafe
A la Carte Traditional British
A family-run business welcoming cyclists, walkers, cavers, climbers, paragliders, hangliders, sightseers and holidaymakers. Comfortable B&B in 16th century cottage. Some ensuite rooms. Varied all day menu, all home cooked. Group booking, weekend and midweek special breaks available.

✕ ♀
Typical tariff single/double room
from £20/£36 Beds 6 Open all year
except Xmas Day

RIPON

ABBEY NORDALE
1 & 2 North Parade, North Road, Ripon, Derbyshire HG4 1ES
Tel 01765 603557
B&B
A long established business in a lovely Victorian town house.
Situated close to Ripon town centre but with easy access to local countryside. All rooms are comfortable and clean. Most rooms have private facilities. Price reduction on vegan breakfasts.
P ♀ Cc ♀
Typical tariff single/double room
£20/£24 Beds 10 Open all year

Places to Eat

BONSALL

KINGS HEAD, THE
62 Yeoman Street, Bonsall, Matlock, Derbyshire DE4 2AA
Tel 01629 822703
Public House
Chinese French Indian Italian/Mediterranean Macrobiotic Mexican Organic Snacks/Drinks Spanish Thai Traditional British
An historic 1677 village pub situated on the Limestone Way and in Peak Practice country. Close to Matlock

Bath, Gullivers Kingdom, Heights of Abraham and Bonsall Church. All food is fresh and the menu changes daily.

🐾 ♿ (public entrance/designated parking area/dining area/bar)
Typical 3 course meal £10 Seats 82
Open Mon–Fri 12pm–2pm & 6pm–11pm; Sat–Sun 12pm–3pm & 7pm–10.30pm

BUXTON

WILD CARROT WORKERS CO-OP
5 Bridge Street, Buxton, Derbyshire DE17 6BS
Tel 01298 22843
Cafe Restaurant
A la Carte Snacks/Drinks
Offering value for money lunches during the day and a la carte during the evening. Predominantly vegan menu. Fully licensed with vegan and organic wines and beers. Situated above a wholefood shop which sells a wide range of organic produce including bread, fresh fruit and vegetables.
V ✗ 🍴 (until 9.30pm)
Typical 3 course meal £3 day; £11 eve
Seats 30 Open 12pm–3pm *(summer)* & 5.30pm–11pm Wed; 12pm–3pm & 5.30pm–11pm Thurs; 12pm–3pm & 5.30pm–11pm Fri; 12pm–4pm & 5.30pm–11pm Sat–Sun
VS members' discount 10%

DERBY

CACTUS CAFE
8–9 Blacksmiths Yard, off Sadler Gate, Derby DE1 3PD

Tel 01332 290793
Restaurant
Mexican
A lively contemporary Mexican restaurant serving creative food to the sound of salsa music. £6 two-course menu every Mon and Tues. A wide variety of vegetarian and vegan dishes.
🥢 Cc ♿ (public entrance/dining area/bar)
Typical 3 course meal £10 Seats 56
Open 6pm–10pm Mon–Sat

HOPE VALLEY

HOPECHEST, THE
8 Castleton Road, Hope, Hope Valley, Derbyshire S33 6RD
Tel 01433 620072 Fax 01433 620795
Cafe Delicatessen Take Away
Tea Rooms
Organic Traditional British
Ideal stop for those touring, camping, etc in the Peak District. In addition to food, there are locally-made arts, crafts and gifts — as well as books, cards and fashion items. Something for everyone. Refreshingly different and not to be missed.
P Cc ✗ (by arrangement) ♿ (public entrance/dining area)
Typical 3 course meal £8–£10 Seats 24 + 24 outside Open all week 10am–5pm; *eves by special arrangement*

HOPE VALLEY WI MARKET
Hathersage Methodist Church Hall, Hathersage, Derbyshire
Tel 01433 670282 (market controller)

WI Market

Variety of preserves, bread, cakes, savouries, vegetarian and some vegan food available. Plants and crafts. Useful to order any special items the week before — particularly if vegan.
Open 9.45am–11.30am Fri

LONGLAND'S EATING HOUSE

Main Road, Hathersage, Hope Valley, Derbyshire S32 1BB
Tel 01433 651978
Cafe
Mexican Snacks/Drinks
Traditional British
A large cafe situated above an outdoor equipment shop. Half the dishes are vegetarian, including 2–3 vegan dishes. Lots of mixed salads, soups and snacks.
Note: vegan fried food may be cooked in same oil as vegetarian food.
🎂 Cc ⭐ (dining area)
Typical 3 course meal £7.50 Seats 60
Open 12pm–5pm Mon; 10am–5pm Tues–Fri; 9am–6pm Sat–Sun

WOODBINE CAFE & B&B

See page 35.

DEVON

Places to Stay

BRAUNTON

WHITELEAF AT CROYDE
Croyde Road, Croyde, Braunton, North Devon, EX33 1PN
Tel 01271 890266
B&B Restaurant (summer only)
International
Situated in a rural area only 300 yards from the beach and close to Saunton Sands Golf Course. Beach views from two rooms. Hotel is owner's home and guests are treated as part of the family. Owner is an international chef. Packed lunches and tourist information available.
P 🐾 🎂 Cc ✗ ⭐ (areas) ♿ (public entrance/designated parking area/dining room/restaurant/sun lounge)
Typical single/double room from £25/£30pp Beds 5 Open all year except 2–3 weeks per year
Typical 3 course meal £17 Seats 20
Open Jun–Oct flexible hours for residents; *non-residents 7pm–9pm Mon–Sat by arrangement*

DARTMOOR

TWO BRIDGES HOTEL
Dartmoor, Devon PL20 6QF
Tel 01822 890581 Fax 01822 890575
Hotel Restaurant
A la Carte Snacks/Drinks
Traditional British
A 17th century former coaching hotel in picturesque riverside setting at the very heart of Dartmoor. Luxury rooms including many with four poster beds. A cosy bar featuring own-brewed Jail Ale. Wide range of bar meals. AA 2 Red Rosette award winning restaurant with tempting varied menu.

🐕 🍴 🎵 Cc ✕ 🚭 (areas) ♿ (public entrance/designated parking area/one bedroom, bathroom & WC on same level/dining room/restaurant/bar)
Typical tariff single/double room £40/£69 Beds 29 Open all year
Typical 3 course meal *(restaurant)* £17.50 Seats 80 Open breakfast 7.30am–10am; lunch 11.30am–2pm; dinner 7pm–9.30pm
Typical 3 course meal *(bar)* £12.50 Seats 60 Open lunch 11am–2.30; dinner 6pm–9.30pm
VS members' discount 10%

EXETER

CROFT GUEST HOUSE, THE
Cockwood Harbour, Starcross, nr Exeter, Devon EX6 8QY
Tel 01626 980282 Fax 01626 891768
Website
http://www.smoothhound.co.uk/hotels/croft1.html
Guesthouse
Traditional British
Overlooking Cockwood Harbour and the River Exe Estuary and 2 minutes walk to two of Devon's finest pubs and restaurants (discount card available for guests). 1 mile to Dawlish Warren Bird Reserve and beach. 8 miles from Exeter. Own key. No restrictions. Safe off road parking.
🐕 🍴 🎵 (over 2 yrs) 🚭 (breakfast room)
Typical tariff single/double room £16–£39 Beds 9 Open all year *except Xmas*

HILLCREST CORNER
1 Hillcrest Park, Exeter, Devon EX4 4SH
Tel 01392 277443 Fax 01392 277443
B&B Private House Self Catering
Quiet, peaceful home in flower-filled gardens (if uneaten by deer). Adjacent to beautiful university campus, 1.25 miles from the city centre (lifts available). Semi-rural location with views to Dartmoor and the sea. Tea and coffee making facilities, TV, parking and self-catering kitchen available.
V 🎵 🚭 ♿ (one bedroom, bathroom & WC on same level on first floor)
Typical tariff single/double room £14.50/£29 Beds 3

LYDFORD

SANCTUARY, THE
nr Lydford, Okehampton, Devon EX20 4AL
Tel 01822 820203 Fax 01822 820203
Self Catering
Based at Vegfam's headquarters on the A386, only 10 miles from Okehampton. Situated in 6.5 acres of nature reserve.
VEGAN 🎵
Typical tariff £10pp Beds 3 Open all year

LYNTON

CASTLE HILL HOUSE HOTEL
Castle Hill, Lynton, North Devon EX35 6JA
Tel 01598 752291 Fax 01598 752291
Email Castlehill@btinternet.com

Hotel Restaurant
French Traditional British
A small friendly family-run business providing a relaxing and comfortable Victorian hotel. Set in the heart of Lynton, it has the very best of sea and moor. Two lounges and elegant cosy bedrooms. Disos wine stocked.
♀ ⛩ 🌣 Cc ✕ ⬦ (in restaurant, 1 lounge, some beds)
Typical single/double room £30/£45
Beds 9 Open Feb–Dec
A la carte pricing for restaurant
Open 6.30pm–8pm *depending on time of year*
VS members' discount 5% on bedroom rates — *except Bank Hols & Xmas*

PAIGNTON

SANDPIPER VEGETARIAN HOTEL, THE
14 Roundham Road, Paignton, Devon TQ4 6DN
Tel 01803 551397 Fax 01803 551397
Hotel
Chinese Indian
Italian/Mediterranean Mexican
Traditional British
A family run hotel only 2 minutes from picturesque Paignton Harbour. Close to coves and beaches. Centrally heated, tea/coffee facilities, colour TV, ensuite in all rooms and family suite. Courtesy pick up from Paignton station. Baby listening service. Vegan and vegetarian wines available. Xmas specials available.
V ♀ 🌣 Cc ✕ ♿ (one bedroom, shower & WC on same level/dining room/restaurant/bar/TV lounge)
Typical tariff single/double room £22/£22pp Beds 7 Open all year

PARKHAM

PENHAVEN COUNTRY HOUSE
Parkham, North Devon EX39 5PL
Tel 01237 451388 Fax 01237 451878
Hotel Restaurant
French Italian/Mediterranean
Traditional British
A country house hotel with a charming restaurant. A former rectory nestling in 11 acres of gardens and woods. No children. Pets welcome. Owner vegetarian.
🐕 ♀ Cc ♿ (public entrance/designated parking area/one bedroom,bathroom & WC on same level/dining room/restaurant/bar/TV lounge)
Typical tariff single/double room £55/£110 Beds 12 Open all year
Typical 3 course meal £13.95 Seats 50
Open 12pm–2pm Mon–Fri;
12pm–2pm Sun

PLYMOUTH

BERKELEY'S OF ST JAMES
4 St James Place East, The Hoe, Plymouth, Devon PL1 3AS
Tel 01752 221654
B&B Guesthouse
Traditional British
Small elegant Victorian guest house with luxury ensuite rooms. Non-smokers haven. Situated in a secluded quiet square on Plymouth Hoe. Easy walking distance for promenade, historic

Barbican, city centre, theatre, pavilions, university, ferry, coach and railway stations. Ideal for touring Dartmoor, Devon, Cornwall. ETB commended.

P 🏊 Cc ♿

Typical tariff single/double room £20/£36 Beds 5

SOUTH MOLTON

FERN TOR VEGETARIAN/VEGAN GUEST HOUSE

Meshaw, South Molton, Devon
EX36 4NA
Tel 01769 550339 Fax 01769 550339
Email ferntor@mcmail.com
Website
http://www.ferntor.mcmail.com
Guesthouse
Wholefood
All bedrooms in the newly-built guest annex have ensuite bathrooms, tea making facilities and radios. 12 acres to relax in or to use as a base for exploring Exmoor, North and mid-Devon. Wholefood cuisine prepared by Cordon Vert host. Accessible by public transport. Opening summer 1998.

V 🐾 🏊 ↦✕

Typical tariff double room £20 pp
Beds 3 Open all year

TIVERTON

ANGEL GUEST HOUSE

13 St Peter Street, Tiverton, Devon
EX16 6NU
Tel 01884 253392 Fax 01884 253392
Guesthouse

A comfortable Georgian house in a conservation area of town. All facilities close by. An ideal base for touring the unspoilt Devon countryside. All rooms have colour TVs and drinks facilities. Ensuite available. Parking area and locked shed for bicycles.

P 🏊

Typical tariff single/double room £16/£32 Beds 7 Open all year

TORQUAY

BROOKESBY HALL HOTEL

Hesketh Road, Torquay, Devon
TQ1 2LN
Tel 01803 292194
Hotel
Quietly situated near coastal woodland only 4 minutes to nearest beach and 15 minutes from town centre. Glorious sea views across Torbay. Enjoying a long-established reputation for providing delicious satisfying and health-giving wholefood menu for vegetarians and vegans. Organic produce used when possible.

V 🐾 🏊 ✕ ↦ ♿ (public entrance/WC/dining room/restaurant/TV lounge)
Typical tariff single/double room £28/£56 Beds 10 Open all year
Typical 3 course meal £13.50 Seats 24
VS members' discount 10% 1 week+

Places to Eat

BRAUNTON

WHITELEAF AT CROYDE
See page 37.

DARTMOOR

TWO BRIDGES HOTEL
See page 37.

DREWSTEIGNTON

CASTLE DROGO
Drewsteignton, Devon EX6 6PB
Tel 01647 432629
Restaurant Tea Rooms
Snacks/Drinks Traditional
Owned by the National Trust. Keen to cater for those with food allergies or special diets.
P Cc ✗ ⊁
Seats 50 restaurant; 48 tea rooms
Open: restaurant 12pm–2pm lunch & 2.30pm–5.30 afternoon tea; tea rooms 10.30am–5.30pm

EXETER

CAFE, THE
38 South Street, Exeter, Devon
EX1 1ED
Tel 01392 410855
Cafe
A self-service, licensed cafe where all the food (except bread) is cooked on the premises. A quick service providing vegan soup, salads and at least one hot dish. A lovely garden is provided for customers to eat al fresco.
V Cc ✗ ⊁ (1 section) ঙ (public entrance/dining area/bar)
Typical 3 course meal £8.25–£11.45
Seats 45 + garden seating Open 10am–6pm Mon–Sat

HERBIES

15 North Street, Exeter, Devon
EX4 3QS
Tel 01892 258473
Bistro Restaurant
Wholefood
Extensive menu of good value food from nut and bean burgers to nachos supreme or spinach & aubergine layer with salads or stir fried vegetables. A meal can be finished with a selection of homemade desserts or vegan ice cream. Licensed. A restaurant to suit all pockets and tastes.
V Cc ✗ ঙ (public entrance/dining area)
Typical 3 course meal £9 Seats 50
Open 11am–2.30pm *(last orders)* Mon–Fri; 10.30am–4pm *(last orders)* Sat; 6pm–9.30pm *(last orders)* Tues–Sat

LYNTON

CASTLE HILL HOUSE HOTEL
See page 38.

NEWTON ABBOT

COUNTRY TABLE CAFE, THE
12 Bank Street, Newton Abbot, South Devon TQ12 2JW
Tel 01626 202120
Cafe Restaurant Take Away
Snacks/Drinks
Offers vegans a variety of foods served in unique and relaxed sur-roundings. Exciting salads served daily. Cakes and ice creams are available as well. Lunches are changed daily. Bring your own wine for evening

restaurant. Bookings only for the evening restaurant when vegans are catered for *with* prior notice.
(P) V ✗ ⁕ ⅋ (public entrance/dining area)
Typical 3 course meal £8.20 Seats 44
Open 9am–5pm Mon–Sat; first Sat in month 9am–4.30pm & 7.30pm–10pm
VS members' discount 10% *except specials*

PLYMOUTH

HEART & SOUL
37 New Street, The Barbican, Plymouth Devon PL1 2NA
Tel 01752 263590
Cafe Healing Centre Shop
A natural healing centre offering a broad range of therapies. Shop and cafe attached.
V ⁕
Typical 3 course meal £5.50 Seats 25
Open 10am–5.30pm

PLYMOUTH ARTS CENTRE VEGETARIAN RESTAURANT
38 Lode Street, Plymouth, Devon PL4 0EB
Tel 01752 202616
Cafe Restaurant Snacks/Drinks Take Away
Snacks/Drinks World Cooking
A wide range of vegetarian and vegan dishes served daily. Always at least 1–2 vegan dishes on menu. Other specialities catered for — eg gluten-free. Monthly 'world cooking' nights with a good choice for vegans.
V ⅋ ✗ ⁕ (area)
Typical 3 course meal £5–£7 Seats 55

Open 12pm–2pm Mon–Sat; 5pm–9pm Tues–Sat; light refreshments all day

TOTNES

OLD FORGE AT TOTNES, THE
Seymour Place, Totnes, Devon TQ9 5AY
Tel 01803 862174 Fax 01803 865385
Hotel
Situated in a 600-year-old stone building with coach arch and old English walled garden. A working forge and pottery studio on site, both for hands on experience. Bike hire and whirlpool spa available. All rooms ensuite. No evening meals but serves snacks and afternoon tea. Local shop sells vegan margarine and soya milk.
P ⅋ ⅋ ⁕ ⅋ (public entrance/designated parking area/one bedroom, bathroom & WC on same level/dining room/restaurant/bar/TV lounge)
Typical tariff double room from £52–£72 Beds 10 Open all year

WILLOW VEGETARIAN GARDEN RESTAURANT
87 High Street, Totnes, Devon TQ9 5PB
Tel 01803 862605
Cafe Restaurant Take Away
Indian Italian/Mediterranean Mexican Organic Snacks/Drinks
Popular restaurant serving delicious food prepared from fresh ingredients. Vegan soup, snacks, main dishes and cakes always available. Offers a good selection of organic and vegan wines and beers. Family room includes toys and books for children. Lovely garden

at rear.
V ✕ ᛒᛜ
Typical 3 course meal £10.12 Seats 50
Open 10am–5pm Mon–Sat Jul & Aug;
7pm–11pm Wed–Sat Jul–Aug;
10am–5pm Mon–Sat Sept–Jun;
7pm–11pm Fri–Sat & Wed Sept–Jun

DORSET

Places to Stay

BLANDFORD

ANVIL, THE
Salisbury Road, Pimperne, Blandford,
Dorset DT11 8UQ
Tel 01258 453431
Hotel Restaurant Public House
A la Carte Snacks/Drinks
Traditional British
*A 16th century thatched hotel/inn set
in a typical English country garden. All
rooms ensuite, colour TV, teasmade
and direct dial telephone. Licensed
bar. Non smoking bar. Beamed restaurant with log fire.*
P ᛗ ♀ ♨ Cc ᛒᛜ ᛕ (public
entrance/designated parking
area/WC/dining room/
restaurant/bar)
Typical tariff single/double room
£47.50/£75 Beds 11 Open all year
Typical 3 course meal £8.50 bar food;
£16.50 restaurant Seats bar 24; dining 24; restaurant 40 Open: bar
12pm–2.30pm & 6.15pm–11pm;
restaurant 12pm–2.15pm &
7pm–9.45pm

BOURNEMOUTH

LANGTRY MANOR
26 Derby Road, Bournemouth, Dorset
BH1 3QB
Tel 01202 290550 Fax 01202 290115
Email
langtrymanor@taxtips.demon.co.uk
Website
http://www.taxtips.demon.co.uk/lan
gtrymanor
Hotel
French Traditional British
*Built in 1877 by Edward VII as a love
nest for his mistress Lillie Langtry. A
Tudor style house with a majestic
dining room, stained glass windows,
inglenook fireplace, 4 poster beds,
tapestries and chandeliers. Tastefully
decorated. A perfect getaway and
oasis in the tree-lined streets of
Bournemouth.*
P ᛗ ♀ Cc ᛒᛜ ᛕ (some rooms) ᛕ (public entrance/designated parking
area/one bedroom, bathroom & WC
on same level/dining room/restau-
rant/bar/TV lounge)
Typical tariff single/double room
£69.75/£89.75 Beds 28 Open all year
Typical 3 course meal £19.75 Seats 50
Open 6.30pm–10.30pm

PAVILION HOTEL
22 Bath Road, Bournemouth, Dorset
BH1 2NS
Tel 01202 291266 Fax 01202 559264
Hotel Restaurant
A la Carte Snacks/Drinks
Traditional British
*All bedrooms have ensuite, tea/coffee
making facilities, TV, radio, telephone*

and hairdryers. Large car park, lift, night porter and room service available. 3 star hotel. STB 4 crowns commended.
🐕 ⬛ ⬛ ⬛ (public entrance/designated parking area/one bedroom, bathroom & WC on same level/dining room/restaurant/bar/TV lounge)
Beds 44 Open all year
Typical 3 course meal £12 Seats 80
Open from 6.30pm (8.30pm last orders)
VS members' discount 10%

ST ANTOINE GUEST HOUSE
2 Guildhill Road, Southbourne, Bournemouth, Dorset BH6 3ET
Tel 01202 433043
Guesthouse
Traditional British
Family-run guesthouse only minutes from the sea and river. Comfortable rooms with WHB tea/coffee and some ensuites. A quiet area on bus routes to Bournemouth and Christchurch. Off road parking.
P ⬛ ⬛
Typical tariff single/double room £18/£36 Beds 7

SAN REMO HOTEL
7 Dudley Road, Westcliff, Bournemouth, Dorset BH2 5JQ
Tel 01202 290558
B&B Hotel
Traditional British
A quiet and peaceful hotel concentrating on cleanliness and freshly cooked food. More suited to older guests. Special diets by arrangement.
P 🐕 ⬛ ⬛ (dining room) ⬛ (public

entrance/designated parking area/one bedroom, bathroom & WC on same level/dining room/restaurant/bar/TV lounge)
Typical tariff single/double room £27/£30 Beds 18 Open Easter–Oct
Seats 42

SWALLOW HIGHCLIFF HOTEL
St Michael's Road, Bournemouth, Dorset BH2 5DU
Tel 01202 557702
Hotel Restaurant
A la Carte French Snacks/Drinks
Traditional British
Bournemouth's largest hotel, with a spectacular cliff top location. Minutes from pier and town centre. Choice of two restaurants, both of which cater for vegans and can accommodate any diet. Indoor/outdoor pools, sauna, steam room, spa bath, gym, tennis court, driving net, putting green and snooker room.
🐕 ⬛ ⬛ Cc ✗ ⬛ ⬛ (public entrance/designated parking area/one bedroom, bathroom & WC on same level/dining room/restaurant/bar/TV lounge)
Typical tariff single/double room £85/£130 Beds 157 Open all year
Typical 3 course meal £20 Seats 120 & 35 Open terrace restaurant 12.30pm–2.30pm & 7pm–10pm; Robert Wild Room 7pm–10pm Mon–Sat

BRIDPORT

MONKTON WYLD SCHOOL
See **SPECIAL INTEREST**, page 228.

CHRISTCHURCH

FAIRWINDS GUESTHOUSE
24 Stour Road, Christchurch, Dorset
BH23 1PS
Tel 01202 483260
B&B Guesthouse
Traditional British
*A family-run and elegant Edwardian
house within easy reach of the town
centre, beaches, riverside walks.* No
evening meals.
P ✝ 📕 ✖
Typical tariff single/double room
£20/£16pp Beds 2

DORCHESTER

KINGCOMBE CENTRE, THE
See **SPECIAL INTEREST**, page 228.

LYME REGIS

FIRLEAS
8 Conway Close, Lyme Regis, Dorset
DT7 3BE
Tel 01297 443528
Guesthouse Private House
Chinese Indian Organic
*Situated in a quiet cul-de-sac above
Lyme Regis overlooking the sea. Quiet
garden where meals are offered to
disabled visitors. Disabled access on
the ground floor only. Single and twin
beded rooms available with hand
basins and second toilet.*
V 📕 Cc ✖ ↻ (public entrance/desig-
nated parking area/one bedroom,
bathroom & WC on same level/dining
room/TV lounge)

Typical tariff single/double room
£15.50/£31 Beds 2
Typical 3 course meal £9 Seats 6 *Eve
meals by arrangement*
VS members' discount 5% *3 nights+*

SHAFTESBURY

SUNRIDGE HOTEL
Bleke Street, Shaftesbury, Dorset
SP7 8AW
Tel 01747 853130 Fax 01747 852139
B&B Hotel Restaurant
Traditional British
*A small quality listed building dating
from 1877. Offers a friendly service in
a quiet town. Tastefully furnished and
modernised to include all the essen-
tials for a comfortable stay for either
the business person or holiday guest.
Indoor pool and sauna.*
P Cc ✖
Typical tariff single/double room
£39.50/£57.50 Beds 9 Open Feb–Dec
Typical 3 course meal £13.45 Seats 20
Open 7pm–8.30pm

SWANAGE

CLARKE, CAROL
30 Cluny Crescent, Swanage, Dorset
BH19 2BT
Tel 01929 421394
B&B
*Only 2 minutes to coastal path and
country park. Sea views.*
V ✖
Typical tariff single/double room
£15/£14pp Beds 2 Open all year
VS members' discount 10%

SEASHELLS HOTEL
7 Burlington Road, Swanage, Dorset
BH19 1LR
Tel 01929 422794
Hotel
A friendly family-run hotel. Situated opposite a safe sandy beach, golf, sailing, windsurfing and spectacular coastal hill walks. Health club and pool in hotel. Ample car parking area or can arrange lifts from the train/bus station.
V 𝕙 ✕ ⟰ ⌖ (public entrance/designated parking area/one bedroom, bathroom & WC on same level/dining room/restaurant/bar/TV lounge)
Typical tariff single/double room £18-£22/£18-£22pp Beds 10 Open all year
Typical 3 course meal £12 Seats 24

WAREHAM

ORCHARD, THE
West Road, West Lulworth,
Wareham, Dorset BH20 5RY
Tel 01929 400592
B&B
A family run B&B business with comfortable accommodation in a relaxed atmosphere. Home-grown produce when possible. Safe off road parking in walled garden. Easy access to Purbeck Hills, Poole, Bournemouth, Dorchester and Weymouth.
𝕙
Typical tariff double room from £28
Beds 3 Open all year *except Xmas*

TILIA HOUSE
115 East Street, Corfe Castle,

Wareham, Dorset BH20 5EG
Tel 01929 480043
B&B Private House
Organic Special Diets
A lovely energy line and healing spot. Lots of trees. Dowsing, meditation and New Age gossip sessions available.
V 𝕙 ⟰
Typical tariff double room £30 Beds 2
Open all year

WEYMOUTH

ROOKERY NOOK
Chapel Lane, Osmington, Weymouth,
Dorset DT3 6ET
Tel 01305 835933
B&B Private House
A modern home situated in a picturesque village near Weymouth. An ideal base from which to walk and tour. Visit NT houses, gardens or relax in the secluded garden or conservatory. Pretty ensuite twin bedroom, colour TV, radio, beverage facilities. Vegetarian or vegan breakfast. Guide books and maps to borrow.
V ⟰
Typical tariff single/double room
£25.30/£18.20pp Beds 1 Open
Mar–Nov
VS members' discount 10% *3 nights+*

Places to Eat

BLANDFORD

ANVIL, THE
See page 44.

England

BOURNEMOUTH

SALAD CENTRE
667 Christchurch Road, Bournemouth, Dorset BH7 6AA
Tel 01202 393673
Bistro Cafe Restaurant Take Away Tea Rooms
Fast Food Restaurant Snacks/Drinks Wholefoods
Dishes prepared daily on site using only pure and natural ingredients. These include raw fresh fruit and vegetables, Dorset-milled wholemeal flour, raw dark sugar, nuts, sun-dried fruits, brown rice, pulses, beans and herbs. Foods or ingredients containing dyes, colouring matter, artificial preservatives and other added chemicals do not feature!
V ✗ ⇸ ⚷ (public entrance/dining area)
Typical 3 course meal £5.25 Seats 60
Open 10am–5pm Mon–Sat
VS members' discount 5%

SWALLOW HIGHCLIFF HOTEL
See page 45.

SHAFTESBURY

SUNRIDGE HOTEL
See page 46.

EAST SUSSEX

Places to Stay

BRIGHTON

BRIGHTON TWENTY ONE, THE
21 Charlotte Street, Brighton, East Sussex, BN2 1AG
Tel 01273 686450/681617
Fax 01273 695560/681617
Email the21@pavilion.co.uk
Website http://www.chelsoft.demon.co.uk/21.htm
B&B
Fully ensuite and luxurious rooms. Large variety of choice for breakfast including 'scrambled eggless'. Fourposter beds and period furniture in some rooms. The bridal suite has an ivy-clad conservatory and courtyard. Special discounts available.
P ⚘ Cc ⇸ (some rooms)
Typical tariff room/suite £35.65/£57.75 Beds 7 Open all year

DUDLEY HOUSE
10 Madeira Place, Brighton, East Sussex BN2 1TN
Tel 01273 67694
Guesthouse
Relaxed, comfortable atmosphere. Tastefully decorated, spacious bedrooms with private bathrooms, colour TV, central heating and sea view. Standard rooms available. Excellent location close to the sea front, conference centre and all amenities.

48

This distinguished hotel is ideally placed for all major attractions.

All rooms are fully en-suite and exquisitely furnished.

Try our patio suite with its own conservatory and court yard.

Try the Victorian room with period furniture. Why not stay in the unique twin Green room.

Enjoy a delicious breakfast — either vegan, vegetarian, continental or full English cooked.

21 Charlotte Street
Brighton BN2 1AG
Tel: 01273 686450/681617
Fax: 01273 695560
e-mail: the21@pavilion.co.uk
http://www.chelsoft.demon.co.uk/21.htm

THE TWENTY ONE

OFFERS
10% off for 2 nights
20% off for 4 nights
30% off for 7 nights
(OFF OUR NORMAL TARIFF)

En-suite rooms from only
£17.50
per person per night sharing a room for a minimum of seven nights

49

P 🏠 ⚒✕
Typical tariff double room £25/£38
Beds 6 Open all year

FUNCHAL GUEST HOUSE

17 Madeira Place, Brighton, East
Sussex BN2 1TN
Tel 01273 603975 Fax 01273 603975
B&B
*A family-run guest house in central
Brighton close to the coach/railway
stations, Palace Pier, Royal Pavilion
and The Lanes. All rooms are comfortably furnished with colour TV, satellite
and video channel, radio/alarm and
free tea/coffee. Theatres, cinemas and
night clubs just a stroll away.*
🐾 🏠 Cc
Typical tariff single/double room
£14/£28 Beds 5

GRAND, THE

Kings Road, Brighton, East Sussex
BN1 2FW
Tel 01273 321188 Fax 01273 202694
Email grandbri@pavilion.co.uk
Web site
http://www.brighton.co.uk/hotels/gr
and
Hotel Leisure Club Restaurant
Table d'Hote Traditional British
*A separate vegetarian menu is avail-
able on request and anything on the
menu which is not suitable can be
adapted to suit guests' requirements.*
🐾 ⬜ 🏠 Cc ✕ ⚒✕ ♿ (public
entrance/designated parking
area/one bedroom, bathroom & WC
on same level/dining room/restau-
rant/bar/TV lounge)
Typical tariff single/double room
£145/£180 Beds 200 Open all year
Typical 3 course meal lunch £19.50;
dinner £25.50 Seats 120 Kings
Restaurant Open Mon–Sun
7.30am–10am, noon–2.30pm,
7pm–10.30pm

HARVEY'S

1 Broad Street, Brighton, East Sussex
BN2 1TJ
Tel 01273 699227 Fax 01273 699227
Guesthouse
Traditional British
*Located in a very central position.
Large clean bedrooms with colour TVs
and central heating. Some bedrooms
have private facilities and sea views.
Situated almost opposite the Palace
Pier, The Lanes, shops and entertain-
ment.*
🏠 (7 yrs+) ✕ ⚒✕
Typical tariff double room £30–£50
Beds 7 Open all year *except Xmas*
VS members' discount 10% *except
Bank Hols & July*

PASKINS HOTEL

18–19 Charlotte Street, Brighton, East
Sussex BN2 1AG
Tel 01273 601203 Fax 01273 621973
Email welcome@paskins.co.uk
Website http://www.paskins.co.uk
B&B Guesthouse Hotel
Organic
*A stylish 'green' B&B in a quiet street
in one of Victorian England's most
perfectly preserved conservation
areas. Most of the food is organic
and Paskins is very proud of its tradi-
tional vegetarian and vegan break-
fasts. All rooms are tastefully and*

individually designed.
♀ 家

Typical tariff single/double room
£30/£58 Beds 20 Open all year
VS members' discount 10% *excluding
Bank Hols*

ROWLAND HOUSE

21 St Georges Terrace, Brighton, East
Sussex BN2 1JJ
Tel 01273 603639
Guest House
*A RAC listed guesthouse set in a
quiet, charming Victorian terrace just
off the Kemptown shopping area and
near the famous Royal Crescent home
of stars and celebrities. A commitment
to cleanliness plus freedom to come
and go. Friendly atmosphere, good
food, good service and individual
attention assured.*
P 👭 Cc
Typical tariff single/double room
£20/£40 Beds 11 Open all year
VS members' discount 10%

HASTINGS

BARNETT, DEREK & MARGRIT

99 Lower Park Road, Hastings, East
Sussex TN34 3LE
Tel 01424 437623
B&B Private House
*Clean friendly private house in
Hastings overlooking the beautiful
Alexandra Park.*
V 👭 ♨ ঙ (one bedroom, bathroom
& WC on same level/dining)
Typical tariff double room £28
(£14pp) Beds 1 Open all year

RYE

JEAKE'S HOUSE

Mermaid Street, Rye, East Sussex
TN31 7ET
Tel 01797 222828 Fax 01797 222623
Email jeakeshouse@btinternet.com
Website http://www.s-h-
systems.co.uk/hotels/jeakes.html
B&B Hotel
Traditional British
*Standing on a beautiful ancient cob-
bled street, Jeake's House was once
the private residence of poet and
author Conrad Potter Aiken. Elegant
luxurious rooms with telephone, TV
and hot drinks tray. Comfortable oak
beamed parlour and book-lined bar.*
♀
Typical tariff single/double room
£22.50/£63 Beds 12 Open all year

ST LEONARDS ON SEA

COPPERBEECHES

41 Chapel Park Road, St Leonards on
Sea, East Sussex TN37 6JB
Tel 01424 714026
B&B Private House
Organic *(when available)*
*A relaxed friendly Victorian guest-
house situated within walking distance of Hastings town centre, station
and the beach. Offers a high standard
of accommodation, cooking, service
and cleanliness at very reasonable
prices. Off road parking for 4 cars.*
P 👭 (with notice) 家 ♨ ঙ (public
entrance 3 steps/one bedroom,
bathroom & WC on same level/
dining room)

Typical tariff single/double room
£15/£30 Beds 3 Open all year
VS members' discount 10%

TOWER HOUSE HOTEL
28 Tower Road West, St Leonards on
Sea, East Sussex TN38 0RG
Tel **01424 427217** Fax 01424 427217
Hotel
Traditional British
*The ambience of a country house but
situated close to all amenities. All
rooms have ensuite, TV, tea making
facilities, hair dryer, toiletries and
direct dial 'phones. Roaring log fires
in the winter. Separate licensed bar
and sun lounge which leads to flow-
ered patio and gardens. Easy road
parking. All meals are freshly prepared
and varied.*
P 盃 Cc ⁑ (bedrooms & dining
room)
Typical tariff single/double room
£34/£45.55 Beds 12 Open all year
Typical 3 course meal £12
**VS members' discount 1 night free
with week booking; 3 night breaks**

SEAFORD

SILVERDALE, THE
Sutton Park Road, Seaford, East
Sussex BN25 1RH
Tel **01323 491849** Fax 01323 891131
Email silverdale@mistral.co.uk
Website http://www.mistral.co.uk/sil-
verdale/silver.htm
**B&B Guesthouse Hotel Restaurant
Self Catering**
A la Carte Traditional British
Situated only 5 minutes from the
*beautiful Cuckmere Valley Bird
Sanctuary and Seven Sisters Country
Park. Part of the Heritage Coast and
in an Area of Outstanding Natural
Beauty. First class home cooking with
special diets catered for. All rooms
have TVs, clock radios, direct dial
telephones, fax/modem lines, email
facilities, tea/coffee making facilities
and canopied beds.*
♀ 盃 Cc ✗ ⁑ (some rooms)
Typical tariff single/double room
£20/£40 Beds 11 Open all year
Typical 3 course meal £16 *Open for
residents only*
VS members' discount 10% *except
specials*

Places to Eat

BRIGHTON

BURLINGTON PUBLIC HOUSE, THE
8 St Georges Road, Kemptown,
Brighton, East Sussex BN2
Tel **01273 683334**
**Public House Restaurant Take
Away**
*A vegetarian and vegan pub restau-
rant serving a full menu plus snacks,
daily specials and soups.*
V ✗ ♿ (public entrance/designated
parking area/dining area/bar)
Seats 120 Open 11.30am–10.30pm
VS members' discount 10%

GEORGE, THE
Trafalgar Street, Brighton, East Sussex
BN1 5EQ
Tel **01273 681055**

Public House Restaurant
Chinese Fast Food French Indian
Italian/Mediterranean Japanese
Lebanese Mexican Snacks/Drinks
Spanish Thai Traditional British
*Situated in the North Lanes of
Brighton and serving 100% vegetar-
ian/vegan food for about 10 years.
Outstanding reputation for food and
a relaxed atmosphere.*
V Cc ✗ ✸ ൠ (public entrance/din-
ing area/bar)
Typical 3 course meal £8.10 Seats 80
Open pub hours — food:
12pm–8.30pm Mon–Thurs;
12pm–7pm Fri–Sat; 12pm–5pm Sun

INFINITY FOODS CO-OP
25 North Road, Brighton, East Sussex
BN1 1YA
Tel 01273 603563 Fax 01273 675384
Email sales@infinityfoods.co.uk
Take Away Wholefood Shop
Fast Food Organic Snacks/Drinks
*A natural and organic wholefood
co-operative store selling the highest
quality products. A wide range of
delicious vegan breads baked daily on
the premises. Sweet and savoury,
vegetarian and vegan take away
foods.*
V

SNOOKIES
29 Tidy Street, Brighton, East Sussex
BN1 4EL
Tel 01273 677712
**Bistro Cafe Restaurant Sandwich
Bar Take Away Tea Rooms**
A la Carte Indian
Italian/Mediterranean Organic

Snacks/Drinks
*A small cafe/restaurant catering for
carnivores, vegetarians and vegans.
Soup and nut roast is always vegan.
Separate food preparation areas for
meat and vegetarian/vegan dishes.*
✗
Typical 3 course meal £10 Seats 28
Open 10am–10pm — ring to confirm

TROGS RESTAURANT & CAFE BAR
124 Kings Road, Brighton, East Sussex
BN1 2FA
Tel 01273 326302
Fax 01273 326302
Cafe Bar Restaurant
*Situated opposite the West Pier on
Brighton's seafront. A gourmet
vegetarian and vegan restaurant plus
a cafe bar with outside seating.*
V Cc ✸
Restaurant — Typical 3 course meal
£18 Seats 40 Open 6pm–10pm all
year
Cafe Bar — Seats 30 covered + outside
terraces Open 12pm–2pm &
6pm–11pm all year
VS members' discount 10%

**VEGETARIAN & VEGAN SANDWICH
SHOP, THE**
92a Trafalgar Street, Brighton, East
Sussex BN1 2ER
Tel 01273 623332
Sandwich Bar
Organic
*Sandwiches, organic breads, salads,
cakes, homemade organic soups and
health drinks.*
V Cc ✸
Seats 4 Open 8am–5.30pm Mon–Sat

HOVE

FROGANS RESTAURANT
117 Western Road, Hove, East Sussex
BN3 1DC
Tel 01273 773586
Cafe Restaurant Take Away
French Indian Italian/Mediterranean
Japanese Organic Thai
Traditional British
Good value for money organic food.
90% of dishes are vegan and 80% or
more of the food used is certified
organic which means it is produced
without chemical fetilisers, pesticides
or herbicides. Every effort is made to
recycle.
V ✗ 💺
Typical 3 course meal £7.75 *(lunch)*
Seats 18 + outside in summer
Open 10am–5pm Sun, Mon & Wed;
10am–9.15pm *(last orders)* Thurs–
Sat

SANCTUARY CAFE
51–55 Brunswick Street East, Hove,
East Sussex BN3 1AD
Tel 01273 770002
Cafe Restaurant
A "Bohemian hangout for the
discerning existentalist punter"
[Impact magazine]. A three floor
cafe/restaurant serving vegetarian
food, fabulous pastries and cakes,
loose teas, fresh ground coffee,
alcohol and entertainment in the
basement including music, film,
poetry and theatre.
V Cc ✗ 💺
Typical 3 course meal £15 Seats 120
Open 10am–11.30pm

LEWES

SEASONS OF LEWES
199 High Street, Lewes, East Sussex
BN7 2NS
Tel 01273 473968
Cafe Restaurant Take Away Tea
Rooms
Organic
A small family business run by
mother and daughter. Three quarters
of the menu is vegan and over half
the ingredients are organic.
Everything is made on the premises
and only stainless steel and glass
cookware is used. "Food for people
who care about what they eat."
Frozen individual meals and outside
catering available.
V ✗ 💺
Typical 3 course meal £8 Seats 40
Open 10am–6pm Tues–Sat

ST LEONARDS ON SEA

CHUTNEY BALTI HOUSE
375 London Road, St Leonards on
Sea, East Sussex TN37 6PP
Tel 01424 439436
Restaurant Take Away
Indian
Easy to find — situated in Silverhill on
one of the main roads running
through St Leonards. Established since
1994. Provides a selection of dishes
for vegetarians/vegans. Discount 10%
off minimum order of £10.
P Cc
Typical 3 course meal £15 Seats 35
Open 5.30pm–11pm Wed–Mon

PASTA PASTA
8 Grand Parade, St Leonards on Sea,
East Sussex TN38 0DD
Tel 01424 423608
Restaurant Take Away
Italian/Mediterranean
*Busy established restaurant situated
on the sea front in St Leonards. A
friendly atmosphere and outstanding
food at affordable prices. Pasta,
pizzas and a selection of salads from
the salad bar are available. "Come
and try us!"*
Cc ✕
Typical 3 course meal £12 Seats 50
Open 11am–11pm Mon–Fri

SEAFORD

SILVERDALE, THE
See page 52.

WADHURST

WEALDEN WHOLEFOODS
High Street, Wadhurst, East Sussex
TN5 6AA
Tel 01892 783065
Cafe Shop
Organic
*Wholefood shop with licensed cafe at
rear. A relaxed and homely atmosphere with friendly staff. Cosy log fire
in the winter and a pretty garden in
the summer. A wide range of
products is available including fresh
organic fruit and vegetables (deliv-
ered twice weekly).*
v ✕ ♨ ᕐ (public entrance/dining
area)
Typical 3 course meal £7–8 Seats 15

Open 9am–5.15pm Mon–Tues &
Thurs–Sat; 9am–4pm Wed

EAST YORKSHIRE

Places to Stay

BEVERLEY

**RUDSTONE WALK COUNTRY HOTEL
& COTTAGES**
South Cave, Brough, nr Beverley, East
Yorkshire HU15 2AH
Tel 01430 422230 Fax 01430 424552
B&B Farmhouse Hotel Self Catering
A la Carte Traditional British
*Renowned for its hospitality and good
food. Loved by business and holidaymakers alike. Tastefully converted
farm buildings next to farmhouse
where meals are served. All rooms
have ensuite, colour TV, telephone
and tea-making facilities, trouser
press, hairdryer and radio alarm.*
P ᕐ (by arrangement only) ♀ ☷ Cc
ᕐ (designated parking area/one bedroom, bathroom & WC on same
level/bar)
Typical tariff single/double room
£43/£58 Beds 21
Typical 3 course meal £16.50 Seats
10–22 Open 12pm–3pm & 7pm–1am

TUDOR ROSE HOTEL
Wednesday Market, Beverley, East
Yorkshire HU17 0DG
Tel 01482 882028
Hotel Public House Restaurant
A la Carte Snacks/Drinks

Traditional British

*All guests are assured a warm wel-
come to the elegant grade II listed
building which is situated in the
picturesque market town of Beverley.
Only 2 minutes from the railway
station and close to Beverley Minster.
8 miles from Hull and 3 miles from
Leconfield.*

P 🐕 ⛾ 🏠 Cc ✕ ⊭

Typical tariff single/double room
from £18/£39 Beds 7 Open all year
Typical 3 course meal £3.95 bar; £6.95
restaurant
VS members' discount 5%

BRIDLINGTON

ABBEY COURT HOTEL
31 Horsforth Avenue, Bridlington,
East Yorkshire YO25 3DG
Tel 01262 401402
B&B Hotel
Traditional British
*A small family-run hotel providing dis-
counts for OAPs and children. A bar
and TV lounge available. Some bed-
rooms ensuite. Tea/Coffee making
facilities in all rooms.*
P 🐕 (small animals, out of season) ⛾
🏠 ✕
Typical tariff single/double room
£15–£21 Beds 12 Open all year
Typical 3 course meal £20

SEAWIND'S GUEST HOUSE
48 Horsforth Avenue, Bridlington,
East Yorkshire YO15 3DF
Tel 01262 676330
Guesthouse
Traditional British

Car park available.
P ⛾ 🏠
Typical tariff single/double room
£13/£26 Beds 7 Open all year

COTTINGHAM

ROSEDALE B&B
9 Skidby Road, Little Weighton,
Cottingham, East Yorkshire
HU20 3UY
Tel 01482 846074
B&B
*A quiet country location approxi-
mately 10 miles from Hull city centre.
All rooms have TV plus tea and coffee
making facilities. Family room available, which includes a double and
two single beds, ensuite facilities
and a games room. Ample off road
parking.*
🐕 🏠 ⊭ ♿ (public entrance/desig-
nated parking area/one bedroom,
bathroom & WC on same level/dining
room/TV lounge)
Typical tariff single/double room
£15/£30 Beds 3 Open all year

Places to Eat

BEVERLEY

TUDOR ROSE HOTEL
See page 55.

ESSEX

Places to Stay

CHELMSFORD

SOUTH LODGE HOTEL
196 New London Road, Chelmsford,
Essex CM2 0AR
Tel 01245 264564 Fax 01245 492827
Hotel Restaurant
A la Carte Snacks/Drinks
Traditional British
*A friendly family-run 3 star hotel just
outside Chelmsford town centre.
Situated in pleasant grounds, it
provides an ideal base for visiting
business people. A full vegetarian and
vegan section is available on the a la
carte menu.*
🛏 ♀ ⚲ Cc ✗ ⅍ (areas)
Typical tariff single/double room
£59/£70 Beds 41 Open 24 hours
Typical 3 course meal £13.50 Seats 40
Open Mon–Fri 7am–9am &
12pm–2.30pm & 6.30pm–9.30pm;
Sat–Sun 7pm–10pm

Places to Eat

CHELMSFORD

FARMHOUSE FEAST RESTAURANT
The Street, Roxwell, Chelmsford,
Essex CM1 4PB
Tel 01245 248583 Fax 01245 248583
Restaurant
Organic Traditional British
*Situated in a late 15th century
beamed building in the centre of
Roxwell village. Retains many original
features, including a friendly ghost.
Fresh seasonal food, carefully
prepared to suit all tastes with an
interesting menu for vegetarians and
vegans.*
✗ ⅍ ⚷ (public entrance/dining
area)
Typical 3 course meal £14.50 Seats 86
Open Tues–Fri lunch & dinner

SOUTH LODGE HOTEL
See left.

COLCHESTER

CHAMPAGNE CHARLIE'S
105 High Street, Colchester, Essex
CO2 8BX
Tel 01206 369372 Fax 01206 579906
Restaurant Wine Bar
A la Carte Snacks/Drinks
Traditional British
*Two storey wine bar (downstairs) and
restaurant (upstairs). A special vege-
tarian and vegan menu is available. All
food is freshly cooked and nothing is
frozen.*
Cc ✗ ⅍
Typical 3 course meal £11.95 Seats 65
Open 11am–11pm Mon–Sat;
12pm–10.30pm Sun

GLOUCESTERSHIRE

Places to Stay

BADMINTON

PETTY FRANCE HOTEL
Dunkirk, Badminton, South
Gloucestershire GL9 1AF
Tel 01454 238361 Fax 01454 238768
Email hotel@pettyfrance.telme.com
Website
http://www.ds.dial.pipex.com/pet-
tyfrance/
Hotel Restaurant
International Traditional British
*A small country manor hotel with
award winning food. Situated on the
edge of the Cotswolds close to Bath
and Bristol.*
🐕 ♀ 🏧 Cc ✕ 🍴 ♿ (public
entrance/designated parking
area/one bedroom, bathroom & WC
on same level/dining room/restau-
rant/bar/TV lounge)
Typical tariff single/double room
£69/£89 Beds 20 Open all year
Typical 3 course meal £16.95 Seats 70
Open Mon–Sun 12–2pm &
7pm–10pm
VS members' discount 5% *except
public hols*

CHELTENHAM

HALLERY HOUSE HOTEL
48 Shurdington Road, Cheltenham,
Gloucestershire GL53 0JF
Tel 01242 578450 Fax 01242 521403
Email hallery.house@bigfoot.com
Website
http://www.Glos.IBP.co.uk/hotels/hal
lery/index/htm
Hotel
A la Carte Italian/Mediterranean
Traditional British
*A family-run hotel located in a
Victorian villa on the south side of
Cheltenham Spa. Prides itself on
customer service and excellent food.
Caters for all tastes and diets and
welcomes all. Cycling and walking
packages available.*
P (better choice with notice) ♀ 🐕 🏧
Cc ✕ 🍴
Typical tariff single/double room
£38/£58 Beds 16 Open all year
Typical 3 course meal £15.95 Seats 22
Open Mon–Sun 7pm–last orders
VS members' discount 10% *except
package deals*

**PRESTBURY HOUSE HOTEL &
RESTAURANT, THE**
The Burgage, Prestbury, Cheltenham,
Gloucestershire GL52 3DN
Tel 01242 529533 Fax 01242 227076
Website
http://www.smoothhound.co.uk/hot
els/prestbur.html
Hotel Restaurant
French Traditional British
*A 300-year-old country manor house
hotel situated in secluded 5 acres of
grounds beneath Cleeve Hill. Only
1.5 miles from Cheltenham town
centre. Ensuite rooms, log fires, four
poster beds and spa baths. Facilities
include bike hire, croquet and hill
walking. AA/RAC 3 star. ETB 4 crown*

commended.
♀ ♨ Cc ✗ ➿ ♿ (public
entrance/designated parking
area/one bedroom, bathroom & WC
on same level/dining room/restau-
rant/bar)
Typical tariff single/double room
£73.50/£91 Beds 17 Open all year
Typical 3 course meal £25 Seats 65
Open all year
**VS members' discount: any 2 nights
for 2 people sharing, dinner and B&B
— £53pp per night** *not during race
meetings*

WOTTON UNDER EDGE

COOMBE LODGE
Wotton Under Edge, Gloucestershire
GL12 7NB
Tel 01453 845057
B&B Private House
*A family-run Georgian country house
in the South Cotswolds. Large garden,
beautiful views and scenic walks from
the door. Spacious and tastefully
decorated rooms with period furniture, including four poster bed. All
rooms equipped to high standard
with wash basin, beverage facilities
and TV. Guests' own sitting room.
Sauna available.*
V ♞ ♨ ➿
Typical tariff single/double room
£28/£44 Beds 3 Open all year *except
Xmas & New Year*

> Please mention the Vegan
> Travel Guide when contacting a
> listed business or advertiser

Places to Eat

BADMINTON

PETTY FRANCE HOTEL
See page 58.

CHELTENHAM

ORANGE TREE, THE
317 High Street, Cheltenham,
Gloucestershire GL50 3HW
Tel 01242 234232
Restaurant Take Away
Chinese French Indian
Italian/Mediterranean Macrobiotic
Mexican Snacks/Drinks Spanish
Thai
*Short walk from the heart of
Cheltenham town centre. A relaxing
jazz/classical atmosphere and an
exciting daily array of speciality
organic vegetarian and vegan dishes
from around the world. Something
to suit every appetite and pocket.
Fully licensed for organic wines,
beers, lagers and ciders.*
V Cc ✗ ➿ (areas)
Typical 3 course meal £9–£12 Seats
40 + courtyard seating Open
9am–4.30pm Mon; 9am–9pm
Tues–Wed; 9am–9pm Thurs;
9am–9.10pm Fri–Sat
VS members' discount 10% *2 courses
per person+*

**PRESTBURY HOUSE HOTEL &
RESTAURANT, THE**
See page 58.

STROUD

MILLS CAFE
Witheys Yard, High Street, Stroud,
Gloucestershire
Tel 01453 752222
Cafe Restaurant Tea Rooms
Around the World Organic
Snacks/Drinks
*Down an alley off the high street,
a leafy courtyard and cafe with
other small shops. Established for
11 years serving espresso and
cappucino coffee, tea, juices and
alcohol. Home made cakes, soups,
salads, sandwiches and hot meals for
lunch. Some vegan food always
available, more possible with prior
notice.*
� (area)
Typical 3 course meal £10.15 Seats 40
+ 30 outside Open 8.30am–6pm
Mon–Sat; 6pm–11pm Fri–Sat

MOTHER MATURE
2 Bedford Street, Stroud,
Gloucestershire GL5 1AY
Tel 01453 758202 Fax 01453 752595
Cafe Delicatessen Sandwich Bar
Take Away
Fast Food Snacks/Drinks
*A town centre food shop on 3 floors
serving 'food you can trust' and
where traditional values count. 90%
vegetarian food with some vegan
dishes.*
✗ ✗ ♿ (public entrance)
Typical 3 course meal £7.10 Seats 36
Open 9am–5.30pm Mon–Sat; Cafe
9am–4.30pm

HAMPSHIRE

Places to Stay

BISHOP'S WALTHAM

ANCHOR COTTAGE
Bank Street, Bishop's Waltham,
Hampshire SO32 1AN
Tel 01489 894935
B&B Private House
*Quiet comfortable accommodation in
a modern cottage. Attractive setting
close to village centre with shops,
banks, pubs, restaurants, etc. Tea/
coffee making facilities in each room.
Central heating, constant hot water,
bath and shower. Pretty garden.
Private off street car parking. Superb
four course vegetarian and vegan
breakfasts.*
V ✗
Typical tariff single/double room
£17/£34 Beds 2 Open all year

ISLE OF WIGHT

BROOKSIDE FORGE HOTEL
Brookside Road, Freshwater, Isle of
Wight PO40 9ER
Tel 01983 754644
Hotel
Traditional British
*A recently converted hotel located in
pleasant terraced gardens in a quiet
tree-lined road. Close to all three Bays
in West Wight. All rooms are well
equipped with colour TV, tea/coffee
making facilities and hairdryers.*

Pleasant dining room and comfortable lounge and bar. Private car park. Good home cooked food and a warm welcome.
P 🐾 ♀ 盃 Cc ✕ 🍴 (areas)
Typical tariff single/double room £19.50/£39 Beds 9 Open all year
Typical 3 course meal £8.95 Seats 24 Open all year
VS members' discount 10%

CLARENDON HOTEL, THE
The Wight Mouse Inn, Chale, Isle of Wight PO38 2HA
Tel 01983 730431
Freehouse Hotel
A la Carte Fast Food Snacks/Drinks Traditional British
A 17th century coaching inn with charm and character standing in its own grounds. All rooms have colour TVs and all bathrooms have hairdryers. Excellent food and hospitality. The Wight Mouse Inn is attached to the hotel and has open fires and live music every evening.
🐾 盃 Cc ✕ 🍴 (area) ♿ (public entrance/designated parking area/one bedroom, bathroom & WC on same level/dining room/restaurant/bar/TV lounge)
Typical tariff single/double room £25–£35/£50–£70 Beds 15
Open all year
Typical 3 course meal £10 Seats 200
Open all year

DIVYA-KRUPA
Kemming Road, Whitwell, Isle of Wight PO38 2QT
Tel 01983 731279

B&B Chalet Private House
Italian/Mediterranean Macrobiotic Mexican Organic Spanish
Peaceful bungalow with new and updated facilities situated in a small picturesque village. Lovely garden to relax in. Surrounded by farms and downs. Beautiful walks to coast. On main travel routes. Chalet also available. Vegan cook.
V 盃 🍴
Typical tariff single/double room £15pp Beds 4 Open all year *except Xmas & first week Jan*

SEAWARD GUEST HOUSE
14–16 George Street, Ryde, Isle of Wight PO33 2EW
Tel 01983 563168 Fax 01983 563168
B&B Guesthouse
Chinese French Indian Italian/Mediterranean
Only 2 minutes walk from Hovercraft terminal, railway and bus station. Close to the ice rink, pier, bowling alley, public swimming pool, dotto train, fun fair and beaches. All rooms have hot and cold water, tea/coffee facilities. Packed lunches and evening meals by arrangement. Bike hire and courtesy coach available.
盃 🍴 (areas) ♿ (public entrance/one bedroom, bathroom & WC on same level)
Typical tariff single/double room £15/£30 Beds 7 Open all year
Typical 3 course meal £7

> **Please mention the** Vegan Travel Guide **when contacting a listed business or advertiser**

England

LYNDHURST

STABLE END
Emery Down, Lyndhurst, Hampshire
SO43 7FJ
Tel 01703 282504
B&B
Traditional British
*A welcoming family home. Converted
Victorian stables and Edwardian
cottage. Relaxed atmosphere with
rambling garden and ample parking
facilities. Lovely forest views with
ponies usually outside the gate.*
🍴✖

Typical tariff single/double room
£20/£20pp Beds 2 Open Jan–Dec

PORTSMOUTH

HAMILTON HOUSE
95 Victoria Road North, Southsea,
Portsmouth, Hampshire PO5 1PS
Tel 01705 823502 Fax 01705 823502
B&B Guesthouse
*Delightful family-run guesthouse. 5
minutes from ferry terminals, railway
stations, Guildhall, University and city
centre. Colour TV and tea/coffee making facilities in all rooms. Large family
rooms available. Early breakfast served
for ferry passengers. RAC 4 crowns,
AA acclaimed and ETB 2 crown
commended.*
P ♨ ✖ (areas)
Typical tariff double room from £36
Beds 9 Open all year

> **Please mention the** Vegan
> Travel Guide **when contacting a
> listed business or advertiser**

Places to Eat

HAVANT

COUNTRY KITCHEN
Havant Arts Centre, Old Town Hall,
East Street, Havant, Hampshire
PO9 1BS
Tel 01705 486505 Fax 01705 498577
Cafe Restaurant Take Away
Organic Snacks/Drinks
*Enjoy a triple experience – the Arts
Centre and Museum in the same
building, as well as the locally
renowned bakes, soups, unique
quiches and cakes of Country Kitchen.
The menu changes daily but there is
always something for vegans. Free
re-fill filter coffee, newspapers and
non-smoking. Licensed. Friendliness is
its trademark.*
V ✖ 🍴 ♿ (public entrance/desig-
nated parking area/dining area/bar)
Typical 3 course meal £6.95 Seats 48
Open 9.30am–4.30pm Mon–Sat

ISLE OF WIGHT

CLARENDON HOTEL, THE
See page 61.

SOUTHAMPTON

SAFFRON VEGETARIAN BISTRO
5 Bedford Place, Southampton,
Hampshire SO5 2DB
Tel 01703 369666
Bistro
The chef won the 1996/7 Winter

Soup Competition in BBC Good Food magazine with a vegan soup. Half the items on the menu are suitable for vegans and many other items can be adapted.

V Cc ✕ ⊭

Typical 3 course meal £12.95 Seats 24
Open 11am–2.30pm Mon–Sat;
7pm–11pm Wed–Sat

TOWN HOUSE, THE
59 Oxford Street, Southampton,
Hampshire SO14 3DL
Tel 01703 340446
Restaurant
Fine cuisine in one of the first vegetarian restaurants in the country to be recommended by Egon Ronay. Considered to be Southampton's leading vegetarian restaurant.
V Cc ⊭
Typical 3 course meal £12.95 Seats 28
Open 12pm–2pm Tues–Fri;
7pm–9.30pm Tues–Sat

SOUTHSEA

COUNTRY KITCHEN
59 Marmion Road, Southsea,
Hampshire PO5 2AX
Tel 01705 811425
Cafe Restaurant Take Away
Organic Snacks/Drinks
Renowned for delicious food, made daily on the premises. Menu changes daily. Many fat-free dishes and always something for vegans. Speciality teas, free re-fill coffee and take away service. Free newspapers and plenty of smiles.
V ✕ ⊭ & (public entrance/desig-

nated parking area/dining area/bar)
Typical 3 course meal £6.95 Seats 70
Open 9.30pm–5pm Mon–Sat

HEREFORDSHIRE

Places to Stay

HAY ON WYE

OLD POST OFFICE, THE
Llanigon, Hay on Wye, Herefordshire
HR3 5QA
Tel 01497 820008
B&B
A 17th century listed house full of character. Warm and welcoming with oak beams, oak floorboards and antique furniture. Set in outstandingly beautiful Brecon Beacons National Park, very close to the Black Mountains and only 2 miles from the world famous second hand book town of Hay on Wye.
V 🐴 ⊭
Typical tariff double room £30–£40
Beds 3 Open all year
VS members' discount 10% *1 week+ & special rates at quiet times*

HEREFORD

POPLARS, THE
Ewyas Harold, Hereford HR2 0HU
Tel 01981 240516 Fax 01981 240516
B&B Private House
Victorian house, with character, is situated in the Golden Valley. Relax in

the sitting room, enjoy the lovely views. Ideal for walking in the Black Mountains, visiting historic churches and ruined castles. Sumptuous breakfasts. Evening meal and packed lunches by arrangement for B&B guests only.

V 盉 ✕ ᐟ✹

Typical tariff single/double room £17/£32 Beds 3 Open all year
Typical 3 course meal £14 Seats 5

KINGTON

PENRHOS COURT
Kington, Herefordshire HR5 3LH
Tel 01544 230720 Fax 01544 230754
Hotel Restaurant School of Food & Health
Italian/Mediterranean Organic
The first restaurant to be awarded the Soil Association Organic symbol. Delicious four course dinner with emphasis on vegetables, grains, seeds and fruit. A vegan option for the main course and all remaining courses vegetarian or vegan. Vegan chef/owner.

♀ 盉 Cc

Typical tariff single/double room £55/£80 Beds 15 Open 7.30pm–9.30pm (restaurant)
VS members' discount 5%

VOWCHURCH

OLD VICARAGE GUEST HOUSE, THE
Golden Valley, Vowchurch, Herefordshire HR2 0QD
Tel 01981 550357
Fax 01981 550357

Guesthouse
Warm hospitality guaranteed in Victorian house of character in the peaceful Golden Valley. Home of Lewis Carroll's brother. Attractively presented, quality breakfasts. Dinners by arrangement using fresh local homecooked produce. Restful nights in attractive ensuite rooms.

P 🐾 (by arrangement) 盉 ᐟ✹

Typical tariff single/double room £19/£19pp Beds 3 Open all year except Xmas

Places to Eat

HEREFORD

PULSE CAFE, THE
89 East Street, Hereford HR1 2LU
Tel 01432 268473
Cafe Restaurant Take Away
Fast Food Italian/Mediterranean Mexican Snacks/Drinks Spanish Thai
A limited company and workers co-operative. Main attractions include raw energy salads, luscious cakes, possibly the best coffee in town. Colourful, friendly and professional. Live music, cabaret nights, party nights and theme food nights.

V ✕ ᐟ✹ (until 3pm)

Typical 3 course meal £7.50 Seats 40 Open 9am–5pm Tues–Sat; 10am–3pm Sun

KINGTON

PENRHOS COURT
See left.

ROSS ON WYE

OAT CUISINE
47 Broad Street, Ross on Wye,
Herefordshire HR9 7DY
Tel 01989 566271
Bistro Cafe Shop Take Away
Snacks/Drinks
*A three in one business including a
bistro/cafe, a take away service and a
shop where everyone is welcome.
Taste is considered 'everything' and
nearly all the food is made on the
premises. Eat in or take away but
don't forget to sample the huge
range of salads available.*
V ✗ ⊁ ♿ (public entrance/dining
area)
Typical 3 course meal £7.50 Seats 25
Open 8am–5pm Mon–Fri; 8am–5pm
Sat; 11am–4pm Sun

HUMBERSIDE

Places to Stay

HULL

ACORN GUEST HOUSE
719 Beverley High Road, Hull,
Humberside HU6 7JN
Tel 01482 853248 Fax 01482 853248
Guesthouse
Chinese Italian/Mediterranean
Traditional British
*Small family-run guesthouse with
large south facing gardens. Situated
on the main A1079 Hull to
Beverley/York Road.*

P 🐕 🛏 ✗
Typical tariff single/double room
£18.22/£36 Beds 4
Typical 3 course meal £5 Seats 8 *(residents only)*

WHEATSHEAF HOUSE
Maint Street, Welnick, Hull, East
Yorkshire HU12 0RY
Tel 01964 630390
B&B
Continental Breakfast
Traditional British
*Situated in a 350-year-old beamed
building and within easy reach of
Spurn Point Bird Sanctuary. A friendly
and personal customer-oriented bed
and breakfast. Private bathroom,
lounge and dining room with TV,
games and books available.*
P 🛏
Typical tariff single/double room
£15/£30 Beds 3

Places to Eat

HULL

GT'S OMELETTE HOUSE
11–12 Albion Street, Hull,
Humberside HU1 3TD
Tel 01482 328603 Fax 01482 221473
Email tambards@aol.com
Bistro Restaurant
Traditional British
*Privately run and owned restaurant.
All meals freshly cooked and made to
order. Pure vegetable oil only used in
coatings and meals cooked in olive oil
by request. No frozen chips or burg-*

ers. Fully licensed. Located in the town centre.
Cc ✗ ⊬ ⌖ (public entrance/dining area)
Typical 3 course meal £8 Seats 80
Open 9am–8pm Mon–Sat

HITCHCOCKS VEGETARIAN RESTAURANT
1–2 Bishop Lane, High Street, Hull, Humberside HU1 1PA
Tel 01482 320233
Restaurant
Afro Caribbean Cajun Chinese French Indian Italian/Mediterranean Lebanese Mexican Spanish Thai
A buffet style menu is available with normally around 20 different dishes. Customers can help themselves and eat at much as they like. This includes a starter, dessert and coffee or tea. The theme for the evening is chosen by the first person to book eg Chinese or Mexican. Bookings preferred but not essential.
V ✗ ⊬ (on request) ⌖ (dining area/bar)
Typical 3 course meal £10 Seats 60
Open 8.15pm
VS members' discount 20% *on full price*

STUDIO 10¹/₂
10¹/₂–11 King Street, Hull, Humberside HU1 2JJ
Tel 01482 224625
Email ppoma@global.co.uk
Cafe Restaurant
A la Carte Italian/Mediterranean Organic Snacks/Drinks
Cc ✗ ⊬ ⌖ (public entrance/desig-nated parking area/dining area/bar)
Typical 3 course meal £1–£11 Seats 100 Open 10am–5pm; 6pm–10pm

HULL

ZOO CAFE, THE
80b Newland Avenue, Hull, East Yorkshire HU5 3AB
Tel 01482 494352
Cafe
Indian Italian/Mediterranean Mexican Snacks/Drinks
A very friendly, lively and relaxed cafe.
V
Seats 35 Open 10am–6pm Mon–Sat

KENT
Places to Stay

ASHFORD

WATERKANT GUEST HOUSE
Moat Road, Headcorn, Ashford, Kent TN27 9NT
Tel 01622 890154
B&B Guesthouse Private House
Traditional British
Situated on the edge of the attractive old Wealden village of Headcorn and nestling in beautiful gardens. Shops, buses and railway station a short distance away. Bedrooms contain 3 poster beds, tea/coffee making facilities and TV. Ensuite or private facilities available. Visitors' private sitting room and summerhouse.
P ⊞ ⊬

Typical tariff double room from
£18pp Beds 2 Open all year
VS members' discount 10%

BROADSTAIRS

DEVON HURST HOTEL
Eastern Esplanade, Broadstairs, Kent
CT10 1DR
Tel 01843 863010 Fax 01843 868940
Hotel
Snacks/Drinks Traditional
Small family-run seafront hotel situ-
ated on the Eastern Esplanade over-
looking the English Channel. Home
cooking with any diet catered for. All
rooms ensuite with colour TV, hairdry-
ers, tea-making facilities and clock
radios. Day trips to Ostende and
France can be booked via the hotel.
P ♀ Cc ✕ 🐾 (over 5 yrs) ⬛✻ (some
beds)
Typical tariff double room £44 Beds 9
Open 1pm–12am
Typical 3 course meal £10 Seats 20
Open breakfast 8.30am–9am; dinner
6pm

CANTERBURY

TANNER OF WINGHAM, THE
44 High Street, Wingham,
Canterbury, Kent CT3 1AB
Tel 01227 720532
B&B Restaurant
Traditional British (*with a difference*)
Situated in historic village only 6 miles
from Canterbury and Sandwich.
Heavily beamed building dating from
1440. Monthly changing imaginative
meals. 8 vegetarian and/or vegan

main courses always available (6 on
Sun).
🐾 ♀ 🈺 Cc
Typical tariff single/double room
£20/£39 Beds 5 Open all year
Typical 3 course meal £15 Seats 60
Open 7pm–9pm *(last orders)*
Mon–Sat; 12.30pm–1.30pm *(last*
orders) Sun

WALTHAM COURT HOTEL &
CHIVES RESTAURANT
Kake Street, Petham, Canterbury,
Kent CT4 5SB
Tel 01227 700413 Fax 01227 700127
Email
sgw.chives@waltham@dial.pipex.com
Website http://www.s-h-
systems.co.uk/hotels/waltham.html
Hotel Restaurant
New English/World
Situated only 12 minutes from
Canterbury and 20 minutes from the
Channel Tunnel. Surrounded by some
of the most beautiful countryside in
Southern England. Ideally situated for
touring or for a hideaway. All rooms
are ensuite with colour TV, radio
alarm, and tea/coffee making facili-
ties. Chives Restaurant is well known
for its vegetarian and vegan food.
♀ 🈺 Cc ⬛✻ (areas) ♿ (designated
parking area/one bedroom, bathroom & WC on same level/restau-
rant/bar)
Typical tariff single/double room
£40/£60 Beds 4 Open all year
Typical 3 course meal £17 Open dinner Wed–Sat; lunch Sun
VS members' discount 5% *short*
break rates only

EAST PECKHAM

ROYDON HALL
See **SPECIAL INTEREST**, page 229.

EDENBRIDGE

JESSOPS
Tonbridge Road, Bough Beech,
Edenbridge, Kent TN8 7AU
Tel 01892 870428
B&B
*A 15th century Kentish cottage with
beams, open fireplaces, large garden
and pond with ducks and geese.
Situated on the B2027 but surrounded by open countryside. Easy
access to the M25, Gatwick, Dover
and Euro Star.*
P ⊁ & (public entrance/designated
parking area/one bedroom, bathroom & WC on same level/dining
room)
Typical tariff single/double room
£20/£20pp Beds 3 Open all year

FOLKESTONE

ROSA VILLA GUEST HOUSE
237 Dover Road, Folkestone, Kent
CT19 6NH
Tel 01303 251415
Email rosa@booklinks.u–net.co.uk
Website
http://www.netlink.co.uk/users/shep-
way/rosa/htm
Guesthouse
*Friendly, family-run guesthouse close
to all amenities. Member of the
Vegetarian Society Food & Drink
Guild. All breakfasts freshly cooked to*
*order. Full English vegan breakfast on
menu. Family rooms available. All
rooms have tea/coffee making facilities, colour TV, washbasins and complimentary toiletries.*
⊛ ⊁
Typical tariff single/double room
£18.21/£30.36 Beds 5 Open all year
except Xmas & New Year
VS members' discount 5%

LAMBERHURST

**LAMBERHURST TEA ROOMS &
CHRA PASTA**
The Down, Lamberhurst, Kent
TN3 8ES
Tel 01892 890891 Fax 01892 526133
B&B Restaurant Tea Rooms
Italian Traditional Snacks/Drinks
*A 19th century beamed property sur-
rounded by common land. Ideal loca-
tion for touring and walking. Close to
Scotney Castle, Bayham Abbey ruins
and Bewl Water. Advance bookings
for B&B. Dine by candlelight in a cosy
beamed restaurant with music and
atmosphere.*
P ⊛ Cc ⊁ (bedrooms) & (public
entrance/WC/dining room/restau-
rant)
Typical tariff single/double room
from £21/£35 Beds 2 Open Mar–Dec
— closed Xmas & New Year
Typical 3 course meal £12.95 Seats
30+ Open 7.30pm–10.30pm
Thurs–Sat

TUNBRIDGE WELLS

OLD PARSONAGE, THE
Church Lane, Frant, nr Tunbridge
Wells, Kent TN3 9DX
Tel 01892 750773 Fax 01892 750773
B&B
Traditional British
*Award winning Georgian country
house, peacefully situated by the
church in the pretty village of Frant.
Overlooking Lord Abergavenny's
Deer Park on one side and church
on the other. Offers superb accom-
modation including luxurious ensuite
bedrooms, antique furnished
reception rooms and flower-filled
conservatory.*
P 🐕 🏛 Cc ⚓
Typical tariff single/double room
£42/£65 Beds 3 Open all year

RUSSELL HOTEL, THE
80 London Road, Tunbridge Wells,
Kent TN1 1DZ
Tel 01892 544833 Fax 01892 515846
Email russell_hotel@globalnet.co.uk
Website
http://www.globalnet.co.uk/~rus-
sell_hotel
Hotel
A la Carte
*The hotel is situated near the town
centre and is accessible 24 hours a
day. A classical restaurant is situated
within the hotel with an a la carte
menu. All meals are prepared to order
with fresh ingredients and market
vegetables.*
P ⚥ Cc ⚓ (some rooms)
Typical tariff single/double room

£68/£80 Beds 24 Open all year
Typical 3 course meal £20 Seats 40
Open breakfast 7am–9.30am
Mon–Sat *(8am–10am Sun & Bank
Hols)*; lunch 12pm–2.30pm; dinner
7pm–10pm Mon–Sat *(7pm–9pm Sun
& Bank Hols)*

Places to Eat

ASHFORD

GOOD INTENT, THE
Frith Road, Aldington, Ashford, Kent
TN25 7HQ
Tel 01233 720426
Public House Restaurant
*A cosy, friendly country inn with an
excellent vegetarian and vegan menu.
Pool and darts available.*
V (menu) **⚥ Cc**
Typical 3 course meal £10 Seats 20
Open 12pm–2.30pm & 6pm–11pm

BIRCHINGTON

SMUGGLERS RESTAURANT
212 Canterbury Road, Birchington,
Kent CT7 9AQ
Tel 01843 841185 Fax 01843 841237
Restaurant
A la Carte French Traditional British
*The leading a la carte restaurant in
the area with customers coming from
a 50 mile radius. Approximately 2% of
the menu is vegan and 6% suitable for
vegetarians.*
Typical 3 course meal £10–£20 Seats
70 Open 11.45am onwards; 6.30pm
onwards — except Mon

CANTERBURY

CANTERBURY WHOLEFOODS
10 The Borough, Canterbury, Kent,
CT1 2DR
Tel 01227 464623 Fax 01227 764838
Take Away Wholefood Shop
Chinese Indian
Italian/Mediterranean Japanese
Lebanese Macrobiotic Mexican
Organic Thai
*A wholesale and retail store run as a
workers' co-operative with 3 of the 10
members being vegan. An extensive
range of vegan products available
including fresh, chilled and frozen
foods. Organic fruit and vegetables
always available. Vegan take away
rolls, Sosmix rolls, etc made daily.*
V
VS members' discount 5%

TANNER OF WINGHAM, THE
See page 67.

WALTHAM COURT HOTEL &
CHIVES RESTAURANT
See page 67.

EAST PECKHAM

ROYDON HALL
See **SPECIAL INTEREST**, page 229.

FOLKESTONE

INDIA, THE
1 The Old High Street, Folkestone,
Kent CT20 1RJ
Tel 01303 259155
Restaurant

French Indian
*The Chef and Patron is Monsieur Ali
Ashraf, formerly of the famous Rama
Sita Restaurant in Holland Park,
London. Hailed as the creator of
'Nouvelle Cuisine Indienne'.
Traditional Indian cooking using
freshly ground spices and fine herbs
as used in ancient times. More exotic
and specialised dishes require 24
hours notice.*
東 Cc
Typical 3 course meal £12.50 Seats 46
Open 12pm–2pm & 6pm–10.30pm —
except Mon, Xmas Day & Boxing Day
VS members' discount 10% *cash pay-
ments*

LAMBERHURST

LAMBERHURST TEA ROOMS &
CHRA PASTA
See page 68.

LANCASHIRE
Places to Stay

BLACKPOOL

IVERNIA, THE
10 Kirby Road, Blackpool, Lancashire
FY1 6EB
Tel 01253 21636
Guesthouse
*Family-run guesthouse just off the
promenade, close to all amenities.
Centrally heated rooms with tea-
making facilities and TV. The owners*

eat mainly vegan food so vegan food and drink (including alcohol) present no problem. Evening meals available for extra £4. Advanced booking preferred.

♀ 🏃 ⇝ (dining room)
Typical tariff single/double room £10–£15/£20–£30 Beds 10 Open Easter–Oct — other times by arrangement

WILDLIFE HOTEL, THE
39 Woodfield Road, Blackpool, Lancashire FY1 6AY
Tel 01253 346143
B&B
Established for 8 years and situated close to attractions and sea. Run by a committed vegan and animal rights supporter. All rooms ensuite. "Your reputation is a credit to not only the town, but also to our Association" (The Hotel & Guesthouse Association). Has flourished against all odds.
V 🐈 ♀ 🏃 ⇝ ♿ (has accommodated wheelchairs but no specific access ramps)
Typical tariff single/double room £16/£16pp Beds 10 Open all year
VS members' discount 10%

CHORLEY

SHAW HILL HOTEL, GOLF & COUNTRY CLUB
Preston Road, Whittle le Woods, Chorley, Lancashire PR6 7PP
Tel 01257 269221 Fax 01257 261223
Golf Course Hotel Leisure Centre
Private House Restaurant
Sandwich Bar

A la Carte Snacks/Drinks
Magnificent Georgian exterior with many original features and lavish furnishings. Superbly appointed, tranquil and comfortable with a reputation for friendly attentive service. Pool, gym, sauna, solarium, etc at the leisure centre (opening summer 1998).
Lancashire Life Restaurant of the Year 1996/7.
🐈 ♀ 🏃 Cc ✗ ♿ (public entrance/one bedroom, bathroom & WC on same level/dining room/restaurant/bar/TV lounge)
Typical tariff single/double room £65/£80 Beds 30 Open all year — except Xmas Day evening, Boxing Day & New Years Day
Typical 3 course meal £14.50 Seats 90 Open Mon–Fri 12pm–1.45pm & 7pm–9.45pm

CLITHEROE

STIRK HOUSE HOTEL
Gisburn, nr Clitheroe, Lancashire
Tel 01200 445581 Fax 01200 445937
Country Club Hotel
A la Carte French
Italian/Mediterranean Snacks/Drinks
Traditional British
A 16th century manor house with open fires, beautiful restaurant and conference facilities for up to 240. Rural setting with easy access and safe parking. Other facilities include a pool, squash court, gym, solarium, toning tables, steam room, sauna, hot spa and beautitian. A happy hotel. Miserable customers not welcome!
P ♀ 🏃 Cc ✗ ⇝ (restaurant) ♿ (pub-

WILDLIFE HOTEL
Licensed

39 Woodfield Road, Blackpool FY1 6AX
Tel. 01253 346143

Paradise for vegans and vegetarians

Small friendly hotel only 2 minutes from the sea and near all the attractions

No Smoking • All en-suite • TV and Tea/Coffee in all rooms • Full central heating
Parking available • B&B from £16pp • Open all year round

100% Vegan & Vegetarian

lic entrance/one bedroom, bathroom
& WC on same level/bar/TV lounge)
Typical tariff single/double room
£60/£80 Beds 50 Open all year
Typical 3 course meal £15 Seats 90
Open breakfast 7.30am–9.30am;
lunch 12pm–2pm; dinner 7pm–10pm

PRESTON

BARTON GRANGE HOTEL
Garstang Road, Barton, Preston,
Lancashire PR3 5AA
Tel 01772 362551 Fax 01772 361267
Hotel
French Italian/Mediterranean
Mexican Snacks/Drinks
Traditional British
*Recently re-developed capturing the
charm and character of the original
building which was built in the early
1900s. Guests will enjoy the garden
and a new cafe/bar restaurant. Other
features include a pool, whirlpool,
sauna, gym, games room, hair and
beauty salon.*
♀ 🏃 Cc ♿ (public entrance/desig-
nated parking area/bathroom & WC
on same level/dining room/restau-
rant/bar/TV lounge)
Typical tariff single/double room
£73/£33pp Beds 50 Open all year
Typical 3 course meal £16 Seats 100
Open 9am–10pm Mon–Fri

RUFFORD

RUFFORD ARMS HOTEL
380 Liverpool Road, Rufford,
Lancashire L40 1SQ
Tel 01704 822040 Fax 01704 822040

Hotel Restaurant
A la Carte
*Privately run, modern hotel in a semi-
rural location. All rooms ensuite with
TV and tea making facilities. Popular
restaurant renowned for its first class
cuisine. Close to Ormskirk, Southport
and Preston. Easy access to motor-
ways.*
♀ 🏃 Cc ✕ ⛙ ♿ ((public
entrance/designated parking
area/bathroom & WC on same
level/dining room/restaurant/bar/TV
lounge)
Typical tariff single/double room
£32.95/£37.95 Beds 14
Typical 3 course meal £10–£15 Seats
60 Open 12pm–2pm &
6.30pm–10pm Mon–Sun

TODMORDEN

SCAITCLIFFE HALL
Burnley Road, Todmorden, Lancashire
OL14 7DQ
Tel 01706 818888 Fax 01706 818825
Hotel
Modern British
*Beautiful 17th century country house
situated in 16-acre grounds. State of
the art conference and banqueting
facilities. Award winning gardens.
Beautifully appointed bedrooms
including suites and four posters.
Gym, pool, snooker room and private
dining room. Highest quality modern
British cuisine, including vegan dishes.*
🐎 ♀ 🏃 Cc ♿ (public entrance/desig-
nated parking area/one bedroom,
bathroom & WC on same level/dining
room/restaurant/bar/TV lounge)

Typical tariff single/double room
£48.50/£64 Beds 30 Open 24 hrs
Typical 3 course meal £19.65 Seats 65
Open Mon–Sat 12pm–2pm &
6.30pm–9pm; Sun 12pm–4pm

Places to Eat

BLACKPOOL

LENNARDS EATING HOUSE
8 Deansgate, Blackpool, Lancashire
FY1 1BN
Tel 01253 628167
Restaurant
A la Carte Snacks/Drinks
Traditional British
*Husband and wife business for 14
years, serving homemade pies and
cakes. All vegetables are fresh. Soya
margarine and soya milk always in
stock. Vegetarian and vegan food is
personally prepared.*
🍴✖ (small area)
Seats 50 Open 8.30am–5.30pm
VS members' discount 10%

BOLTON

COOKING THE BOOKS
150 Deansgate, Bolton, Lancashire
BL1 1BB
Tel 01204 526999 Fax 07070 600103
Cafe
Organic Snacks/Drinks
Traditional British
*A friendly coffee shop and book shop
combined. Able to provide food for
lots of different diets and uses some
organic vegetables.*
Cc ♿ (public entrance/designated

parking area/dining area)
Seats 17 Open 9am–6pm Mon–Sat

PATAGONIA CAFE
129 Bradshawgate, Bolton, Lancashire
BL2 1BL
Tel 01204 528533
Cafe Expresso Bar Take Away
Snacks/Drinks Traditional British
*The only American-style coffee house
in Bolton with American style choice
and service. The best coffee this side
of the Atlantic with 20 different vari-
eties of whole beans which are
ground to order and packaged to
take home. The freshness and quality
of the menu items is its trademark.
Easy to find off the A666.*
✖ 🍴 ♿ (public entrance/dining
area)
Typical 3 course meal £6–£10 Seats
34 Open 9am–5pm Mon–Sat

BURNLEY

RED TRIANGLE CAFE
160 St James Street, Burnley,
Lancashire BB11 1NR
Tel 01282 832319
Cafe Restaurant
*Run by a co-op and serving delicious
home made food in a warm and cosy
atmosphere. A cafe with blackboard
menu during the day and a restaurant
with table service in the evening.
Acoustic music for evenings once a
month. Buffets for parties, meetings
and conferences can be arranged on
the premises or for outside catering.*
V ♿ (disabled parking bay 3 doors
away/toilets upstairs with double

hand rail)
Typical 3 course meal £8 Seats 24
Open 10.30am–7pm Tues–Sat;
7.30pm–10pm Tues–Wed *(advance
booking only)*; 7.30pm–10pm Fri–Sat

CHORLEY

**SHAW HILL HOTEL, GOLF &
COUNTRY CLUB**
See page 71.

CLITHEROE

B'S BAR CAFE
At the Wellsprings, Sabden Road,
Clitheroe, Lancashire BB7 9HN
Tel 01200 427722
Brasserie
French Italian/Mediterranean
Snacks/Drinks
*A Mediterranean style restaurant and
bar in a rural setting on the 'nick of
Pendle'. The chef caters sensitively for
vegans and vegetarians, especially
when given prior notice. "I could not
fault either the meal, the atmosphere,
the friendly staff or the value for
money." (Vegan Society member).*
P Cc ♿ (public entrance/dining area)
Typical 3 course meal £15 Seats 70
Open 12pm–9.30pm summer;
12pm–3pm & 6pm–9.30pm winter;
bar snacks until 10pm

JIGSAW PANTRY
The Trinity Centre, Parson Lane,
Clitheroe, Lancashire BB7 2JY
Tel 01200 427886
Cafe Delicatessen
Organic Snacks/Drinks

*The cafe and market delicatessen is
run by young adults with learning difficulties as part of their vocational
training. The delicatessen can be
found at: 1 Cabin, New Market Road,
Clitheroe. It sells at least one vegan
sandwich and can make to order on
site.*
V ✗ 🍴 ♿ (public entrance/desig-
nated parking space/dining area/toi-
let)
Typical 3 course meal £5.50 Seats 24
Open cafe 12pm–1.15pm Mon–Wed;
deli Tues, Thurs & Sat

LANCASTER

LIBRA
19 Brock Street, Lancaster LA1 1UR
Tel 01524 61551
Cafe Restaurant Take Away
Chinese International
Italian/Mediterranean Organic
Snacks/Drinks
*A friendly ground floor cafe with
counter service. All soups, main meals
and some cakes are usually suitable
for vegans. Two dining areas.*
V ✗ 🍴 ♿ (public entrance)
Typical 3 course meal £7.50 Seats 34
Open 9am–5pm Mon–Sat

WHALE TAIL, THE
78a Penny Street, Lancaster LA1 1XN
Tel 01524 845133
Cafe
Snacks/Drinks
*Renowned for its creative approach to
both cooking and life! Quick snacks
and leisurely meals provided in this
spacious friendly cafe. Excellent value*

*full vegetarian or vegan breakfast
available 7 days a week.*
V X ᵇ✕
Typical 3 course meal £6 Seats 60
Open 9am–5pm Mon–Fri; 9am–6pm
Sat; 10.30am–3pm Sun

PRESTON

NASEEB TANDOORI HOUSE
121 Church Street, Preston,
Lancashire PR1 3BT
Tel 01772 562082 **Fax** 01772 562032
Restaurant
Indian
*Established for 14 years providing an
extensive menu including many vege-
tarian/vegan dishes especially pre-
pared from the sub-Continent.*
♀ ♨ cc X ᵇ✕ ♿ (public
entrance/dining area/bar)
Typical 3 course meal £8.10 Seats 160
Open 5pm–late Mon–Sun

RUFFORD

RUFFORD ARMS HOTEL
See page 73.

TODMORDEN

BEAR WHOLEFOOD SHOP & CAFE
29 Rochdale Road, Todmorden,
Lancashire
Tel 01706 819 690
Cafe Take Away Wholefood Shop
Organic
*A co-operative run by women. Very
accommodating and will help if they
can. Located in a lovely old light and
airy building with lots of plants.*

*Friendly and welcoming. The only
place in Todmorden selling vegetarian
wholefoods. Easy to find. Bring own
bottle. No corkage.*
V X ᵇ✕ (areas)
Typical 3 course meal £7.50 Seats 30
Open 9.30am–5.30pm Mon–Sat

LEICESTERSHIRE
Places to Stay

LEICESTER

DODGY DICK'S BACKPACKER'S HOSTEL
157 Wanlip Lane, Birstall, Leicester
LE4 4GL
Tel 0116 267 3107
Backpacker's Hostel
*A small cosy backpacker's hostel cater-
ing mainly for the 16–26 age group
(not a rule). All wholemeal bread and
cakes are homemade and vegan. All
meals are cooked to order. Guests are
informed of every ingredient used to
make meals. No self catering.*
P ᵇ✕
Typical single tariff £8–£10 Beds 2 +
summer house Open 5pm–10pm
arrivals; 7am–10am departures
VS members' discount 25% 7 nights+

Please mention the Vegan
Travel Guide **when contacting a
listed business or advertiser**

Places to Eat

LEICESTER

GOOD EARTH, THE
19 Free Lane, Leicester LE1 1JX
Tel 0116 262 6260
Restaurant
Lunch time only restaurant situated on the first and second floors of the building. Established in 1965.
V ✗ ⓦ
Typical 3 course meal £7.50 Seats 100
Open 12pm–3pm Mon–Fri;
12pm–5pm Sat

WHOLE TRUTH, THE
19 Belvoir Street, Leicester LE1 6SL
Tel 01162 542722
Cafe Restaurant Take Away
Organic Snacks/Drinks
Situated on first and second floor premises. Offering a wide selection of vegetarian and vegan cuisine.
V ⓦ
Typical 3 course meal £10.95 Seats 82
Open 10am–4pm Mon–Sat;
7pm–10pm Fri

LOUGHBOROUGH

CACTUS CAFE
17 High Street, Loughborough,
Leicestershire LE11 2PY
Tel 01509 214585
Restaurant
Mexican
A lively contemporary Mexican restaurant serving creative food to the sound of salsa music. Live music every

Wednesday. £6 two-course menu every Monday and Tuesday. A wide variety of vegetarian and vegan dishes.
杰 **Cc** ⓗ (public entrance/dining area/bar)
Typical 3 course meal £10 Seats 56
Open 6pm–10pm Mon–Sat

LINCOLNSHIRE

Places to Stay

LINCOLN

YOUTH HOSTEL ASSOCIATION
77 South Park, Lincoln LN5 8EZ
Tel 01522 522076 Fax 01522 567424
B&B Self Catering
Traditional British
A membership organisation costing £10 a year, which includes discounts to many local attractions.
杰 **Cc** ✗
Typical tariff double room
£21.50/dormitory £8.80 Beds 8
Open 7.30am–10am & 5pm–11pm
Typical 3 course meal £4.40 Seats 40
Open breakfast 8am; dinner 7pm

Places to Eat

LINCOLN

BELL INN, THE
Far Lane, Coleby, Lincoln, Lincolnshire
LN5 0AH
Tel 01522 810240 Fax 01522 811800

Public House
A la Carte Snacks/Drinks
Traditional British
*An 18th century inn full of character
and charm with open log fires in the
winter. Situated on the Viking Way
only 10 minutes from Lincoln and 15
minutes from Newark. Good quality
home made food (including vegan on
request). Thursday night is for vegetarians with a black board full of
home made meals.*
🐕 ♀ ☲ Cc ✕ ⇥ (restaurant)
Typical tariff double room £34.50
Beds 3 Open 11am
Typical 3 course meal £12–15 Seats
30 restaurant; 20 lounge; 30 bar
Open Mon–Fri 11.30am–3pm &
5.30pm–11pm; Sat 11.30am–11pm;
Sun 9.30am–11.30 & 12pm–10.30pm

LOUTH

LOUTH WHOLEFOOD SHOP
7–9 Eastgate, Louth, Lincolnshire
LN11 9NB
Tel 01507 602411
Take Away Wholefood Shop
Organic Snacks/Drinks
*A wide variety of vegetarian and
vegan foods available including take
away pasties and pies. Also sells a
large range of snacks and drinks —
including organic wines suitable for
vegans.*
V
Open 9am–5pm Mon–Sat

LONDON

Places to Stay

SE13

BAILEYS B&B
77 Belmont Hill, Lewisham, London
SE13 5AX
Tel 0181 852 7373
Fax 0181 473 7777
B&B
*A large refurbished house near
Greenwich. 15 minutes from London.
5 minutes from the station (zone 2).
TVs in all rooms, central heating, etc.*
☲
Typical tariff single/double room
£20/£40 Beds 4 Open all year

SW4

GEORGIAN HOUSE HOTEL
35 St George's Drive, London
SW4 4DG
Tel 0171 834 1438
Fax 0171 976 6085
Email georgian@wildnet.co.uk
Website
http://www.smoothhound.hotel-
world
B&B
Traditional British
*A cosy and relaxed family run B&B.
Professional and helpful staff. Great
location for sightseeing, shopping and
the West End. Victoria coach/railway
station within a short walk. Breakfast
included in the price. Special student*

rooms and family rooms available. 2 crowns.

P 㡯 Cc

Typical tariff single/double room £19.39/£32.55 Beds 34 Open 8am–11pm all year

W1

KENWOOD HOUSE HOTEL
114 Gloucester Place, off Baker Street, London W1H 3DB
Tel 0171 935 3473/9455
Fax 0171 224 0582
B&B Hotel
Traditional British
A family-run friendly B&B hotel in a wonderfully central location between Oxford Street, Regents Park and Madam Tussauds. Serving breakfast only in the dining room. Two vegetarian restaurants nearby. Have had many vegan guests stay.
㡯 Cc
Typical tariff single/double room £46/£60 Beds 16

W2

DUKE & LEINSTER HOTEL, THE
34 Queen's Gardens, Leinster Terrace, Bayswater, London W2 3AA
Tel 0171 258 0079
Fax 0171 262 0741
Email duke_of_leinster_hotel
Hotel
Centrally located only 2 minutes walk from Hyde Park and 15–20 minutes from Oxford Street shopping. All rooms have ensuite, TV (including satellite major channels), hairdryer

and direct telephone. Children up to 2 years free of charge.

P 㡮 㡯 Cc

Typical tariff single/double room £54/£74 Beds 41 Open all year

W3

ACTON GRANGE GUEST HOUSE
317 Uxbridge Road, Acton, London W3 9QU
Tel 0181 992 0586
Fax 01256 355456
Guesthouse
A small friendly family-run establishment. Central location with easy access to the West End and Heathrow Airport.
P ⥅
Typical tariff single/double room £25/£45 Beds 6 Open 8am–10pm

WC1

QUAKER INTERNATIONAL CENTRE
1-3 Byng Place, London WC1E 7JH
Tel 0171 387 5648
Fax 0171 383 3722
Email qic@btinternet.com
Guesthouse
P 㡯 ⥅ (public room) ♿ (one bedroom, bathroom & WC on same level/dining room/public room)
Typical tariff single/double room £30/£46 Beds 25 Open all year — except Xmas–New Year

Places to Eat

E1

CAFE SPICE NAMASTE
16 Prescot Street, London E1 8AZ
Tel 0171 488 9242
Fax 0171 488 9339
Restaurant
Indian
Vibrant and contemporary designed restaurant renowned for its high standard of Indian cuisine. Scintillating dishes created by chef/owner Cyrus Todiwala who provides a great variety of the culinary styles on offer across India.
Cc ✗ ൟ (public entrance/dining area/bar)
Typical 3 course meal £18 Seats 110
Open Mon–Fri 12pm–3pm & 6.15pm–10.30pm; Sat 6.30pm–10.30pm

E2

CHERRY ORCHARD
241 Globe Road, Bethnal Green, London E2 0JD
Tel 0181 980 6678
Email cherryorchard@compuserve.com
Restaurant
Around the World
Run by Buddhist women and serving homemade vegetarian and vegan dishes throughout the day. Recipes are changed daily and the atmosphere is calm and friendly. Also available for parties and functions as well as outside catering.
V Cc ✗ ൟ
Typical 3 course meal £7 Seats 48
Open 11am–3pm Mon; 11am–7pm Tues–Fri; hot food available 12pm–3pm & 5pm–7pm

FRIENDS FOODS
83 Roman Road, London E2 0QN
Tel 0181 980 1843
Fax 0181 980 5077
Email khemavir@aol.com
Health Food Shop Take Away
Macrobiotic Organic Snacks/Drinks
Traditional British
Catering for vegans and special diets with a wide range of take away drinks and snacks plus an emphasis on organic products and produce.
V Cc ൟ
Open 9.30am–6pm Mon, Weds, Thurs & Sat; 10am–6pm Tues; 9.30am–7pm Fri
VS members' discount 10%

GALLERY CAFE
21 Old Ford Road, Bethnal Green, London E2 9PL
Tel 0181 983 3624
Cafe
Cosmopolitan
Quickly becoming a favourite after opening in January 1996. Run by a team of Buddhist men with a friendly and helpful service. Soups and hot meals are usually vegan and there are sandwiches with vegan fillings. Soya milk is available.
V Cc ൟ
Typical 3 course meal £6 Seats 48 + outside Open 10.30am–5pm Mon;

12pm–5pm Tues; 10.30am–5pm
Wed–Sat

THAI GARDEN, THE
249 Globe Road, Bethnal Green,
London E2 OJD
Tel 0181 981 5748
Restaurant
Thai
Established for 8 years. A set vegetarian menu comprising some vegan dishes. Listed in all major guides and winner of Time Out *Best Vegetarian Meal in May 1991.*
Cc ⬛✖ ⬛ (public entrance/dining area)
Typical 3 course meal £15 Seats 32
Open 12pm–2.45pm & 6pm–10.45pm

E8

GREEN DOOR CAFE
The Print House, 18 Ashwin Street,
London E8 3DL
Tel 0171 249 6793
Fax 0171 275 9914
Cafe Take Away
Chinese Indian
Italian/Mediterranean Mexican
Snacks/Drinks Take Away Thai
Traditional British
Well established cafe offering a full range of vegan foods including breakfasts, soups, main courses, desserts, salads and sandwiches. A full take away service and an extensive range of foods including vegetarian, vegan, gluten free and organic.
V ✖ ⬛ ⬛ (public entrance/designated parking area/dining area/bar)
Typical 3 course meal £6.50 Seats 32

Open 9am–3pm Mon–Fri

E11

PEACHES HEALTH FOODS
143 High Street, Wanstead, London
E11 2RL
Tel 0181 530 3617
Health Food Store
A huge selection of foods available including supplements and a number of organic products — such as organic wine suitable for vegans and vegetarians.
V
Open 9am–6pm Mon–Fri;
9am–5.30pm Sat

E15

PURPLE ONION CAFE, THE
39 Water Lane, Stratford, London
E15 4NL
Tel 0181 519 3228
Fax 0181 519 3228
Cafe Take Away
Fast Food Snacks/Drinks
A wide range of good hearty food, funky atmosphere and friendly service. Cafe on two floors available for hire. Dinner parties and buffets catered for.
V ✖ ⬛
Typical 3 course meal £10 Seats 75
Open 10.30am–7pm

E17

HORNBEAM & GANNETS
458 Hoe Street, Walthamstow,
London E17 9AH

Tel 0181 558 6880
Cafe Take Away Restaurant
Organic Snacks/Drinks
Urban environmental centre with an in-house cafe. Homemade organic vegetarian and vegan food plus vegan alcohol available. Group bookings outside normal hours. Not-for-profit community business. Free environmental library, meeting place, information point, etc.
V ✷ ✗ (on request) ঙ (public entrance/dining area)
Typical 3 course meal £8.50 Seats 30–40 Open 12pm–3pm Mon; 12pm–3.30pm Tues, Thurs, Fri; 7pm–10pm Fri; 10am–4.30pm Sat

EC1

ANGLO ANATOLIAN RESTAURANT
123 Stoke Newington Church Street, London EC1V 0HX
Tel 0121 923 4349
Restaurant
Turkish
Cc ✗
Seats 30 Open 6pm–12am Mon–Fri; 12pm–1am Sat & Sun
VS members' discount 10%

CARNEVALE
135 Whitecross Street, London EC1Y 8JL
Tel 0171 250 3452
Fax 0171 336 6322
Email carnevale.demon.co.uk
Website http://www.carnevale.demon.co.uk
Restaurant Sandwich Bar Take Away

A la Carte Italian/Mediterranean Snacks/Drinks
Fresh and tasty food using seasonal produce. Many meat-eaters come and enjoy the food not realising it is vegetarian and vegan. Meals are served 12pm–3pm and 5.30pm–10.30pm. Snacks and drinks area available at all other times.
V ✷ ✿✗ Cc (Switch & Delta)
Typical 3 course meal £15 Seats 25
Open 10am–10.30pm Mon–Sat

FRESHLANDS
196 Old Street, London EC1V 9FR
Tel 0171 250 1708
Natural Remedy Centre Organic Food Shop Sandwich Bar Take Away
Fast Food Macrobiotic Organic
The City's leading organic food store established in 1977 and recently refurbished. Stocks a wide range of organic wholefoods and specialises in high quality vegan foods. Extensive wholesome take away features vegan hot soup of the day and vegan salad bar. 100 yards from Old Street underground station, exit 6.
Cc
Open 10.30am–6.30pm Mon–Fri; 10.30am–4.30pm Sat

RYE WHOLEFOODS
35 Mydletton Street, London EC1R 1UA
Tel 0171 278 5878
Take Away Wholefood Shop
Organic Snacks/Drinks
Food created in an imaginative and perceptive way. Nice, generous atmos-

phere. Organic vegan cakes, huge range of salads, sandwiches — eg butterbean pâté or smoked tofu. Renowned for its soups — eg Jerusalem artichoke, carrot & coriander or brown lentil & mixed vegetables. Situated between the Angel and the Barbican.
V ✗ ᵂ⁺

Typical 3 course meal £4 Seats 12
Open 8.30am–4pm Mon–Fri
VS members' discount 10%

STEPHEN BULL RESTAURANT
71 St John Street, London EC1M 4AN
Tel 0171 490 1750
Restaurant
Modern British
One of three restaurants in central London. Listed in all the major food guides and always serving at least three vegetarian dishes. Happy to accommodate vegans and those with special dietary requirements. Notice is preferable but not essential.
P Cc ✗ ᵂ⁺ (public entrance/dining area/bar)
Typical 3 course meal £17.28 Seats 70
Open lunch & dinner Mon–Fri; dinner Sat; *closed 1 week at Xmas*

EC2

MOSHI MOSHI SUCHI
Unit 24, Liverpool Street Station, London EC2M 7QH
Tel 0171 247 3227
Fax 0171 248 1807
Restaurant
Japanese
A limited vegan menu is available here where they pride themselves on catering for people from all walks of life. Japanese fast food available at affordable prices.
🚇 Cc ✗ ᵂ⁺ ♿ (public entrance/designated parking area/dining area/bar)
Typical 3 course meal £10 Seats 70
Open 11.30am–9pm Mon–Fri

PLACE BELOW RESTAURANT, THE
St Mary Le Bon Church, Cheapside, London EC2V 6AU
Tel 0171 329 0789
Fax 0171 329 0789
Email bill@theplacebelow.telme.com
Restaurant Take Away
Award winning, principally vegetarian restaurant situated in the Norman crypt of the Bow Bells Church. Provides freshly cooked food prepared from the finest ingredients. Serves a vegan hot dish on Tues and Thurs. A vegan main course and salad is on the menu daily.
Cc ᵂ⁺
Typical 3 course meal £13 Seats 80
Open 7.30am–2.30pm Mon–Fri

EC3

FUTURES! RESTAURANT
8 Botolph Alley, London EC3R 8DR
Tel 0171 283 9697
Fax 0171 621 9508
Cafe Wine Bar
A la Carte Chinese French Indian Italian/Mediterranean Mexican Snacks/Drinks Spanish Thai Traditional British
Located in the lovely Broadgate devel-

opment above Liverpool Street Station. A European flavour with large sunny terraces, outside seating and a bright conservatory. No food served at night when Futures! becomes a bar. Menu changes monthly with daily specials.

V ♀ Cc & (WCs) ⚒ (some areas)
Typical 3 course meal £12 Seats 120
Open 7.30pm–10pm Mon–Fri

FUTURES! VEGETARIAN TAKE AWAY
8 Botolph Alley, London EC3R 8DR
Tel 0171 623 4529
Fax 0171 621 9508
Take Away
Chinese French Indian
Italian/Mediterranean Mexican Thai
Traditional British
All food freshly cooked on the premises each day. The menu is faxed to 200 companies every night and is available on Reuters. A delivery service is available within the City at lunch time.
V ⚒
Typical 3 course meal £6.85 Seats none Open Mon–Fri 7.30am–10am & 11.30am–3pm

N1

BENNETT & LUCK
212 Upper Street, London N1 1RL
Tel 0171 226 3422
Fax 0171 354 0212
Health Food Shop Take Away
A health food shop with a vegan and vegetarian take away counter service. A good range of vegan foods is available.

V 🏛 Cc ⚒
Open 9am–7pm Mon–Fri; 9am–6pm Sat

CALZONE PIZZA BAR
35 Upper Street, London N1
Pizza Bar Restaurant Take Away
Italian/Mediterranean
Made to order fresh pizzas and pasta dishes. 'Make your own' pizza parties for children. A fast but friendly personal service in a clean and modern environment. Good value for money. Other branches in NW3, SW10 and W11.
Cc ✗ (highchair available)
Typical 3 course meal £12.15 Seats 32
Open Mon–Sun

CHARMINAR VEGETARIAN RESTAURANT
21 Chapel Market, Islington, London N1 9EZ
Tel 0171 278 9322
Restaurant
Indian Snacks/Drinks
Choose from a daily special or the buffet available day or night. Alternatively 'eat as much as you like' from 25 different dishes — including a starter, main course, salad, chutneys, soup, deserts, etc. 90% of the dishes are vegan.
V 🏛 Cc ⚒ & (public entrance/WC/dining area/bar)
Typical 3 course meal £5 Seats 65
Open Mon–Thurs 12pm–2.30pm & 5.30pm–11.30pm; Fri–Sun 12pm–11.30pm
VS members' discount 10%

INDIAN VEGETARIAN
BHELPOORI HOUSE

92–93 Chapel Street, London N1 9EX
Tel 0171 837 4607
Fax 0171 263 7512
Website http://www.indianveg.co.uk.
Restaurant
A la Carte Indian Organic
Self Service Buffet
A large, very busy and successful restaurant, established 11 years. Well known for quality food and prices. Self service buffet is very popular.
V Cc
Typical 3 course meal £5.25 Seats 145
Open 12pm–11.30pm Mon–Sun
VS members' discount 10%

MILAN VEGETARIAN RESTAURANT

52 Caledonian Road, Kings Cross, London N1 9DP
Tel 0171 278 3812
Restaurant
Indian
V ⍓✗
Typical 3 course meal £10 Seats 24
Open Mon–Sat 12pm–3pm &
6pm–10pm

TONY'S NATURAL FOODS

10 Caledonian Road, London N1 9DT
Tel 0171 837 5223
Bistro Cafe Sandwich Bar
Fast Food Organic Snacks/Drinks
Take away food for vegetarian and vegan customers including fresh sandwiches, soup and cake. Also sells vegetarian and vegan remedies, organic/non-organic vegetables and bread baked mostly on the premises.
V Cc

Typical 3 course meal £10 Seats 20

N6

CAFE VERT

Jacksons Lane Centre, 269a Archway Road London N6 5AA
Tel 0181 348 7666
Fax 0181 348 2424
Cafe Take Away
Snacks/Drinks
Based in a large community and arts centre opposite Highgate tube station. Serves an ever changing menu of dishes from around the world. Also outside or onsite catering for weddings, parties Free entry to live jazz Sunday lunchtimes.
V ⍓ ♿ (public entrance/designated parking area/dining area/bar)
Typical 3 course meal £8.50 Seats 70
Open 10am–9pm Mon–Sat;
12pm–3.30pm Sun

N16

BLUE LEGUME, THE

101 Stoke Newington Church Street, London N16 0UD
Tel 0171 923 1303
Fax 0171 249 6300
Cafe Restaurant Take Away
A la Carte French
Italian/Mediterranean Mexican
Organic Snacks/Drinks Spanish Thai
Traditional British
An all day food package serving 50% vegetarian and vegan foods such as roast pepper and cashewnut burger, salsa and salad. A wide range of beverages is available from carrot, celery

and beet juice to soya barleyccino. All served in a relaxed convivial atmosphere.

✗ ♿ (dining area)

Typical 3 course meal £13.50 Seats 32 indoors; 10 pavement Open 9.30am–6.30pm Tues & Wed; 9.30am–11pm Thurs & Fri; 10.30am–11pm Sat; 10.30am–6.30pm Sun

KARNAPHULI RESTAURANT

20 Stoke Newington Church Street, London N16 0LU
Tel 0171 254 0661
Home Delivery Service Restaurant Take Away
Indian

Classic Indian cuisine concentrating on healthy foods using quality and authentic foods and spices. Satisfying healthy meals with an emphasis on providing a choice for the customer. 50% of the menu is vegetarian.

Cc

Seats 50 Open Mon–Sun 12pm–2pm & 5.30pm–12am *except Xmas Day & Boxing Day*
VS members' discount 10%

RASA RESTAURANT

55 Stoke Newington Church Street, London N16 0AR
Tel 0171 249 0344
Restaurant
A la Carte Indian

A traditional south Indian restaurant serving more Kerala food than anywhere else. Dishes are made using the freshest spices and herbs and are suitable for vegan and wheat-free diets.

The chef creates a certain ambience with the superbly presented food. Recommended by the Good Food Guide 1997.

V 🍽 Cc ♿ (public entrance/dining area)

Typical 3 course meal £10 Seats 43 Open 12pm–3pm Thurs–Sat; 6pm–12am Mon–Sun

VORTEX, THE

139–141 Stoke Newington Church Street, London N16 0UH
Tel 0171 254 6516
Fax 0171 249 8226
Cafe Jazz Bar
Italian/Mediterranean Snacks/Drinks
Cafe during the day and music venue from 7pm onwards. Entry fee is charged during evenings.

Cc ✗

Typical 3 course meal £8–£10 Seats 90 Open 11am–6pm & 7pm–11pm

YUM YUM THAI RESTAURANT

30 Stoke Newington Church Street, London N16 0LU
Tel 0171 254 6751
Fax 0171 241 3857
Website http://www.egonronay.com
Restaurant Take Away
Thai

A classical Thai restaurant specialising in good quality food in a relaxed atmosphere. Dairy products are not used except in some desserts.

Cc ♿ (public entrance, designated parking area/dining area/bar)

Typical 3 course meal £15 Seats 120 Open 12pm–2.30pm Mon–Sun; 6pm–10.45pm Sun–Thurs;

6pm–11.15pm Fri–Sat

N22

GREEN HOUSE, THE

Unit 65–67, Market Hall, Wood Green
Shopping City, Wood Green, London
N22
Tel 0181 881 1471
Cafe Health Food Shop Take Away
Snacks/Drinks
*A vegan and vegetarian cafe plus
health food shop. Hot dishes, snacks
and drinks available each day in the
cafe. Take away service. A one–stop
vegan haven selling a cheap range of
vegan foodstuffs including loose nuts,
dried fruit, etc.*
V ✕ ⇞ (preferred)
Typical 3 course meal £3.30 Seats 6
Open Mon–Sat: cafe 9am–4pm; shop
9am–6pm

POPCORN IN THE PARK

The Grove, Alexandra Park, London
N22 4AY
Cafe
Chinese French Indian
Italian/Mediterranean
Japanese Lebanese Mexican
Snacks/Drinks Spanish Thai
Traditional British
*A small day centre for those with
learning difficulties, operating as a
'cafe', producing tasty international
'slow' food — including Marine Ices,
Cafe Direct and other ethically sound
items. No cheques, no Coca-Cola, no
cards, no capuccino, no crisps, no
candy, no junk! Run by the Actual
Workshop for Haringey MENCAP.*

VEGAN ✕ ⇞ ♿ (open and accessible to all)
Typical 3 course meal £5 Seats 500
(incl outside in the park!) Open
10am–5pm Mon–Fri *except 2 weeks
at Xmas*

NW1

DIWANA RESTAURANT

121 Drummond Street, London
NW1 2HL
Tel 0171 387 5556
Fax 0171 380 0560
Email krzysztof@bogo.co.uk
Restaurant
Indian
*A family-run restaurant established in
1972. The first Bhel Poori House in
London. Lots of awards and recommendations.*
V Cc
Typical 3 course meal £7 Seats 100
Open 12pm–11.30pm

VEG

41 Castlehaven Road, Camden Town,
London NW1 8RJ
Tel 0171 482 4449
Restaurant
Chinese
*Serves both traditional and spicy
modern Chinese cooking, developed
by preserving the culinary rigour of
the ancients and supplementing it
with its own imaginative tastes. Also
at SW3.*
VEGAN ⇞
Typical 3 course meal £15 Seats 120
Open lunch & eves all week

NW3

CALZONE PIZZA BAR
66 Heath Street, London NW3
Pizza Bar Restaurant Take Away
Italian/Mediterranean
Made to order fresh pizza and pasta dishes. 'Make your own' pizza parties for children. A fast but friendly personal service in a clean and modern environment. Good value for money. Other branches in N1, SW10 and W11.
Cc ✗ (highchair available)
Typical 3 course meal £12.15 Open Mon–Sun

KAROON RESTAURANT
289 Finchley Road, London NW3 6ND
Tel 0171 681 7080
Fax 0171 681 7001
Restaurant Take Away
Iranian
Serves a selection of vegan starters, main courses and sweets.
Cc
Typical 3 course meal £10 Seats 40
Open 12pm–12am
VS members' discount 10%

MANNA RESTAURANT
4 Erskine Road, Primrose Hill, London NW3 3AJ
Tel 0171 722 8028
Fax 0171 722 8028
Website http://www.manna.veg.com
Restaurant
A la Carte Gourmet Global
One of Britain's oldest vegetarian restaurants situated in the pretty village of Primrose Hill. The aim of the restaurant is to serve delicious food, beautifully presented in relaxing surroundings. According to the 1998 Time Out Guide it succeeds. There are always two vegan choices in each section of the menu and a range of organic vegan wines and beers.
V Cc ✗ (on request) ⁑ (area) ♿ (public entrance/dining area/bar)
Typical 3 course meal £15 Seats 50
Open 7pm–11pm Mon–Sun

NW4

RAJEN'S
195–197 West Hendon Broadway, London NW4
Tel 0171 203 8522
Restaurant Take Away
Serves customers with a smile!
V Cc ✗
Typical 3 course meal £4.99 Seats 80
Open 12pm–10pm Mon–Sun

NW6

ORGANIC CAFES, THE
25 Lonsdale Road, Queens Park, London NW6 6RA
Tel 0171 372 1232
Fax 0171 372 1232
Cafe Restaurant
Organic Modern European
The chef will prepare a vegan meal if there is nothing on the menu.
✗ ⁑ (area)
Typical 3 course meal £15 Seats 35
Open 9.30am–9.30pm *(last orders)* Mon–Fri; 9.30am–10.30pm Sat–Sun

SURYA INDIAN VEGETARIAN RESTAURANT

59–61 Fortune Green Road, West Hampstead, London NW6 1DR
Tel 0171 435 7486
Restaurant Take Away
Indian
Established 10 years ago, this family-run restaurant is highly acclaimed by all major food critics. The menu and prices have not changed since the day it opened. It has built a reputation for excellent food, excellent service and affordable prices.
V Cc &. (bathroom & WC on same level/dining room/restaurant)
Typical 3 course meal £10 Seats 32
Open 6pm–10.30pm Mon–Sun; 12pm–2.30pm Sun
VS members' discount 5%

NW10

SABRAS

263 High Road, Willesden Green, London NW10 2RX
Tel 0181 459 0340
Restaurant
Indian
Established since 1973, it remains one of the top restaurants for properly cooked homestyle Indian vegetarian cuisine. Many satisfied vegans come again and again as many dishes are cooked with no animal ingredients. Fresh food may take a little longer to arrive from the kitchen but the quality will be remembered for a long time.
V Cc ⁕ (area) &. (public entrance/dining area)
Typical 3 course meal £15 Seats 32

Open 6.30pm–10.30pm Tues–Sun

SE1

COOPERS NATURAL FOODS

17 Lower Marsh, Waterloo, London SE1 7RJ
Tel 0171 261 9314
Health Food Shop Take Away
Fast Food Snacks/Drinks
A health food shop with take away food cooked on the premises. Vegetarian with some daily vegan items. Fresh soup, salad, sandwiches, cakes (some vegan), pizza or quiche. Food cooked daily and often sold out by 2pm. Shop stocks huge range of food and other supplies. Handy for a visit to South Bank.
V Cc ⁕ &. (public entrance)
Open 8.30am–5.30pm Mon–Fri; 10am–1pm Sat *(no cooked food)*

SE8

HEATHER'S RESTAURANT

74 McMillan Street, Deptford, London SE8 3HA
Tel 0181 691 6665
Restaurant Take Away
A licensed restaurant selling a wide range of organic vegan wines, beers and spirits. 'Eat as much as you like buffet' is 90%–100% vegan and includes soups, hot food, salads and puddings. Regular women only and jazz nights. Outside catering.
V ⁕
Typical 3 course meal £12 Seats 90
Open 7pm–11.30pm Tues–Sat; 12.30pm–3.30pm & 6.30pm–9.30pm Sun

SE18

KANCHAN VEGETARIAN RESTAURANT
62a Plumstead High Street, London SE18 1SL
Tel 0181 317 0202
Restaurant Take Away
Indian
Pure vegetarian Indian food from western and southern India. Also caters for parties of 100–200 guests. Details of ingredients of dishes are explained fully on the menus.
V ✥
Seats 24 Open 11am–8.30pm
Tues–Sun

SE24

ROTI ROTI
127 Dulwich Road, Herne Hill, London SE24 0NG
Tel 0171 737 7440
Restaurant Take Away
Trinidadian
A friendly, intimate restaurant serving home made food – including a range of starters and specials which may be made vegan with prior notice. A private dining room overlooking the park is ideal for parties of up to 25 persons. DJ on Friday nights.
P ✕ ♿ (public entrance/dining area)
Typical 3 course meal £11.25 Seats 50
Open 12pm–11pm Mon–Thurs;
12pm–12am Fri–Sat

Please mention Vegan Travel Guide when contacting a listed business or advertiser

---

SE27

HOLLYHOCKS
10 Knights Hill, West Norwood, London SE27 0HY
Tel 0181 766 8796
Tea Rooms
Snacks/Drinks
Charming tearooms serving traditional tea-time fare, light meals and daily specials in a relaxed atmosphere with friendly staff. Delightful decor and period furnishings make for a unique culinary experience. Recommended by Time Out.
V ✕ ✥
Typical 3 course meal £9.50 Seats 24
Open 10am–5pm Tues–Sun & last Fri of each month for eve buffet

SW1

MATSURI
15 Bury Street, London SW1Y 6AL
Tel 0171 839 1101
Fax 0171 930 7010
Restaurant
Japanese
*Matsuri, meaning festival in Japanese, has a huge dining area set in exceptionally stylish surroundings.
Experience authentic Japanese cuisine including a teppan-yaki where the food is cooked in front of you on a grill table by your own personal chef.*
Cc
Typical 3 course meal £30 Seats 133
Open 12pm–2.30pm & 6pm–10pm

WILKINS NATURAL FOODS
61 Marsham Street, London

SW1P 3DP
Tel 0171 222 4038
Fax 0171 222 4038
Sandwich Shop
Snacks/Drinks Take Away
Situated in an office area of London quite close to Westminster Abbey and Houses of Parliament. Vegan options available 2–3 times a week depending on suppliers. Telephone first to check availability.
V Cc
Open 9am–5pm Mon–Sat

WOODLANDS RESTAURANT

37 Panton Street, off Haymarket,
London SW1 4EA
Tel 0171 839 7258
The largest Indian vegetarian restaurant group serving the finest cuisine.
V
Typical 3 course meal £13 Seats 65
Open Mon–Sun 12pm–2.45pm &
6pm–10.45pm

SW3

VEG

8 Egerton Garden Mews,
Knightsbridge, London SW3 2EH
Tel 0171 584 7007
Restaurant
Chinese
Serves both traditional and spicy modern Chinese cooking, developed by preserving the culinary rigour of the ancients and supplementing it with its own imaginative tastes. Also at NW1.
VEGAN �ᐟᐟ
Typical 3 course meal £15 Seats 80
Open lunch & eves all week

SW4

CAFE ON THE COMMON

2 Rookery Road, Clapham, London
SW4 9DD
Tel 0171 498 0770
Cafe
Snacks/Drinks
A cafe situated in the park. Very busy when hot and sunny. Provides vegetarian and vegan breakfasts, cakes, salads, rich main meals, crumpets, muffins and a large selection of health drinks. Open for large dinner party bookings in the evening with a set 3 course meal. More than half the menu is vegan.
V ✗ ᐟᐟ (public entrance/designated parking area/dining area/bar)
Typical 3 course meal £10 Seats 30
indoors; 100 outdoors Open
10am–6pm

SW6

WINDMILL WHOLEFOODS

486 Fulham Road, Fulham London
SW6 5NH
Tel 0171 381 2372
Cafe Restaurant Take Away
A la Carte Fast Food Snacks/Drinks
A funky, comfortable and friendly restaurant offering an extensive vegetarian and vegan menu. Wholefood menu is changed daily. All food is prepared fresh daily and some items are organic.
V Cc ✗ ᐟᐟ (public entrance/dining area)
Typical 3 course meal £11 Seats 60
Open 11am–11pm Mon–Sat

SW10

CAFE ORGANIC
The Auction Rooms, 71 Lots Road,
London SW10 0RN
Tel 0171 351 7771
Cafe
Thai
A small cafe set in an antique auction gallery in Chelsea. Principally vegan but cow's milk is used in tea/coffee on request. One or two dishes are Thai. Tea and cake available.
V ✗ ☞✖
Typical 3 course meal £5–£7 Seats 25
Open 10am–4pm Fri–Sun;
9am–7.30pm Mon

CALZONE PIZZA BAR
335 Fulham Road, London SW10 9TW
Tel 0171 352 9797 Fax 0171 352 9898
Pizza Bar Restaurant Take Away
Italian/Mediterranean
Made to order fresh pizza and pasta dishes. 'Make your own' pizza parties for children. A fast but friendly personal service in a clean and modern environment. Good value for money. Other branches in N1, NW3 and W11.
Cc ✗ (highchair available)
Typical 3 course meal £12.15 Seats 32
Open 10am–12am Sun–Thurs;
10am–12.45am Fri–Sat

SW16

SHAHEE BELPOORI
1547 London Road, Norbury, London
SW16 4AD
Tel 0181 679 6275
Restaurant

Indian
A well-known restaurant with a huge range of vegan dishes. Menu items marked with an asterisk are suitable for vegans. Those marked with a dot can also be made suitable for vegans on request. Helpful, friendly staff and a relaxed and unhurried atmosphere. "Best vegetarian and vegan restaurant in South London" (BBC Vegetarian).
V 🏧 Cc ♿ (public entrance/designated parking area/dining area/bar)
Typical 3 course meal £7 Seats 75
Open Mon–Sun 12pm–2.30pm &
6pm–11pm — *incl Bank Hols*
VS members' discount 10% *food*

WHOLEMEAL VEGETARIAN CAFE
1 Shrubbery Road, Streatham,
London SW16 2AS
Tel 0181 769 2423
Cafe Restaurant
A friendly cafe established in 1978 providing a perfect oasis in the middle of Streatham. Vegan and organic alcohol available. Menu changes constantly but there is always one vegan special, and vegan starters and desserts. Close to all bus routes and easy to find next to Streatham Police Station.
V Cc ✗ ☞✖ ♿ (public entrance/dining area)
Typical 3 course meal £10 *(including wine)* Seats 38 Open 12pm–10pm
Mon–Sun; *closed Bank Hols*

SW17

SREE KRISHNA SOUTH INDIAN RESTAURANT
192–194 Tooting High Street, London

SW17 0SF
Tel 0181 672 6903/4250
Restaurant
South Indian (Kerala)
An exclusive restaurant established in 1973. The oldest and only classical family restaurant in South West London, close to Tooting Broadway Station. Provides authentic South Indian food, distinctive because of the unique combination of freshly ground spices and herbs and little use of oil or fat.
Cc ♿ (public entrance/dining area/bar)
Typical 3 course meal £10 Seats 120
Open 12pm–3pm & 6pm–11pm
Sun–Thurs; 12pm–3pm & 6pm–12am
Fri–Sat

SW18

GRAIN SHOP, THE
567 Battersea Park Road, London SW18
Tel 0171 229 5571
Restaurant Take Away Wine Bar
Vegetarian and vegan meals to eat in or take out. Also sells organic breads baked at its Portobello Road branch.
V
Seats 32

W1

CARAVAN SERAI AFGHAN RESTAURANT
50 Paddington Street, London W1M 3RQ
Tel 0171 935 1208
Fax 0171 486 0255

Restaurant
Afghan
The only restaurant in the UK specialising in cuisine from Afghanistan. Has been featured in countless newspapers and magazines, and has appeared on numerous radio and television shows. Try it for a unique experience and rewarding meal.
♀ ♨ Cc ⬛ ♿ (public entrance/designated parking area/dining area/bar)
Typical 3 course meal £15 Seats 55
Open Mon–Sun 12pm–3pm & 6pm–11.30pm

COUNTRY LIFE
3–4 Warwick Street, London W1R 5WA
Tel 0171 434 2922
Restaurant Shop Take Away
A la Carte Buffet
Opening April 1998 as a restaurant, a natural food shop and a health education charitable trust promoting a healthy Christian lifestyle. The lunch time buffet is vegan except for the use of honey in some deserts, which is clearly labelled.
V ✗ ⬛
Typical 3 course meal lunch £5; a la carte £15 Seats 75 Open lunchtime buffet 11.30am–3pm Sun–Fri; afternoon tea 3pm–5.30pm; a la carte 5.30pm–9pm Sun–Thurs

GAYLORD
79–81 Mortimer Street, London W1N 7TB
Tel 0171 580 3615/0171 636 0808
Fax 0171 636 0860
Restaurant Take Away

A la Carte Indian Snacks/Drinks
*Established in 1966 in the UK and still
under the same management.
Branches in most of the big cities in
the world including New Delhi,
Bombay, New York, San Francisco,
Manchester, Chicago and the
Bahamas. Pioneers of fine authentic
Indian cuisine in the world.*
♀ Cc ✻ ⌖ (public entrance/desig-
nated parking area/dining area/bar)
Open Mon–Sat 12pm–3pm &
6pm–11.30pm; Sun 12pm–3pm &
6pm–11pm
VS members' discount 10% *food*

LA PORTE DES INDES
32 Bryanston Street, London
W1H 7AE
Tel 0171 224 0055
Fax 0171 224 1144
Restaurant
Indian
*Noted for its fine Indian cuisine.
Employs eight specialist chefs to pre-
pare meals from different areas of
India. The interior was renovated by
architect Yves Burton and contains a
stunning white marble staircase link-
ing two floors, a 40' high Mogul
waterfall, exotic plants and flowers.*
Cc ✗ ✻ (section)
Typical 3 course meal £35 Seats 300
Open Mon–Fri 12pm–2.30pm &
7pm–12am; Sat 7pm–12am; Sun
12pm–3pm & 6pm–10.30pm

MANDEER
21 Hanway Place, London W1P 9DG
Tel 0171 323 0660
Fax 0171 580 3470

Restaurant
Indian
*Established in 1960. Excellent Indian
vegetarian and vegan cuisine including vegan Kulfi ice cream.
Note:* Ring before visiting — may be
relocating.
Cc ✻
Typical 3 course meal lunch £3.50; eve
meal £12.50 Seats 50–60 Open
Mon–Sat 12pm–3pm & 5.10pm
onwards; *closed Bank Hols & Xmas
week*

MILDREDS
58 Greek Street, Soho, London
W1V 5LR
Tel 0171 494 1634
Fax 0171 494 1634
Cafe Take Away
*Established in the West End for 9
years. The menu changes daily.
Organic produce used when possible.
Organic wines and beers also avail-
able. Take away main dishes and pud-
dings less 40p.*
✻
Typical 3 course meal £11.50 Seats 36
Open 12pm–11pm Mon–Sat;
12pm–6.30pm Sun

NUTHOUSE WHOLEFOOD
VEGETARIAN RESTAURANT
26 Kingly Street, London W1
Tel 0171 437 9471
Cafe Restaurant Take Away
Wholefood Shop
Organic
*Established 35 years ago and situated
in a convenient position behind
Hamleys in Regent Street, close to*

Oxford Circus underground. All food is made on the premises to own unique recipes. Vegan starters, main meals, salads, desserts, snacks and cakes all available.

✗ ᨆ (area) ♿ (small step at door/parking area with disabled badge only/dining area/bar)
Typical 3 course meal £7 Seats 60
Open 10am–8pm *(last orders)* Mon–Sat

SMOLLENSKY'S AMERICAN BAR & RESTAURANT
1 Dover Street, London W1X 3PJ
Tel 0171 491 1199
Fax 0171 409 2214
Restaurant
American
A newly refurbished American bar and restaurant offering a menu reflecting some of the many culinary influences across the United States. The ambience is a touch more formal than in the past, but the restaurant has retained its efficient and friendly American standard of service.
Cc

STEPHEN BULL RESTAURANT
5–7 Blandford Street, London W1N 3AA
Tel 0171 486 9696
Restaurant
Modern British
One of three restaurants in central London. Listed in all the major food guides and always serving at least three vegetarian dishes. Happy to accommodate vegans and those with special dietary requirements. Notice is
preferable but not essential.
P Cc ✗ ♿ (public entrance/dining area/bar)
Typical 3 course meal £17.28 Seats 110 Open lunch & dinner Mon–Fri; dinner only Sat; *closed 1 week at Xmas*

WOODLANDS RESTAURANT
77 Marylebone Lane, off Marylebone High Street, London W1M 4GA
Tel 0171 486 3862
Restaurant
South Indian
The largest Indian vegetarian restaurant group serving the finest cuisine.
V
Typical 3 course meal £13 Seats 75
Open Mon–Sun 12pm–2.45pm & 6pm–10.45pm

YO! SUSHI
52 Poland Street, London W1U 3DF
Tel 0171 287 0443
Fax 0171 287 2324
Home Delivery Service Restaurant
Japanese
Famous high tech sushi bar featuring the world's longest conveyor belt, robots, automated water dispensers, remote drinks trolleys and according to the Sunday Times, London's best sushi and cooked foods — including vegan.
Cc ᨆ
Typical 3 course meal £12 Seats 125
Open 12pm–12am Mon–Sun

Please mention the Vegan Travel Guide **when contacting a listed business or advertiser**

W2

VERONICA'S RESTAURANT
3 Hereford Road, Bayswater, London
W2 4AB
Tel 0171 229 5079
Fax 0171 229 1210
Restaurant
Organic Macrobiotic
Traditional British
*Award winning restaurant specialising
in British historic food. Official cater-
ers to the Historic Royal Palaces with
authentic recipes spanning 600 years.
Geared towards healthy food.
Everything made on the premises with
many vegetarian and vegan options.*
Cc ✕ ⚒ (public entrance/designated
parking area/dining area/bar)
Typical 3 course meal £16–£25 Seats
70 Open 12pm–3pm Mon–Fri;
6.10pm–11.30pm Mon–Sat
VS members' discount 10% *lunches &
Mon–Fri dinners*

W3

MAXIM RESTAURANT
155 Northfield Avenue, West Ealing,
London W13 9QT
Tel 0181 567 1719
Fax 0181 932 7067
Restaurant
Chinese
*Managed and run by Mrs Chow who
has been in the trade for the last 25
years — since the restaurant opened.
Redecorated and updated three times
during the last 25 years, still the best
Chinese restaurant in West London.
Mr Chow is now 71-years-old and still*
working and in charge of the kitchen.
Cc
Typical 3 course meal £15 Seats 100
Open Mon–Sat 12pm–2.30pm &
6.30pm–12am; Sun 6.30pm–12am

W8

BYBLOS MEZZA OF LEBANON
262 Kensington High Street, London
W8 6ND
Tel 0171 603 4422
Restaurant
Lebanese
*A family-run restaurant, established
since 1968, serving Lebanese vegetar-
ian and vegan meals. All dishes boast
high fibre and low fat natural ingredi-
ents with positively no additives.*
Cc ✕ ⚒ (public entrance/dining
area/bar)
Typical 3 course meal £10 Seats 50
Open 11.45am–11.45pm
VS members' discount 10%

PHOENICIA RESTAURANT
11–13 Abingdon Road, London
W8 6AH
Tel 0171 937 0120
Fax 0171 937 7668
Restaurant Take Away
Lebanese
*A family-run business established in
1980. A meal in Lebanon is a social
occasion and the waiters here will be
delighted to explain how to eat the
traditional Lebanese way. All dishes
are prepared to order. For favourite
dishes that are not on the menu customers should order in advance. Own
bread baked in clay oven.*

Cc ♿ (public entrance/designated
parking area/dining area/bar)
Typical 3 course meal £22 Seats 120
Open 12pm-12am Mon–Sun

W11

CALZONE PIZZA BAR
2 Kensington Park Road, London W11
Pizza Bar Restaurant Take Away
Italian/Mediterranean
*Made to order fresh pizza and pasta
dishes. 'Make your own' pizza parties
for children. A fast but friendly per-
sonal service in a clean and modern
environment. Good value for money.
Other branches in N1, NW3 and SW10.*
Cc ✗ (highchair available)
Typical 3 course meal £12.15 Open
Mon–Sun

GRAIN SHOP, THE
269a Portobello Road, London
W11 1LR
Tel 0171 229 5571
Take Away
Snacks/Drinks
*Vegan and vegetarian prepared meals
to take out. Vegan and sugar-free pas-
tries plus organic bread baked on the
premises. Yeast- and wheat-free
breads available.*
V

W12

BLAH BLAH BLAH
78 Goldhawk Road, Shepherds Bush,
London W12 8HA
Tel 0181 746 1337
Restaurant

*A friendly, lively restaurant specialis-
ing in vegetarian cuisine with multi-
national influences reflected in the
menu — eg sushi (vegan), stuffed
Jamaican banana leaves and homemade pasta dishes. Always vegan
options available — eg soup, two
starters and two main courses.
Booking advised in evenings.*
V ♿ (public entrance/dining area)
Typical 3 course meal £15.95 Seats 60
Open Mon–Sat lunch & eves

WC1

CHAMBELI OF RUSSELL
SQUARE, THE
146 Southampton Row, London
WC1B 5AG
Tel 0181 810 6444
Restaurant Take Away
Indian
*Provides good food, good service and
a romantic atmosphere. Renowned in
London for the best curry and
Tandoori dishes. Fully licensed and air
conditioned. Relaxed and informal
surroundings. Awarded two stars by
the AA. Recommended by* What's On
and Bloomsbury *magazine. Parties
welcome. Special business lunches
available.*
Typical 3 course meal £12.50 Seats 65
Open 12pm–12am

WC2

BUNJIES COFFEE HOUSE
27 Litchfield Street, London
WC2H 9HJ
Tel 0171 240 1796

Restaurant
Italian/Mediterranean
🍽✖
Typical 3 course meal £7.50 Seats 40
Open 12pm–11pm
VS members' discount 10%

CARRIE AWAZE DESIGNER SANDWICHES
27 Endell Street, London WC2H 9BA
Tel 0171 836 0815
Restaurant Sandwich Bar Take Away
Indian
Established nearly 20 years ago and regional winner of the Guardian/Snapple's Sensational Sandwich Contest. Good selection of imaginative vegetarian and vegan sandwiches and hot food. Friendly tranquil atmosphere. Owner plays classical sitar.
🍽✖
Typical 3 course meal £10 Seats 20
Open 10am–8pm Mon–Fri;
12pm–7.30pm Sat; 12pm–5pm Sun

CHINA CITY RESTAURANT
25a Lisle Street, London WC2
Tel 0171 734 3833
Fax 0171 434 3723
Restaurant
Chinese
Conveniently situated in the heart of Soho Chinatown and close by all amenities such as theatres, cinemas, casinos, night clubs and hotels. China City is one of the largest and most modern Chinese restaurants in Chinatown. Private function rooms available with karaoke.

Cc 🍽✖
Typical 3 course meal £10 Seats 500
Open 12pm–11.30pm

FOOD FOR THOUGHT
31 Neal Street, Covent Garden, London WC2H 9PA
Tel 0171 836 9072/0239
Catering Service Restaurant Take Away
A la Carte Chinese French Indian Italian/Mediterranean Japanese Lebanese Mexican Spanish Thai Turkish
Ideally located for hungry shoppers and pre-theatre diners, providing a warm welcome and excellent value. The innovative menu is changed daily and reflects the influences of world cuisine. All dishes are 100% vegetarian with vegan and gluten-free options and are prepared daily on the premises.
V 🍽✖
Typical 3 course meal £7.80 Seats 48
Open 9.30am–8.30pm Mon–Sat;
12pm–4pm Sun; 12pm–4pm Bank Hols; *closed Easter Sun, Xmas & New Year*

NEAL'S YARD SALAD BAR
2 Neal's Yard, Covent Garden, London WC2H 9DP
Tel 0171 836 3233 Fax 0171 836 3233
Cafe
Opened at the beginning of the 1980s, Neal's Yard Salad Bar was the first vegetarian establishment in the Yard. All the salads are made with non-dairy ingredients and most of the hot dishes are vegan. A soya fruit shake is also available. The juices are

sweetened with apple juice concentrate instead of sugar.

V

Typical tariff £10 Open 10am–9pm Mon–Sun

STEPHEN BULL RESTAURANT

12 Upper St Martin's Lane, London WC2H 9DL

Tel 0171 379 7811

Restaurant

Modern British

One of three restaurants in central London. Listed in all the major food guides and always serving at least three vegetarian dishes. Happy to accommodate vegans and those with special dietary requirements. Notice is preferable but not essential.

P Cc ✗ ⅋ (public entrance/dining area/bar)

Typical 3 course meal £17.28 Seats 55 Open lunch & dinner Mon–Fri; dinner only Sat; *closed 1 week at Xmas*

TIBETAN RESTAURANT, THE

17 Irving Street, Leicester Square, London WC2H 7AU

Tel 0171 839 2090

Restaurant

Tibetan

The first and only restaurant in the UK featuring traditional cuisine from the Roof of the World.

禾

Typical 3 course meal £10 Open Mon–Sat 12pm–2.45pm & 5pm–10.45pm

WORLD FOOD CAFE

1st Floor, 14 Neals Yard, London WC2H 9DP

Tel 0171 379 0298

Cafe

Indian Italian/Mediterranean Lebanese Mexican Spanish Thai

Dishes are globally inspired by street food that has been enjoyed whilst travelling in Europe, Asia, Africa, Latin America and the Caribbean. Open plan with all homemade wholesome food prepared in front of customers. The cafe is designed to be user-friendly to single people and all seating is communal.

V 🐾

Typical 3 course meal £15 Seats 42 Open 12pm–5pm Mon–Sat

MANCHESTER

Places to Eat

60/40 CAFE

448 Wilmslow Road, Withington, Manchester M20 3BW

Tel 0161 374 1796

Email 60/40@usa.net

Cafe

Indian Italian/Mediterranean Mexican Snacks/Drinks

A lively cafe/bar which is unobtrusively vegetarian. Casual, relaxed atmosphere. Regular clientele include local residents, local business professionals, students and vegetarians from afar. Friendly staff are more than happy to adapt meals to suit customer requirements. Renowned breakfasts available all week.

V Cc ✗ ☺ (public entrance/dining area/bar)
Typical 3 course meal £8.50 Seats 60
Open 10am–12.30am Mon–Sat;
10am–12am Sun

AMIGOS RESTAURANT
14 Oxford Road, Manchester M1 5QA
Tel 0161 236 8438
Fax 0161 236 8438
Restaurant
Mexican
Established 17 years ago and serving mainly Mexican food. This restaurant has a licensed bar and Happy Hours which include half price meals. A vegan section is marked on the menu. A party room is available with a disco and a free meal voucher is available to pre-booked parties of 4+.
Cc ✗ ✚ ☺ (public entrance/dining area)
Typical 3 course meal £8–£9 Seats 60
Open 12pm–11pm Mon–Fri

CACHUMBA CAFE
220 Burton Road, West Didsbury,
Manchester M20 2LW
Tel 0161 445 2479
Cafe Take Away
A la Carte Indian *(North & South)*
Thai Ugandan Vietnamese
World Food
Menu changes from time to time but some current vegan dishes include Spiced Okra and Onions, Courgette with Mustard and Cumin Seeds, Ugandan Mtoki, and Gujarati Style Vegetables.
☗ ✗ ☺ (public entrance/dining area/bar)

Typical 3 course meal £5.10 Seats 30
Open 6pm–10pm

CAFE GALLERY
City Art Gallery, Mosley Street,
Manchester M2 3JL
Tel 0161 228 3268
Fax 0161 236 7369
Restaurant
Around the World Continental
Located in the City Art Gallery in Manchester, it has a unique and relaxing atmosphere with seating on different levels. Decorated with works of art and displays.
Cc ✚✗
Typical 3 course meal £9.50 Seats 110
Open 10am–4.30pm Mon–Sat;
12pm–4.30pm Sun
VS members' discount 10%

CAFE POP
34–36 Oldham Street, Manchester
M1 1JN
Tel 0161 237 9688
Fax 0161 237 9688
Cafe Take Away
Chinese Indian
Italian/Mediterranean Mexican
Snacks/Drinks Spanish Thai
World Foods
A rare breed of cafe catering for vegans (well the ones who can open the door) with quality, variety and imagination. The only cafe in Britain with its own collection of design and ephemera from the 50s onwards. Visit before you die.
✗ ✚ ☺ (public entrance/dining area)
Typical 3 course meal £7.50 Seats 60+

Open 9.30am–5.30pm Mon–Sat;
10.30am–4.30pm Sun *(seasonal)*
VS members' discount 10%

FALLEN ANGELS VEGETARIAN RESTAURANT

263 Upper Brooke Street, Chorlton on
Medlock, Manchester M13 0HR
Tel 0161 273 4327
Restaurant
Organic World Food
*Situated close to Manchester
University and opposite Manchester
Royal Infirmary. An intimate vegetar-
ian and vegan restaurant serving
home made food. Friendly and
relaxed atmosphere. Decorated with
unusual paintings based on Hopi
Indian cave paintings. Bring a bottle.
£1 corkage per table.*
V ✗ ঙ (public entrance, dining area)
Typical 3 course meal £13 Seats 28
Open Tues–Fri 12pm–2pm &
5.30pm–10.30pm; Sat 6pm–11pm;
Sun 6pm–9pm; *booking required
Fri–Sat*
VS members' discount 10% *main
meals*

GAYLORD INDIAN RESTAURANT

Amethyst House, Spring Gardens
(next to Post Office), Manchester
M2 1EA
Tel 0161 832 4866/6037
Restaurant
Indian
*An extensive vegetarian menu. Food is
cooked daily using pure corn oil and
fresh vegetables and pulses.*
Cc
Typical 3 course meal £11.95 Seats 90

Open 12pm–2.30pm Mon–Sun;
6pm–11.30pm Mon–Sat; 6pm–11pm
Sun

GREENHOUSE LICENSED VEGETARIAN RESTAURANT, THE

331 Great Western Street, Rusholme,
Manchester M14 4AN
Tel 0161 224 0730
Fax 0161 256 0943
Restaurant
A la Carte Snacks/Drinks World Food
*Located at the junction of Great
Western Street and Heald Grove and
just 170 yards from Wilmslow Road in
the centre of Rusholme. Offers a selec-
tion of over 100 dishes from around
the world. Approximately 50% are
suitable for vegans. Egon Ronay
recommended.*
V Cc ✗ ✖ ঙ (public entrance/din-
ing area/no toilet)
Typical 3 course meal £8.50 Seats 37
Open 12pm–11pm *(last orders)*
Mon–Sat; 12pm–10.30pm *(last
orders)* Sun; *bookings only for 24, 25
& 31 Dec, 14 Feb*

KALLISH CAFE

New Aeon Books, 110–112 Tib Street,
Manchester M4 1LR
Tel 0161 839 9293
Email
kallish@newaeonbooks.demon.co.uk
Website http://www.newaeo
books.demon.co.uk/kallish.html
Snack Bar
Snacks/Drinks
*The snack bar is part of a bookshop
which specialises in esoteric, mysteries,
paganism and general counter*

culture. Serves top tea, classic coffees and nourishing nosh with comfy chairs. Friendly atmosphere and cheap food. Can sit around all day browsing through books and eating!

V Cc & (public entrance/dining area)
Seats 21 Open 10am–6.30pm Mon–Sat; 12pm–4.30pm Sun
VS members' discount 10% +/– depending on order!

MARKET RESTAURANT, THE

104 High Street, Manchester M4 1HQ
Tel 0161 834 3743
Restaurant
Modern English

A small friendly family-run restaurant with freshly prepared food using seasonal ingredients. The whole menu changes every 4–6 weeks. At least a third of the dishes are suitable for vegetarians (vegans with prior notice).

P Cc & (public entrance/dining area/bar)
Typical 3 course meal £18 Seats 45
Open 6pm–9.30pm *(last orders)* Wed–Fri; 7pm–9.30pm *(last orders)* Sat

MISTY'S VEGETARIAN CAFE

Unit 3, Longsight Shopping Centre, 531 Stockport Road, Longsight, Manchester M12 4JH
Tel 0161 256 3355
Cafe

A local friendly cafe producing a wide range of food at affordable prices. A massive selection of vegan food. All cakes are vegan, made with organic flour and baked on site. Vegan cheesecakes, puddings and 'ice

cream'. All day vegan breakfasts, shakes etc. Outside catering also available.

V ✖ & (public entrance/designated parking area/dining area)
Typical 3 course meal £5 Seats 25
Open 9am–6pm Mon–Wed & Sat; 11am–5pm Sun

ON THE EIGHTH DAY CO-OP

107–111 Oxford Road, Manchester M1 7DU
Tel 0161 273 1850 (cafe) **Tel 0161 273 4878** (shop) Fax 0161 273 4878
Email 8th-day@eighthy.demon.co.uk
Website http://www.eighthy.demon.co.uk
Cafe Outside Catering Shop Take Away

A workers' co-operative which first opened in 1970. Visit the cafe for freshly cooked, wholesome food. Vegan options are always available but bring your own bottle. Visit the shop for supplies of organic produce, vegetarian/vegan food and homoeopathic medicines. Outside catering, gourmet evenings and cookery classes also available.

V Cc ✖ ⬥ & (public entrance/designated parking area/dining area)
Typical 3 course meal £5.50 Seats 100
Open cafe 9am–7pm Mon–Fri & 10am–4.30pm Sat; shop 9.30am–5.30pm Mon–Sat

UNICORN GROCERY

89 Albany Road, Chorlton, Manchester M21 0BN
Tel 0161 861 0010
Fax 0161 861 7675

Email unicorn@grocery.demon.co.uk

Wholesome Food Store

A large, friendly store run by a workers' co-operative selling the widest range of quality organic fruit and vegetables in Manchester. Also provides over 500 wholefood lines — including organic bread, snacks, wines and beers. A consistent policy on sugar-free food of non-animal origin. Children's play area plus bicycle and car parking available.

VEGAN

YELLOW BRICK CAFE

47 Old Birley Street, Hulme,
Manchester M15 5RF

Tel 0161 227 9008

Cafe

A small, friendly cafe providing vegetarian and some vegan dishes. Will cater in-house for special occasions. Outside catering also available. A fast delivery service is planned and customers will be able to telephone, fax or email for take away food.

V ✕ ⬢✖

Typical 3 course meal £6 Seats 24
Open 7.30am–3pm Mon–Fri;
11am–4pm Sun

MERSEYSIDE

Places to Stay

BIRKENHEAD

VICTORIA GUEST HOUSE

12 Shrewsbury Road, Oxtow,
Birkenhead, Merseyside L43 1UX

Tel 0151 652 8379

B&B Guesthouse Private House

Traditional British

A friendly, family-run guesthouse just outside Birkenhead. Comfortable centrally heated rooms with TV and tea/coffee making facilities. Large garden and parking. Shops and pubs nearby. Accessible by bus and train and only 3 miles from junction 3 of the M53.

P 🏛 Cc ⬢✖

Typical tariff single/double room
£22/£40 Beds 4 Open all year

HOYLAKE

KING'S GAP COURT HOTEL

The King's Gap, Hoylake, Wirral,
Merseyside L47 1HE

Tel 0151 632 2073

Fax 0151 632 0247

Hotel Restaurant

Traditional British Various Styles

Old established 3–4 crown hotel with restaurant and separate banqueting for 200 people. Near to shops, railway, championship golf courses and seashore. Ideal base for visiting Wales, Chester and Liverpool.

🐕 ♀ 🜍 Cc 🍴 ♿ (public entrance/
designated parking area/dining
room/restaurant/bar/TV lounge)
Typical tariff single/double room
£36/£52 Beds 28 Open Mon–Sun
Typical 3 course meal from £8.95
Seats 40–200 Open Mon–Sun: lunch
12pm–2pm; dinner 6pm–9pm

LIVERPOOL

AACHEN HOTEL
89–91 Mount Pleasant, Liverpool,
Merseyside L2 5TB
Tel 0151 709 3477
Fax 0151 709 1126
Website
http:www.connect.org.uk/mersey-
mall/Aachen/
Hotel Restaurant
A la Carte Snacks/Drinks
Traditional British
*Double winner of both Best Small
Hotel North West and Best Hotel
Merseyside. In the heart of Liverpool's
city centre. Convenient for all road,
rail and sea links. Within walking
distance of all attractions. Famous for
'eat as much as you like' breakfast.
3 crown commended. AA & RAC
recommended.*
P ♀ 🜍 Cc ♿ (public entrance/desig-
nated parking area/one bedroom,
bathroom & WC on same level/dining
room/restaurant/bar/TV lounge)
Typical tariff single/double room
from £24/£38 Beds 18 Open 3
Jan–22 Dec
Typical 3 course meal £17 Seats 30
Open 8am–8pm
VS members' discount 10%

Places to Eat

BIRKENHEAD

CAPITOL RESTAURANT
24 Argyle Street, Birkenhead, Wirral,
Merseyside L41 6AE
Tel 0151 647 9212
Fax 0151 647 3793
Restaurant
A la Carte Chinese
*Award winning Chinese restaurant.
Voted Restaurant of the Year in
Merseyside for three consecutive
years. AA rosette 1994, 1995, 1996
and 1997.*
Cc ✖ ♿ (public entrance/designated
parking area/dining area/bar)
Typical 3 course meal £12 Seats 100
Open Mon–Fri 11.30am–2pm &
6pm–11.30pm

HOYLAKE

KING'S GAP COURT HOTEL
See page 104.

LIVERPOOL

AACHEN HOTEL
See left.

LIVERPOOL CYCLE CENTRE/
HUB CAFE, THE
9–13 Berry Street, Liverpool,
Merseyside L1 9DF
Tel 0151 707 9495
Fax 0151 707 1693
Bistro Cafe Wine Bar
A la Carte Italian/Mediterranean

Mexican Snacks/Drinks Spanish Traditional British

The Hub is the social part of Liverpool Cycle Centre with live music, poetry and video news 5 nights a week. A solar powered cafe, low energy lighting is used and rainwater flushes toilets. The furniture and radiators are sculpted entirely from old bikes. Bike hire, massage, bike and eco holidays available.

V & (public entrance/designated parking area/dining area/bar)
Typical 3 course meal £8 Seats 55
Open 9.30am–12am Tues–Sun; 9.30am–7pm Mon

EVERYMAN BISTRO
9 Hope Street, Liverpool, Merseyside L1 9BH
Tel 0151 708 9545 Fax 0151 708 9545
Cafe Restaurant Take Away
Mixed Menu
Established 25 years ago and is one of Liverpool's best known institutions. Situated beneath the Everyman Theatre, it provides well priced food and an inventive style of cooking. David Scott (co-proprietor) is author of The Vegan Diet *and* Simply Vegan.
Cc ⅋✕
Typical 3 course meal £10 Seats 150
Open 10am–12am Mon–Sat

GREEN FISH CAFE
11 Upper Newington, Liverpool, Merseyside L1 2SR
Tel 0151 707 8592
Cafe
Different Styles
Freshly made meals, fine teas and

great coffee.
V ✕
Typical 3 course meal £5 Seats 30
Open 11am–6pm Mon–Sat

MIDDLESEX
Places to Eat

EDGEWARE

CHAI RESTAURANT
236 Station Road, Edgeware, Middlesex
Tel 0181 905 3033
Restaurant Take Away
Chinese (Peking)
A lacto-vegetarian restaurant only 5 minutes from Edgeware underground station. There is a cinema nearby and a pub on the same parade. Chef, Peter Lau from Hong Kong, has 23 years experience as a head chef. Where possible, dishes are cooked according to the requirements of the customer.
V Cc ⅋✕ & (public entrance/dining area)
Typical 3 course meal £12–£15
Seats 45
VS members' discount 5% *when no other offers running*

ENFIELD

MR WING
2–10 Sarnesfield Road, Enfield, Middlesex EN2 6AS
Tel 0181 363 5252

Restaurant
Peking Sezchuan
Cc
Typical 3 course meal £16 Seats 160
Open Mon–Sun

SOUTHALL

A SWEET
106 The Broadway, Southall,
Middlesex UB1 1QF
Tel 0181 574 2821
Cafe Take Away
Indian
*Established in 1970. Aims to provide
authentic north and south Indian food
at reasonable prices in a cafe environ-
ment. Mentioned in various newspa-
pers and publications and on BBC2
and Channel One Cable TV. Limited
variety of vegan foods.*
V ⊁ ♿ (public entrance/dining area)
Typical 3 course meal £7 Seats 20
Open 9am–6pm Tues–Fri; 9am–7pm
Sat; 10am–6pm Sun

**SHAHANSHAH VEGETARIAN
RESTAURANT & INDIAN SWEETS**
60 North Road, Southall, Middlesex
UB1 2JL
Tel 0181 574 1493
Restaurant Take Away
Indian
*Very well known restaurant in the
London area. Has received 8–10
awards and has been recommended
by many newspapers. Food is cooked
on the spot while customers wait.
Indian sweets also available. Plenty of
car parking.*
V 禾 ⊁ ♿ (public entrance/desig-
nated parking area/dining area/bar)
Seats 35+ Open 10am–8pm
Wed–Mon
VS members' discount 10%

TWICKENHAM

FISHERMENS HUT
175 Hampton Road, Twickenham,
Middlesex TW2 5NG
Tel 0181 943 4625
Fax 0181 943 9757
Email mmcma49770@aol.com
Bar Restaurant
A la Carte Organic Traditional British
*Britain's first organic food restaurant
featuring organic wines, vegetables,
bread, oilive oil, etc. Vegan wines and
beers are also available.*
⚲ 禾 Cc ✗ ⊁ ♿ (dining area/bar)
Typical 3 course meal £20 Seats 80
Open 11.30am–3pm & 6pm–12am
VS members' discount 10%

WEMBLEY

WOODLANDS RESTAURANT
402a High Road, Wembley, Middlesex
HA9 6AL
Tel 0181 902 9869
*The largest Indian vegetarian restau-
rant group serving the finest cuisine.*
V
Typical 3 course meal £13 Seats 55
Open 12pm–2.45pm & 6pm–10.45pm
Mon–Sun

> **Please mention the** Vegan
> Travel Guide **when contacting a
> listed business or advertiser**

NORFOLK

Places to Stay

CASTLE ACRE

OLD RED LION, THE
Bailey Street, Castle Acre, nr
Swaffham, Norfolk PE32 2AG
Tel 01760 755557
B&B Guesthouse Private House
Self Catering/Hostel Style
Organic Wholefood
*Centrally situated, serving travellers
who seek 'restauration and repose' in
Castle Acre village. Essentially a B&B
but evening meals available on
request. All meals freshly prepared.
No deep freeze or microwave! Walled
herbaceous garden, private rooms
and dormitories — as well as quiet
spaces for reading and meeting other
guests. Ample parking.*
V 🐐 🜊 🌭
Typical tariff single/double room
£10/£15 Beds 5 Open Jan–Dec
Typical 3 course meal £5–£6.50
Seats 22

NEATISHEAD

REGENCY GUEST HOUSE
The Street, Neatishead, nr Norwich,
Norfolk NR12 8AD
Tel 01692 630233
B&B
*17th century guest house in the cen-
tre of a quiet Norfolk Broads village. 6
miles to the coast and 10 miles to*
Norwich. *Accent on personal service
with a long established name for very
generous vegan and vegetarian breakfasts. Ideal for wildlife, birdwatching,
rambling, cycling and sailing.*
🐐 🜊 🌭 (bedrooms & public areas)
Typical tariff single/double room
from £20–£39 Beds 5 Open all year
VS members' discount *reductions on
1 night+ bookings*

NORWICH

ROSE COTTAGE
33 Holt Road, Gresham, Norwich,
Norfolk NR11 8AD
Tel 01263 577822
B&B
*A Norfolk flint cottage set amidst
beautiful unspoilt countryside and 4
miles from the coast. Woods, heath-
land, salt marshes, clean unspoilt
beaches are all within easy reach.
Meals are provided using wholefoods
and organic produce, mostly from own
garden. Private accommodation with
ensuite facilities. Reflexology available.*
V 🐐 Cc 🌭 🜊 (public menu/desig-
nated parking area/one
bedroom,bathroom & WC on same
level/dining room/TV lounge)
Typical tariff single/double room
£25/£40 Beds 1 Open Mar–Oct

WENDLING

GREENBANKS
Swaffham Road, Wendling, Norfolk
NR19 2AB
Tel 01362 687742
Hotel

Italian/Mediterranean
Traditional British
A small family-run country hotel in the heart of Norfolk. Excellent accommodation and cuisine, catering for a full range of special diets — including a large range of homemade non-meat dishes. Situated in a central position for business or tourism.
🐕 (by arrangement) ⚱ 🏛 Cc ♿
(public entrance/designated parking area/dining area/bar/1 suite) 🍴✖ (in restaurant)
Typical tariff single/double room £38/£52 Beds 5 Open all year
Typical 3 course meal £13–£16.50 Seats 40 Open 12pm–2pm & 7pm–late *(booking necessary)*

WORSTEAD

BARWICK, DICK
Weavers Way, Heath Farm Road, Worstead, Norfolk NR28 0JB
Tel 01692 404570
Caravan Private House
A caravan accommodating 2+ vegans situated in a veganic garden. Very secluded and private with access to the house at all times.
Accommodation available in the house depending on the time and needs of people. No fixed prices. Opportunities to sail and circle dance. Owner has intimate knowledge of Norfolk countryside and Broads.
VEGAN

Please mention the Vegan Travel Guide **when contacting a listed business or advertiser**

Places to Eat

NORWICH

TREEHOUSE, THE
14 Dove Street, Norwich, Norfolk NR2 1DE
Tel 01603 763258
Cafe Restaurant
A co-operative vegetarian restaurant owned by the people who work in it. Most of the food on the daily menu is vegan. It also caters for gluten-free and other special diets. 10% student discount during off peak hours.
V ✖ 🍴✖
Typical 3 course meal £10 Seats 48
Open 10am–5pm Mon–Wed; 10am–9.30pm Thurs–Sat

WELLS NEXT THE SEA

MOORINGS RESTAURANT
6 Freeman Street, Wells Next the Sea, Norfolk NR23 1BA
Tel 01328 710949
Restaurant
A small neighbourhood restaurant featuring local ingredients of all types.
✖ 🍴✖ ♿ (public entrance/dining area/bar)
Typical 3 course meal £21 Seats 30
Open 12.30pm–2pm & 7.30pm onwards

NORTHAMPTONSHIRE

Places to Eat

KETTERING

WELLINGBOROUGH HEALTH FOODS
103 Montague Street, Kettering,
Northamptonshire
See **WELLINGBOROUGH**, below.

WELLINGBOROUGH

WELLINGBOROUGH HEALTH FOODS
22 Silver Street, Wellingborough,
Northamptonshire
Tel 01933 276703 Fax 01933 277532
Email webbers@dial.pipex.com
Website
http://www.ds.dial.pipex.com/town/l
ane/gdh30/whf
Health Food Shop
Snacks/Drinks
One of two independent health food
shops. Established for 24 years.
Cannot guarantee a vegan option
every day — availability depends on
stock. Ring in advance to check.
Able to provide potato and beans,
sweetcorn and ratatouille plus salad
sandwiches if specify vegan margarine
is required.
♿ (public entrance)
Open 8.45am–5.30pm Mon–Sat

NORTHUMBERLAND

Places to Stay

BELFORD

WAREN HOUSE HOTEL
Waren Mill, Belford, Northumberland
NE70 7EE
Tel 01668 214581 Fax 01668 214484
Email laverack@btinternet.com
Hotel Restaurant
Traditional British
A traditional country house hotel
situated on the edge of Bodle Bay
overlooking Holy Island. Bamburgh
Castle only 2 miles away. Superb
accommodation. Freshly prepared
Northumbrian cuisine.
P 🐔 ♔ ♿ (public
entrance/designated parking
area/dining room/restaurant/bar)
Typical tariff single/double room
£80/£110 Beds 10 Open all year
Typical 3 course meal £22.45 Seats 24
Open 7pm–8.30pm *(last orders)*
Mon–Sun

HEXHAM

BATTLESTEADS HOTEL
Wark, nr Hexham, Northumberland
NE48 3LS
Tel 01434 230209 Fax 01434 230730
Email
thebattlesteads@btinternet.com
Website
http://www.btinternet.com/~thebat
tlesteads/

Hotel Public House Restaurant
Italian/Mediterranean Thai
Traditional British
Pool available.
🐾 ♀ 🏠 Cc ✗ ➤ (dining area)
Typical tariff single/double room
£25–£30/£20–£25pp Beds 10
Typical 3 course meal £12.14 Seats 60
Open 12pm–3pm & 6pm–11pm

ROBINSON, MR & MRS
15 Leazes Crescent, Hexham,
Northumberland NE46 3JZ
Tel 01434 606773
B&B
*Situated only 10 minutes from the
town centre and close to Hadrian's
Wall and the Metro Centre. Evening
meal by arrangement. Years of experi-
ence of vegan catering with own son
and use of Animal Free Shopper.*
➤ 🏠 (11+ yrs)
Typical tariff double room £18 pp
Beds 2 Open all year
VS members' discount 10% *2+ nights*

WEST WOODBURN

BAY HORSE INN
West Woodburn, Northumberland
NE48 2RX
Tel 01434 270218 Fax 01434 270118
B&B Public House Restaurant
Fast Food French
Italian/Mediterranean Snacks/Drinks
Traditional British
*An 18th century country inn beside
the River Rede in the Cheviot Hills.
Central for visiting historic castles,
Kielder Water and Forest or shopping
in Newcastle and the Metro Centre.*

*Ensuite bedrooms and children's play
area. Friendly atmosphere and extensive menu including good selection
for vegetarians and vegans.*
♀ 🏠 Cc
Typical tariff single/double room
£25/£40 Beds 5 Open all year
Typical 3 course meal £10.50 Seats 80
Open 12pm–2pm & 6.30pm–9pm
Mon–Sun; 10am onwards for morning coffee

Places to Eat

BELFORD

WAREN HOUSE HOTEL
See page 112.

HEXHAM

BATTLESTEADS HOTEL
See page 112.

WEST WOODBURN

BAY HORSE INN
See left.

NORTH YORKSHIRE

Places to Stay

HARROGATE

AMADEUS VEGETARIAN HOTEL
15 Franklin Road, Harrogate, North
Yorkshire HG12 5EN
Tel 01423 505151 Fax 01423 505151

Hotel

Elegant Victorian house offering excellent standard of accommodation and delicious home-made vegetarian and vegan food to holiday and business guests. Conveniently situated 10 minutes walk from the town centre and half an hour drive from the Dales and North Yorkshire Moors. Ensuite rooms and non-smoking throughout.

V 壺 ⅛✗
Typical single/double room £26/£46
Beds 5 Open all year *except Xmas*

WHARFEDALE HOUSE
28 Harlow Moor Drive, Harrogate, North Yorkshire HG2 0JY
Tel 01423 522233
Guesthouse
A small family-run guesthouse situated only minutes from the town centre. All rooms are ensuite with colour TV, hospitality tray and private telephone. Lovely views across park and woodland. Special break prices available. RAC acclaimed, AA 3 Q recommended and Tourist Board 3 crown commended
P 🐕 壺 ⅛✗ (dining area)
Typical tariff single/double room £28/£48 Beds 8 Open all year

INGLETON

BRIDGE END GUEST HOUSE
Mill Lane, Ingleton, via Carnforth, North Yorkshire LA6 3EP
Tel 015242 41413
Guesthouse
Italian/Mediterranean Traditional British

Situated on the fringe of Ingleton village in the beautiful Yorkshire Dales. Formerly the mill owner's house and a Grade II listed building. Comfortable rooms with ensuite, tea and coffee making facilities, colour TV and central heating. Ideal for touring or just relaxing. ETB three crowns commended.
P 壺 Cc
Typical tariff single/double room £20/£36 Beds 3 guest rooms Open all year
Typical 3 course meal £12 Seats 8
Open 8.30am breakfast; 6.30pm dinner; or by arrangement for guests

PROSPECT COTTAGE
Ingleton, via Carnforth, North Yorkshire LA6 3HE
Tel 015242 41328
B&B Private House
A recently restored cottage in a quiet area notable for its original stained glass and monkey puzzle tree. Discover open fells, crags, wooded glens, waterfalls and caves. Homely accommodation with own entrance, bathroom but no TV or guest lounge. Pick up from Bentham or Ribblehead rail station by arrangement.
V 壺 ⅛✗
Typical tariff single/double room £14.50/£16 Beds 2 Open all year
VS members' discount 15% *2+ nights*

KIRKBY MOORSIDE

LION INN, THE
Blakey Ridge, Kirkby Moorside, North Yorkshire YO6 6LQ

Tel **01751 417320** Fax 01751 417717
**B&B Camping Public House
Restaurant**
A la Carte Traditional British
*A 16th century freehouse located on
the highest point of the North
Yorkshire Moors. Breathtaking views,
open fires burning all day, original
low beamed ceilings and friendly
atmosphere. An extensive bar meal
menu available.*
🐾 ♀ 🏠 Cc ✗
Typical tariff single/double room
£16.50/£22.50pp Beds 10 Open
all year
Seats 125 Open a la carte
7pm–9.30pm Mon–Sun; bar meals
11.30am–10pm Mon–Sun

MIDDLEHAM

GREYSTONES
Market Place, Middleham, North
Yorkshire DL8 4NR
Tel 01969 622016
Guesthouse
Organic Traditional British
*A fine Georgian house with a lovely
view over Middleham's cobbled mar-
ket place. A homely atmosphere, a
warm welcome and an excellent repu-
tation for food. The menu changes
daily and everything is homemade,
using only the best local produce. Bike
hire, drying facilities, walking books
and maps.*
🐾 🏠 ✗ 🍴
Typical tariff double room £54 Beds 4
Open Feb–Nov
Typical 3 course meal £16 Seats 12
Open 7pm for dinner

RICHMOND

KINGS HEAD HOTEL, THE
Market Place, Richmond, North
Yorkshire DL10 4HS
Tel 01748 850220 Fax 01748 850635
Hotel
A la Carte Snacks/Drinks
Traditional British
*A warm and friendly welcome at this
18th century hotel — a focal point of
the cobbled market place. Elegant
restaurant and bar both offering
varied meals with a selection of vegetarian and vegan dishes. The chef will
be happy to cook any dish if there is
nothing on the menu suitable.*
🐾 ♀ 🏠 Cc ✗ 🍴
Typical tariff single/double room
£47/£75 Beds 30 Open all year; bar
11am–11pm; tea room 9.30am–5.30pm;
restaurant 7pm–9.15pm

ROBIN HOODS BAY

MEADOWFIELD B&B
Mount Pleasant North, Robin Hoods
Bay, North Yorkshire YO22 4RS
Tel 01947 880564
B&B
Traditional British
*A small family-run Victorian house in a
quiet historic village on the Yorkshire
coast. Clean, comfortable and well
decorated rooms with central heating,
wash basins and colour TVs. Special
diets catered for. Substantial meals.
Good walking area.*
🍴
Typical tariff single/double room £20/
£32 Beds 5 Open all year *except Xmas*

SCARBOROUGH

BEDFORD HOTEL & LUCAN'S RESTAURANT, THE
The Crescent, Scarborough, North Yorkshire YO11 2PW
Tel 01723 360084 Fax 01723 507374
Email bedford@yorkshirecoast.co.uk
Website
http://www.yorkshirecoast.co.uk/bedford
Hotel Restaurant
French International
Traditional British
The hotel is situated on Scarborough's elegant Regency Crescent. A short stroll to town centre and seafront. Ideal for business conference or pleasure. Lucan's Restaurant is renowned for fine dining in beautiful surroundings.
♀ ☂ ☘ ✕
Typical tariff single/double room
£25/£24pp Beds 30 Open all year
Typical tariff 3 course meal £25 Seats 70 Open 11am–4pm & 6pm–9.30pm

FLOWER IN HAND GUEST HOUSE
Burr Bank, Scarborough, North Yorkshire YO11 1PN
Tel 01723 371471 Fax 01723 507800
Email bazhamps_flower
B&B Guesthouse
A charming 150-year-old listed building in Scarborough's old town. Perched high above the harbour and south bay in the lee of the 11th century castle. All rooms ensuite with TVs, facilities for making hot drinks and sea views. Friendly welcome with great vegan breakfasts.

Cc
Typical tariff single/double room
£25/£35 Beds 3 Open all year

GIRVAN
61 Northstead Manor Drive, Scarborough, North Yorkshire YO12 6AF
Tel 01723 364518 Fax 01723 364518
Hotel Restaurant
A la Carte Fast Food
Italian/Mediterranean Snacks/Drinks
Traditional British
Delightful detached hotel and restaurant overlooking Peasholt Park and close to the sea. Open fire when required. All rooms ensuite, TV and tea/coffee making facilities. A warm welcome.
P ☂ (by arrangment) ♀ ☂ ✕ ⤬
(areas)
Typical tariff single/double room
from £18/£36 Beds 12 Open all year
Typical 3 course meal £8 Seats 40
Open 12pm–6pm *(last orders)*
VS members' discount 5% *low season*

GORDON HOTEL
Ryndleside, Scarborough, North Yorkshire YO12 6AD
Tel 01723 362177
B&B Hotel
Delightful family-run hotel with pleasant views from the lounge and bar. Overlooking Peasholme Park and near all North Bay amenities. Tea and coffee making facilities and TVs in all rooms. Reductions for children sharing. Babysitting available.
OAP discount in low season. Qualified cook will cater for special diets.

P 🐕 ♀ 🏛
Typical tariff single/double room
£18/£36 Beds 11 Open Easter–Nov
VS members' discount 5% *week+ booking*

IVYHOLME HOTEL
30 West Street, Scarborough, North
Yorkshire YO11 2QP
Tel 01723 360649
Guesthouse
Traditional British
A family-run guesthouse offering bed and breakfast. All rooms centrally heated, ensuite, with TV and courtesy tray. Close to esplanade and seafront. Pleased to welcome vegans and happy to provide them with a choice of vegan meals.
P 🏛 ♀ ⅄ ♿ (1 ground floor twin
room)
Typical tariff single/double room
£16.50/£18.50 Beds 6
VS members' discount 5%

PRINCESS COURT GUEST HOUSE
11 Princess Royal Terrace,
Scarborough, North Yorkshire
YO11 2RP
Tel 01723 501922
Guesthouse
Ideally situated for Spa conferences, Esplanade, Italian gardens and within easy walking distance of town centre. Spotless ensuite bedrooms with colour TV, radio, teasmade and central heating. Traditional home cooked food. Reductions for OAPs, families and weekly bookings. Easy parking.
P 🏛
Typical tariff single/double room

£16–£21/£32–£42 Beds 7
Open all year
VS members' discount *£1 off daily rates*

RANWORTH VEGETARIAN GUEST HOUSE
Church Road, Ravenscar,
Scarborough, North Yorkshire
YO13 0LZ
Tel 01723 870366
Guesthouse
Macrobiotic Organic
A Victorian villa in the cliff top village of Ravenscar. Serving vegetarian and vegan wholefoods using many organic ingredients. A lounge is available for guests as well as a play room and large safe garden for children. Ravenscar offers peace, tranquility and open spaces.
V 🐕 🏛 ✕ ⅄
Typical tariff single/double room
£17/£34 Beds 4 Open all year
Typical 3 course meal £8

ROYAL HOTEL
St Nicholas Street, Scarborough,
North Yorkshire YO11 2HE
Tel 01723 364333 Fax 01723 500618
Email theroyalhotel@ukbusiness.com
Website
http://www.mkbusiness.com/theroyalhotel
Cafe Hotel Restaurant
Traditional British
Located in the heart of Scarborough, this famous and historic 4 star hotel has all the comfort and satisfaction guests require. 139 ensuite bedrooms, 9 conference rooms and full leisure

facilities, combined with excellent dining facilities makes this Scarborough's premier hotel.

P ⛄ ♀ 🈺 Cc 🍴✕ (areas) ♿ (public entrance/one bedroom, bathroom & WC on same level/dining room/restaurant/bar/lounge)
Typical tariff single/double room £75/£96 Beds 139 Open all year
Typical 3 course meal £16 Seats 350
Open breakfast 7.30am–10am & dinner 7pm–9pm

SELBOURNE HOTEL
4 West Street, Scarborough, North Yorkshire YO11 2QL
Tel 01723 372822
Hotel
Traditional British
A small family-run hotel on the South Cliff close to the spa, sea front and bus stops. Rooms are mostly ensuite and all have tea making facilities. Catering for individual needs and special diets where possible.
P ♀ 🈺 Cc 🍴✕ (during meals)
Typical tariff single/double room £19.50/£39 Beds 13 Open Jan–Dec
Typical 3 course meal £6 Seats 30
Open breakfast 8.30am–9.30am; dinner 6pm–7pm

SETTLE

SANSBURY PLACE VEGETARIAN GUEST HOUSE
Duke Street, Settle, North Yorkshire BD24 9AS
Tel 01729 823840
Guesthouse
Organic

A small friendly guesthouse in a spacious Victorian property with splendid views of the surrounding limestone scenery. Cruelty-free, environmentally friendly and organic products used wherever possible. Delicious home cooking and special diet catering. Open fires and secluded garden. Bike storage. Nearby railway station.
V 🈺 (over 5 yrs) 🍴✕
Typical tariff single/double room £22/£44 Beds 3 Open all year *except last 3 weeks Jan*
VS members' discount 10% *excl Xmas, New Year & Bank Hols*

SKIPTON

FOX & HOUNDS
Starbotton, nr Skipton, North Yorkshire BD23 5HY
Tel 01756 760269 Fax 01756 760862
B&B Public House
A la Carte Snacks/Drinks
Traditional British
An inn set in the heart of the Yorkshire Dales which caters for vegetarians and vegans. Ideally placed for walking holidays or for people walking the Dales Way.
⛄ ♀ 🈺 Cc 🍴✕
Typical tariff single/double room £30/£50 Beds 2 Open mid Feb–mid Jan
Typical 3 course meal £10 Seats 36
Open food 12pm–2pm & 7pm–9pm; *no food Mon eve*

SYKE HOUSE B&B
Syke House, 103 Raikes Road, Skipton, North Yorkshire BD23 1LS

Tel 01756 793460
B&B Private House
A small family-run business situated in a quiet residential area close to the Yorkshire Dales. Only 2–3 miles from Yorkshire Dales National Park. Accommodating vegans in a sensitive way.
P 🐾 (by arrangement) ♨✖
Typical tariff double room £17.50pp or £35 Beds 2 Open all year

WHITBY

ESTBEK HOUSE HOTEL
Eastrow, Sandsend, Whitby, North Yorkshire YO21 3SU
Tel 01947 893424 Fax 01947 893424
Website http://www.fastfix.com/est bek
B&B Hotel Restaurant Tea Rooms
A la Carte Snacks/Drinks
Traditional British
Elegant lovingly restored Georgian building. Picturesque village by the sea. The hotel has tastefully decorated ensuite furnishings. The kitchen prepares fresh food using local and own produce from vegetable and herb garden. Dinner by candlelight in the Georgian Room. Cosy lounge/bar.
P 🐾 🍴 ♨ ✖ ♨✖
Typical tariff single/double room £29.50/£22.50pp
Typical 3 course meal £15.50 Seats 24
Open Tea Rooms 9am–5.30pm all week; Restaurant 6pm–10.30pm Mon–Sat

FALCON GUEST HOUSE
29 Falcon Terrace, Whitby, North Yorkshire YO21 1EH

Tel 01947 603507
B&B Guesthouse
Situated in a quiet location only seven minutes walk from the centre of Whitby and harbour. Lounge and sunny breakfast room. Parking available near the house. Tea making facilities in all rooms. Reductions available for children.
V ♨ ♨✖
Typical tariff £15pp Beds 2 Open all year

SEACLIFFE HOTEL
12 North Promenade, West Cliff, Whitby, North Yorkshire YO21 3JX
Tel 01947 603139 Fax 01947 603139
Website http://www.sheribansguide-comm/ukireland
Hotel Restaurant
A la Carte Traditional British
A friendly family-run hotel overlooking the sea. All rooms are ensuite with tea making facilities. Candlelit restaurant (also overlooking the sea) provides a good variety of vegetarian dishes using fresh vegetables.
🐾 🍴 ♨ Cc ✖ ♨✖ (restaurant)
Typical tariff single/double room £37.50/£59 Beds 20 Open all year
Typical 3 course meal £17.50 Seats 32
Open 6pm–9pm

WENTWORTH HOUSE
27 Hudson Street, West Cliff, Whitby, North Yorkshire YO21 3EP
Tel 01947 602433
B&B Guesthouse
A Victorian town house offering comfortable and spacious ensuite accommodation. beautifully furnished. Quiet

location, just minutes walk from all attractions in this picturesque historic town. Excellent reputation. ETB 2 crown commended.

🏠 Cc ⤞ ♿ (public entrance/one bedroom, bathroom & WC on same level/dining room)
Typical tariff single/double room £16/£38 Beds 7 Open Jan–Dec excl Xmas & New Year

YORK

DAIRY GUEST HOUSE
3 Scarcroft Road, York, North Yorkshire YO2 1ND
Tel 01904 639367
Guesthouse
Traditional British
Beautifully appointed Victorian house that was once the local dairy! Well equipped cottage-styled rooms around a flower-filled courtyard. Some ensuite rooms and one fourposter bed. Informal atmosphere. Listed as 'commended' by the tourist board.
🏠 ⤞
Typical tariff single/double room £26/£35 Beds 5 Open Feb–Dec

HOLMEWOOD HOUSE HOTEL
114 Holgate Road, York, North Yorkshire YO2 4BB
Tel 01904 626183 Fax 01904 670899
Email
holmwood.house@dial.pipex.com
Website
http://www.smoothhound.co.uk/hotels/holmwood/html
Hotel
A grade II listed buliding situated in

the middle of a 19th century terrace, backing on to one of the prettiest squares in York. Lovingly restored to a family-run hotel which retains the ambience of a private home with peaceful, elegant rooms. All rooms have direct dial telephones, colour TV, hair dryers, radio alarms and coffee/tea making facilities.
Cc ⤞ 🏠 (over 8 yrs)
Typical tariff single/double room £50/£65 Beds 11 Open all year

VEGETARIAN GUEST HOUSE
21 Park Grove, York, North Yorkshire YO3 7LG
Tel 01904 644790
B&B
Special Diets
Spacious Victorian town house in a quiet locality only 10 minutes walk from the centre of York and the Minster. Double rooms are ensuite. Tea making facilities and clock radio are provided in all rooms. Separate sitting room with television. No evening meals.
V ⤞
Typical tariff single/double room £18/£36 Beds 3

Places to Eat

HARROGATE

SUMMERBRIDGE BAKERY
The Main Street, Summerbridge, nr Harrogate, North Yorkshire HG3 4HS
Tel 01423 780844
Bakery Take Away
Fast Food Snacks/Drinks

Traditional British

A village bakery selling 100% vegan bread and a wide selection of vegan sandwiches and cake. One of the proprietors is vegan. The Apricot and Banana Muesli Bar is renowned and runners/joggers buy a tray-full to take home and freeze.

✗ ⊯ ⅄ (public entrance)
Open 8.30am–2pm Mon–Sat

WILD GINGER

5 Station Parade, Harrogate, North Yorkshire HG4 3LG
Tel 01423 566122
Bistro
Situated in the conference town of Harrogate. Boasts a 100% vegan meals menu (dairy milk is served with tea/coffee). An excellent choice of starters, main courses and desserts available. Many organic ingredients used. Organic wines and beers available. All meals served by friendly staff. Recycling policy.
v ✗ ⊯ ⅄ (public entrance/dining area)
Typical 3 course meal £10–£12 Seats 34 Open 10am–4pm Mon–Sat; 10am–9pm *(last orders)* Fri
VS members' discount 5%

KIRKBY MOORSIDE

LION INN, THE
See page 114.

Please mention the Vegan Travel Guide **when contacting a listed business or advertiser**

SCARBOROUGH

BEDFORD HOTEL & LUCAN'S RESTAURANT, THE
See page 116.

GIRVAN
See page 116.

ROYAL HOTEL
See page 117.

SKIPTON

AAGRAH RESTAURANT
Devonshire Place, off Keighley Road, Skipton, North Yorks BD23 2LP
Tel 01756 790807
Restaurant Take Away
Indian
An award winning group of Asian restaurants. Food served is typical Kashmiri as cooked in the owners' homeland. Over 250 dishes on the menu main of which many are vegetarian and vegan. Situated in the centre of Skipton.
Cc ✗ ⊯
Typical 3 course meal £13 Seats 52
Open 6pm–12am Mon–Sat; 6pm–11pm Sun

FOX & HOUNDS
See page 118.

HERBS RESTAURANT
1st Floor, 10 High Street, Skipton, North Yorkshire BD23 1JZ
Tel 01756 790619 Fax 01274 511552
Restaurant
Wholefood

Opened in 1980 at the Healthy Life Natural Food Centre. Offers home-made rolls, soups and savouries made from unadulterated wholefoods together with fresh produce. Prepared by staff who care and served in pleasant surroundings.
V Cc ✕ ⋗ ♿ (public entrance/dining area)
Typical 3 course meal £6.50–£8 Seats 34 Open 9.30am–4.45pm; *closed Tues & Sun*

WENSLEYDALE

TEA TREE
Outhwaite House, Main Street, Hawes, Wensleydale, North Yorkshire DL8 3QL
Cafe Restaurant Tea Rooms
Italian/Mediterranean Snacks/Drinks Traditional British
Intimate teashop serving snacks, cakes and lunches. High quality local crafts, handmade crafts and pottery. Now open in the early evening.
V ✕ ⋗ ♿ (public entrance/designated parking area/dining area/bar)
Typical 3 course meal £8 Seats 30
Open 10am–9pm

WHITBY

MAGPIE CAFE, THE
14 Pier Road, Whitby, North Yorkshire YO21 3PU
Tel 01947 602058 Fax 01947 601801
Restaurant
A la Carte Traditional British
Situated in a distinctive black and white building overlooking the har-bour in the historic Port of Whitby. Run by the same family for three generations. The cafe welcomes families. High chairs, toy boxes, a children's menu and a baby changing room are all available.
Cc ✕ ⋗
Typical 3 course meal £10 Seats 100
Open 11.30am–9pm daily

SEACLIFFE HOTEL
See page 119.

YORK

BLAKE HEAD VEGETARIAN CAFE, THE
104 Micklegate, York, North Yorkshire YO1 1JX
Tel 01904 623767 Fax 01904 625456
Cafe
A light and airy conservatory-style cafe behind one of York's best bookshops. Breakfasts with ground coffee and freshly squeezed fruit juice. Lunchtime hot savouries, freshly prepared salads and cakes. Friendly and committed staff will tell you the ingredients of every dish. Recommended by the Vegetarian Good Food Guide.
V 🕏 Cc ⋗ ♿ (public entrance/dining area)
Typical 3 course meal £7.50 Seats 45
Open 9.30am–5pm Mon–Fri; 9.30am–5.30pm Sat–Sun

ST WILLIAM'S RESTAURANT
College Street, York, North Yorkshire YO1 2JF
Tel 01904 634830 Fax 01904 621800
Restaurant

A la Carte Italian/Mediterranean
Snacks/Drinks
Situated within St William's College, which overlooks York Minster. Food is prepared daily on site using fresh ingredients to suit all tastes. The evening bistro has candlelight and background jazz.
Cc ✗ 🐾 (area) ♿ (designated parking area/dining area)
Typical 3 course meal £9.95 Seats 80–140 Open Mon–Sun 10am–5pm & 6.30pm–9.30pm

NOTTINGHAMSHIRE

Places to Stay

NOTTINGHAM

ST ANDREWS HOTEL
310 Queens Road, Beeston,
Nottingham NG9 1JA
Tel 0115 925 4902
Fax 0115 925 4902
B&B Guesthouse Hotel
French Traditional British
Situated within easy reach of the beautiful Derbyshire Dales and historic Robin Hood country. Comfortable guest lounge with books, board games and TV. All rooms have colour TV, tea/coffee making facilities. Some ensuite and non-smoking rooms. Renowned for its good food and friendly atmosphere.
P 🐾 🛏 🐾 (rooms)
Typical tariff single/double room from £21/£30 Beds 10 Open all year

Typical 3 course meal £8.50 Seats 14
Open Mon–Thurs

Places to Eat

NOTTINGHAM

BLUE NILE
First Floor, 5–9 Heathcote Street,
Hockley, Nottingham NG3 1AF
Tel 0115 941 0976
Restaurant
Egyptian
Nottingham's only Egyptian restaurant, established 15 years. Serves traditional food. Set menu may include a 15 course starter plus the chef's special for only £11.50. Watch out for the occasional belly dancer.
Cc
Typical 3 course meal £10–£11 Seats 60 Open 7pm–late Mon–Sat
VS members' discount

INDIAN EXPERIENCE, THE
5–7 Bentinck Road, Nottingham
NG7 6HD
Tel 0115 942 4922
Restaurant
Indian
A relaxing atmosphere with jazz and some classical Indian music playing in the background. The decor is light with tiled floors, slowly turning ceiling fans, palm plants, wooden screens and concealed lighting. An unhurried and laid back place catering for the early evening trade.
✗ 🐾 ♿ (public entrance/dining area)
Typical 3 course meal £15 Seats 30

Open 6pm–10.30pm Tues–Sat; bar
until 11.30pm
VS members' discount 5% *Fri & Sat*

OLD ANGEL, THE
7 Stoney Street, The Lace Market,
Nottingham NG1 1LG
Tel 0115 950 2303
Public House
Indian Italian/Mediterranean
Mexican Snacks/Drinks
Traditional British
*A young, lively pub with music and
live entertainment. Travellers, dogs,
students and working people are all
catered for together in a relaxed and
friendly atmosphere. Traditionally
catering for meat-eaters and vegetari-
ans the Old Angel now has a range of
vegan foods available.*
🐾 ♀ Cc
Typical main dish £2.50 Seats 150
Open 11am–11pm Mon–Sat;
12pm–10.30pm Sun

RAINBOW CENTRE CANTEEN
188 Mansfield Road, Nottingham
NG1 3HW
Tel 01159 585666 Fax 01159 585666
Cafe
Snacks/Drinks
*A small cafe snack bar situated in an
environmental resource centre.*
VEGAN ⅌
Seats 20 Open 10.30am–5pm
Mon–Sat

SALAMANDER RESTAURANT
23–25 Heathcote Street, Hockley,
Nottingham NG1 3AG
Tel 0115 941 0710

Restaurant
A la Carte Chinese French Indian
Italian/Mediterranean Japanese
Lebanese Mexican Spanish Thai
Traditional British
*A workers' co-operative owned and
run by the people who work there.
Established for over three years serv-
ing high quality vegan cuisine with a
wide and varied choice from a la carte
menu. Fully licensed with an extensive
wine list which is vegan and organic.
Special dietary requirements catered
for with notice.*
VEGAN Cc ⅌ (rooms) ♿ (public
entrance/dining area/bar)
Typical 3 course meal £11 Seats 45
Open Thurs–Sat & Mon–Tues
6pm–10.30pm; Sun 1pm–3.30pm &
6pm–9pm
VS members' discount 10% *food*

OXFORDSHIRE

Places to Stay

OXFORD

ASCOT HOUSE
283 Iffley Road, Oxford OX4 4PQ
Tel 01865 240259 Fax 01865 727669
Email llambertti@classic.msn.com
B&B
*A pretty Victorian house with beauti-
fully refurbished rooms to afford
every comfort. All rooms have ensuite,
colour TV, radio alarm, hairdryer,
tea/coffee, fridge, direct dial telephone and central heating. Buffet*

style breakfast with plenty of fresh fruit, juices, mushrooms, tomatoes, etc. Soya milk provided for vegans.
🏛 Cc ⮾

Typical tariff single/double room from £35/£48 Beds 6 Open all year

BURLINGTON HOUSE

374 Banbury Road, Summertown, Oxford OX2 7PP
Tel 01865 513513 Fax 01865 311785
B&B

A beautiful renovated Victorian house in the prime location of Summertown, north Oxford. A super base for exploring Oxford, the Cotswolds and Bath. Bike hire, telephones and coffee/tea making facilities available. New proprietors ensure a warm hospitable welcome to vegans and vegetarians alike.
P Cc ⮾

Typical tariff single/double room £25/£50 Beds 11 Open all year

COTSWOLD HOUSE

363 Banbury Road, Oxford OX2 7PL
Tel 01865 310558 Fax 01865 310558
Guesthouse

Situated 2 miles north of the centre of Oxford. A stone built house constructed relatively recently to high standards. Bedrooms vary in size but each feature good quality, comfortable furnishings and good equipment.
⮾ 🏛 (over 6 yrs)

Typical tariff single/double room £41/£61 Beds 7 Open all year *except Xmas & New Year*

EARLMONT GUEST HOUSE

322–324 Cowley Road, Oxford OX4 2AF

Tel 01865 240236
Email beds@earlmont.prestel.co.uk
Website
http://www.oxlink.co.uk/oxford/hotels/earlmont/html
B&B Guesthouse

Situated within a 20 minute walk from the city centre on a bus route. Ensuite rooms are equipped with colour TVs, radio-alarm clocks, hairdryers plus tea and coffee making facilities. Budget rooms have colour TVs plus tea and coffee making facilities. Bike hire available.
P Cc ⮾

Typical tariff single/double room £38/£48 Beds 16 Open 7 Jan–20 Dec

GABLES, THE

6 Cumnor Hill, Oxford OX2 9HA
Tel 01865 862153 Fax 01865 864054
B&B

Traditional British
An attractive detached house with a beautiful garden situated close to the city centre, bus and railway stations. Superbly equipped rooms with satellite TV, direct dial telephone, hairdryer and clock/radio. Breakfast only served 7am–9.30am. A warm and friendly welcome guaranteed.
🏛 Cc ✗ ⮾ ♿ (one bedroom, bathroom & WC on same level/dining room/restaurant/bar/TV lounge)

Typical tariff single/double room £24/£42 Beds 6 Open all year *except Xmas & New Year's Eve*

HEATHER HOUSE B&B

192 Iffley Road, Oxford OX4 1SD
Tel 01865 249757 Fax 01865 249757

B&B

Bright and comfortable accommodation within easy walking distance of the historical and commercial heart of Oxford. Business people, academics, tourists and folks visiting friends and family all enjoy the helpful and individual attention. Motto is 'Heather House — where you're most welcome'.

P 🏛 Cc 🏠✖

Typical tariff single/double room £23/£46 Beds 6

PARKLANDS HOTEL

100 Banbury Road, Oxford OX2 6JU
Tel 01865 554374 Fax 01865 559860
Email 100574.3512@compuserve.com
Hotel
Traditional British
A small, friendly hotel willing to provide for guests' needs with a 'Just ask and we try' policy.

🐕 (dogs) 🍴 Cc

Typical tariff single/double room £47/£68 Beds 18 Open all year except Xmas

Typical 3 course meal £10.50 Seats 60
VS members' discount 10%

PINE CASTLE HOTEL

290–292 Iffley Road, Oxford OX4 4AE
Tel 01865 241497 Fax 01865 727230
Email
pinebeds.oxfhotel@pop3.hiway.co.uk
Website
http://www.oxlink.co.uk/oxford/hotels/pine_castle.html
Guesthouse
Traditional British
A well-established family-run guest-

house easily accessible from the Oxford ring road and convenient for the city centre. All rooms ensuite, TV, telephone, tea/coffee tray and hairdryer. ETB 3 crowns highly commended, reflecting the personal attention guests receive.

P (blankets) 🍴 🏛 Cc 🏠✖

Typical tariff single/double room £45/£55 Beds 8 Open all year except Xmas week

THAME

SPREAD EAGLE HOTEL

Cornmarket, Thame, Oxfordshire
OX9 2BW
Tel 01844 213661 Fax 01844 261380
Hotel Restaurant
A la Carte French Snacks/Drinks
Traditional British
An historical coaching inn, carefully modernised, comprising 33 bedrooms and award winning restaurant. Private dining room, large car park and private rooms available.

🏛 Cc ✖ ♿ (public entrance/designated parking area/one bedroom, bathroom & WC on same level/dining room/restaurnt/bar/TV lounge)
Typical tariff single/double room £81.96/£96.95 Beds 33 Open all year
Typical 3 course meal £20 Seats 65
Open 12.30pm–2pm Mon–Sun;
7pm–10pm Mon–Fri; 7.30pm–10pm
Sat; 7pm–9pm Sun

WITNEY

FORGE COTTAGE

East End, North Leigh, Witney,

Oxfordshire OX8 6PZ
Tel 01993 881120
B&B Private House
Traditional British
An old Cotswold cottage traditionally furnished. Home of conservation crazy and cat loving biologist. Firm comfortable beds, drinks facilities and TVs in all rooms. Off road parking. Delicious breakfasts including homegrown and homemade preserves.
🐾 💢

Typical tariff single/double room £16/£40 Beds 2 Open all year *except Xmas, Easter, mid-Jul–mid-Aug*

Places to Eat

OXFORD

GARDENERS ARMS
Plantation Road, Oxford OX2 6JE
Tel 01865 559814
Public House
Italian/Mediterranean
Traditional British
Serving a mixture of students and locals. Beer garden available.
♀ 🍺

Seats 60 Open Mon–Sun
11am–2.30pm & 6.30pm–11pm

NOSEBAG RESTAURANT, THE
6–8 Michael's Street, Oxford
OX1 2DU
Tel 01865 721033 Fax 01865 792290
Restaurant
Traditional British
Established for 26 years and situated in a 15th century building. Serves good wholesome homemade food prepared on the premises, using only fresh ingredients.
P 💢

Typical 3 course meal £10 Seats 52
Open 9.30am–5.30pm Mon; 9.30am–10pm Tues–Thurs; 9.30am–10.30pm Fri–Sat; 9.30am–9pm Sun

UHURU WHOLEFOODS
48 Cowley Road, Oxford OX4 1HZ
Tel 01865 248249
Take Away Wholefood Shop
Fast Food Organic Snacks/Drinks
A wholefood shop stocking a wide range of foods including a range of vegan take away products.
V Cc
Open 10am–6pm Mon–Fri;
9.30am–5.30pm Sat
VS members' discount 5%

THAME

SPREAD EAGLE HOTEL
See page 127.

WITNEY

COUNTRY PIE, THE
63 Corn Street, Witney, Oxfordshire
OX8 7DQ
Tel 01993 703590 Fax 01993 703590
Restaurant
International Traditional British
Good food is served in congenial surroundings with an air of calm efficiency in this 16th century building of Cotswold stone. Recently modernised but maintains its charm. Also caters for private parties, wedding receptions and business luncheons.

Cc ✗ ⊯ ☝ (public entrance/dining area/bar)
Typical 3 course meal £15.20 Seats 40
Open 12pm–2pm Tues–Sun; 7.00pm–9.30pm *(last orders) Tues–Sat*

SHROPSHIRE

Places to Stay

CRAVEN ARMS

LOST LEET MILL
Hopton Heath, Craven Arms,
Shropshire SY7 0QB
Tel 01547 530384
B&B Private House
Set in the beautiful Clun Valley on the Borders with Wales. 10 miles from the historic town of Ludlow, 29 miles from Hereford and 29 miles from Shrewsbury. Lost Leet Mill is one of only two 19th century turbine mills in the country. Packed lunches available but no evening meal.
P ⊮ ⊯
Typical tariff double room £18pp
Beds 2
VS members' discount 5%

GAREN ARMS

GABLES, THE
Broome, Garen Arms, Shropshire
SY7 0NX
Tel 01588 660667 Fax 01588 660799
B&B
Organic Traditional British
A charming house with spacious gar-
dens and the open countryside of the Chen Valley. Situated 8 miles from Ludlow, it is ideal to explore the Long Mynd, Wenlock Edge and Offas Dyke. Evening meals by arrangement.
P ⊮ ⊞ ✗ ⊯ ☝ (designated parking area/one bedroom, bathroom & WC on same level/dining room)
Typical tariff double room £18 Beds 3
Open all year
Typical 3 course meal £10.50 Seats 6

Places to Eat

CHURCH STRETTON

ACORN WHOLEFOOD RESTAURANT & COFFEE HOUSE
26 Sandford Avenue, Church Stretton,
Shropshire SY6 6BW
Tel 01694 722495
Restaurant Take Away Tea Rooms
Food, atmosphere and service count at this restaurant which has been established for 10 years. Nearly all the food is made on the premises. Endorsed by Egon Ronay and other vegetarian and 'teapot trail' guides.
✗ ⊯ ☝ (designated parking area/dining area/tea garden)
Typical 3 course meal £6.80 Seats 45 + tea garden Open winter 9.30am–5.30pm Mon, Thurs, Fri, Sat; summer 9.30am–6.00pm Mon, Wed, Thurs, Fri, Sat, Sun & school holidays; 10am–6pm Bank Hols & Sun

CRAVEN ARMS

SUN INN, THE
Corfton, Craven Arms, Shropshire

SY7 9DF
Tel 01584 861239 Fax 01584 861239
Public House
Traditional British
A small successful pub which has been established for over 12 years. Winner of the Shropshire Star Best Village Pub competition and South Shropshire Access Award for promoting access for the disabled. A selection of vegetarian meals and one vegan meal on the menu.
Cc ✗ ⤞ ♿ (public entrance/designated parking area/dining area/bar)
Typical 3 course meal under £10
Seats 50 Open Mon–Sat 11am–2pm & 6pm–11pm; Sun 12pm–3pm & 7pm–10.30pm; all day Bank Hols

IRONBRIDGE

OLIVERS VEGETARIAN BISTRO
33 High Street, Ironbridge, Telford, Shropshire TF8 7AG
Tel 01952 882961 Fax 01952 882961
Voice 01952 433086
Email oliversvegetarianbistro@btinternet.com
Bistro Cafe Restaurant
Established in 1987. A licensed restaurant with a large selection of main courses, side dishes and desserts. Evening menu changes regularly and can be found on the blackboard in the restaurant. Advisable to book for evening meals.
V 🍴 Cc ⤞ ♿ (dining room)
Typical 3 course meal £11 Seats 45
Open 7pm–9pm Tues–Thurs; 7–10pm Fri; 12pm–3pm, 7pm–10pm Sat; 11am–5pm Sun; open daytime most

Bank Hols & for special events
VS members' discount 10% *with 4% surcharge*

SHIFNALL

RAPHAELS RESTAURANT
4 Church Street, Shifnal, Shropshire TF11 9AA
Tel 01952 461136
Restaurant
A la Carte French
Italian/Mediterranean
Traditional British
An intimate and charming 17th century licensed restaurant situated in the market town of Shifnal. Excellent freshly cooked French, British and vegetarian gourmet dishes. Good Food Guide *and* Les Routiers *award winners.*
P (ensures choice) Cc ✗ ⤞ ♿ (public entrance/designated parking area/dining area/bar)
Typical 3 course meal £14.95 Seats 30
Open 7.30pm–late Tues–Sat; 12pm–2.30pm Sun

SHREWSBURY

GOODLIFE RESTAURANT, THE
Baracks Passage, Wyle Cop, Shrewsbury, Shropshire SY1 1XA
Tel 01743 350455
Cafe Restaurant
Snacks/Drinks Traditional British
Wholefood
An established restaurant/coffee shop situated in a listed 15th century building in one of Shrewsbury's historic passageways. Serving freshly prepared

*meals, homemade cakes and desserts.
Extensive salad bar. All food made
daily on the premises.*
V ✕ ᨪᨪ (area)
Typical 3 course meal £6 Seats 64
Open 9.30am–4.30pm Mon–Sat

SOMERSET

Places to Stay

BRIDGWATER

PARSONAGE FARM
Over Stowey, nr Nether Stowey,
Bridgwater, Somerset TA5 1HA
Tel 01278 733237 Fax 01278 733511
B&B Guesthouse
*A traditional 17th century farmhouse
and organic smallholding in the
Quantock Hills. Delicious vegan and
vegetarian fare using own fresh pro-
duce. Homemade jams and breads.
Friendly and informal atmosphere.
Relaxing log fires and delightful gar-
dens. Hill, wood and moorland walks
on the doorstep.*
ᕦ ᨪᨪ ᨪᨪ
Typical tariff single/double room
£25/£18.21pp Beds 3 Open all year
VS members' discount 5% *accommodation*

POPLAR HERB FARM
Burtle, Bridgwater, Somerset TA7 8NB
Tel 01278 723170
B&B Pirvate House
*Situated in a village location 7 miles
west of Glastonbury. A herb/nursery*

*and smallholding with display herb
gardens and friendly rescued animals.*
V ᕦ ᨪᨪ ᨪᨪ
Typical tariff single/double room
£14/£17 Beds 3 Open all year

BURNHAM ON SEA

PRIORS MEAD
23 Rectory Road, Burnham on Sea,
Somerset TA8 2BZ
Tel 01278 782116 Fax 01278 782116
B&B
*Guests are welcome in this peaceful
Edwardian family home. Large rooms,
king sized beds, ensuite facilities, CTV
and tea/coffee trays. Facilities include
a swimming pool, croquet, secluded
gardens with tennis court and golf
course nearby. Excellent base for
Bath, Bristol, Wells and Cheddar.
Which recommended.*
P ᨪᨪ
Typical tariff single/double room
£20/£34 Beds 3 Open all year except
Xmas

CHARD

ASHANIKA SANCTUARY
Rastra Devas, Holmbush,
Thorncombe, Chard, Somerset
TA20 4PL
Tel 01297 678597 Fax 01297 678597
B&B Private House
Chinese Italian/Mediterrean Organic
*A small private animal sanctuary in des-
ignated Area of Outstanding Natural
Beauty near Lyme Regis. The cosy
period cottage has log fires and beams.
Run by healers so guests or companion*

animals may have healing advice on
alternative medicine if they wish.
VEGAN 🐕 ⚖ ✗ ⊯

Typical tariff single/double room
£27/£27pp for B&B + eve meal
Beds 2
Typical 3 course meal £10 Seats 8
VS members' discount 10%

CREWKERNE

**MEREFIELD VEGETARIAN
GUEST HOUSE**
East Street, Crewkerne, Somerset
TA18 7AB
Tel 01460 73112
Guesthouse Self Catering
16th century guesthouse established
for 10 years. Gardens, large guest
lounge, books, video and games available. Specialising in imaginative vegan
cuisine for those who enjoy eating.
Owner vegan. All meals vegan
although cow's milk and eggs are
available if required by vegetarians.
🐕 (self catering) **V** ⊯ (public areas)
Typical tariff double room £35 Beds 3
Open all year except when owner on
holiday
VS members' discount 10% 1 week+

DUNSTER

GABLES GUEST HOUSE, THE
33 High Street, Dunster, Somerset
TA24 6SF
Tel 01643 821496
Guesthouse Tea Rooms
Snacks/Drinks Traditional British
A three storey Georgian building with
a Victorian facade situated in the

main street of Dunster, just above the
yarn market. Refurbished, fire certificate, licensed and smoke free
throughout. Catering mainly for up to
ten guests serving breakfast and
evening meals.
P ⚖ ⊯ & (public entrance)
Typical tariff single/double room
£25/£45 Beds 5 Open all year
Typical 3 course meal £10.15 Seats 30
Open 11am–5pm during season
VS members' discount 10% (with
advance notice)

EXFORD

EXMOOR LODGE
Chapel Street, Exford, Somerset
TA24 7PY
Tel 01643 831694
B&B
Located in the centre of Exford, overlooking the village green, in the heart
of Exmoor National Park. Combining
healthy food and cruelty-free principles. Evening meals available with
advance booking, ranging from aduki
bean pasties to Indian and Mexican
dishes.
V 🐕 (with notice) ⊯ & (public
entrance/one bedroom, bathroom
[not wide enough for wheelchair] &
WC on same level/dining room)
Typical tariff £15–£21pp Beds 5
Open all year

GLASTONBURY

ARCTURUS B&B
98 Bove Town, Glastonbury, Somerset
BA6 8JG

Tel 01458 831156
B&B
Situated in a quiet location overlooking Glastonbury Tor. A warm friendly welcome in a spiritual vegan home only 5 minutes walk from the town centre. Offers a nurturing and supportive environment with aromatherapy, massage, counselling and healing. Non-smokers only.
VEGAN 🏠 ⚡ ♿ (designated parking area/one bedroom, bathroom & WC on same level/dining room)
Typical tariff single/double room £15/£30 Beds 2 Open Apr–Dec

BROCK COTTAGE
77 Bere Lane, Glastonbury, Somerset
BA6 8BE
Tel 01458 834985
B&B Private House
A small cottage built in 1782 overlooking Glastonbury Abbey, Rural Life Museum and Glastonbury Tor. Tea/coffee maker in all rooms. Tarot counselling by experienced reader. Would suit quiet sensitive people as this is a small cottage.
V 🐕 🏠 (10 yrs+) ⚡ ♿ (one bedroom, bathroom & WC on same level)
Typical tariff single/double room £20/£35 Beds 3 Open all year
VS members' discount 10%

LIGHTSHIP, THE
82 Bove Town, Glastonbury, Somerset
BA6 8JG
Tel 01458 833698
B&B Guesthouse Garden Camping Holiday Cottage Self Catering Take Away

Organic
A cosy retreat in a 17th century terraced cottage made of Somerset stone. Completely self-contained with fully equiped kitchen. Adjoining a spirituality/green centre. Country views, sunny courtyard for eating out. On the Tor route and close to the town centre. The whole cottage or one bedroom can be hired on a nightly or weekly rate.
V 🐕 🏠 ⚡
Typical tariff single/double room £15/£25 Beds 2 Open all year

MATKINS, MS A
5 Bere Lane, Glastonbury, Somerset
BA6 8BD
Tel 01458 832675
B&B Private House
A la Carte Chinese Fast Food Indian Italian/Mediterranean Organic Snacks/Drinks
Situated close to the centre of town and sacred sites. Private bathroom and toilet.
V ⚡
Typical tariff single room £16 Beds 1 Open all year

SHAMBHALA HEALING CENTRE
See **SPECIAL INTEREST**, page 229.

TORDOWN
5 Ashwell, Glastonbury Tor, Somerset
BA6 8BU
Tel 01458 832287 Fax 01458 831100
B&B
Situated on the southern slopes of the Tor. Family-run, warm welcoming, peaceful atmosphere. All rooms have

hot/cold water, tea/coffee making facilities, audio, colour TV, hairdryers and some ensuite. Healing and healing courses available. Car parking. ETB 2 crowns commended.
V ➤ (by arrangement) ⚥ Cc ♿ ⬛✖
(public entrance/one bedroom/bathroom & WC on same level/dining room/TV lounge)
Typical tariff single/double room £15/£30 Beds 7 Open all year
VS members' discount 10%
block bookings

WATERFALL COTTAGE
20 Old Wells Road, Glastonbury, Somerset BA6 8ED
Tel 01458 831207
B&B Private House
Beautiful 17th century cottage radiating peace and harmony. 10 minutes walk to town. Views of the Mendip Hills and Tor and country walks from the garden gate. Healing and aromatherapy massage. Excellent centre to tour SW England.
⬛✖
Typical tariff single/double room £14.50/£14.50pp Beds 4 Open all year

WICK HOLLOW HOUSE
8 Wick Hollow, Glastonbury, Somerset BA6 8JJ
Tel 01458 833595
B&B Private House
Chinese Indian
Italian/Mediterranean
Traditional British
Self contained B&B accommodation in a ground floor annexe. Suite com-prises entrance hall, sitting/breakfast room, bedroom and bathroom. Very spacious and light. Beautiful views of extensive gardens, the Tor and Chalice Hill. Warm welcome assured.
P ➤ ⚥ ⬛✖ ♿ (public entrance/designated parking area/one bedroom, bathroom & WC on same level/dining room/restaurant/TV lounge)
Typical tariff single/double room £28/£40 Beds 1 Open all year

PORLOCK

LORNA DOONE HOTEL, THE
High Street, Porlock, Somerset TA24 8PS
Tel 01643 862404 Fax 01643 863018
Hotel Restaurant
A la Carte Snacks/Drinks
Traditional British
A family-run hotel in the village centre. All room ensuite. An ideal centre for walking on Exmoor. The restaurant is open to non-residents and has an extensive a la carte choice including vegetarian and vegan dishes.
➤ ♀ ⚥ Cc ✖ ⬛✖ (restaurant) ♿
(public entrance/designated parking area/one bedroom, bathroom & WC on same level/dining room/restaurant/bar/TV lounge)
Typical tariff single/double room £24/£44 Beds 15 Open all year except Xmas
Restaurant seats 24 Open Mon–Sun 11am–2pm & 6.30pm–8.30pm

SEAPOINT
Upway, Porlock, Somerset TA24 8QE
Tel 01643 862289 Fax 01643 862289

Guesthouse
Traditional British
A comfortable Edwardian guesthouse with spectacular views over Porlock Bay. Set in the heart of Exmoor's wild heather moorland with deep wooded coombes, clear streams and magnificent coastline. Delicious vegan food, log fires, candlelit dinners and tastefully furnished ensuite rooms with colour TV.
ETB 2 crown highly commended. AA 3 Q recommended.
🐎 ⛩ ✕ ⅙✕
Typical tariff single/double room £21/£42 Beds 3 Open Feb–Nov

WELLS

BURCOTT MILL GUEST HOUSE
Wookey, Wells, Somerset BA5 1NJ
Tel 01744 673118 Fax 01744 673118
Guesthouse
This Grade II listed building is a working water mill. Set in a rural location with lots of animals around and opposite a country pub. Half a mile from Wells on the edge of Somerset wetlands. Rooms are available in the miller's house. Wholemeal flour is milled here and used in the home cooked food.
P 🐎 ⛩ Cc ♿ (disabled access ETB Category 1)
Typical tariff single/double room £19/£25 Beds 6 Open all year

CADGWITH

Hawkers Lane, Wells, Somerset BA5 3JW
Tel 01749 677799

B&B
Traditional British
Modern family home backing on to green fields and only 10 minutes walk to the city centre. Spacious bedrooms.
🐎 ⛩
Typical tariff single/double room £19/£18pp Beds 3 Open all year

WRINGTON

BRACKEN HILL HOUSE
Wrington Hill, Wrington, North Somerset BS18 7PN
Tel 01934 862261 Fax 01934 862875
Email bracken.hill.@btinternet.com
B&B
A peaceful and comfortable country house retreat with beautiful views, cosy fires, TV and complimentary tray in all rooms. Excellent walking country yet within easy driving distance of Bath, Wells and Bristol. ETB highly commended.
🐎 (by arrangement) ⛩ (over 5 yrs) ⅙✕
Typical tariff single/double room £25.50 Beds 4 Open all year except Xmas & New Year

Places to Eat

CHARD

JARRATS RESTAURANT
1–3 Fore Street, Chard, Somerset TA20 1PH
Tel 01460 6613 Fax 01460 6613
Bistro Restaurant
A la Carte Snacks/Drinks
Traditional British

A relatively new family oriented licensed establishment. Clean and friendly. Currently developing a selection of vegan dishes.
Cc ✖ ᴸ✖ (area in Bistro & restaurant)
& (public entrance/dining area/toilet)
Typical tariff bistro £8; a la carte £10
Seats bistro 44; restaurant 40
Open *Oct–Apr:* 9am–6pm
Mon–Thurs; 9am–8pm Fri–Sat; Sun functions only;
May–Sept: 9am–10pm Mon–Thurs; 9am–11pm Fri–Sat; Sun functions only

DUNSTER

GABLES GUEST HOUSE, THE
See page 132.

GLASTONBURY

ASSEMBLY ROOMS CAFE
High Street, Glastonbury, Somerset
BA6 9DU
Tel 01458 834677
Cafe Take Away
Organic Snacks/Drinks
All food is homemade by a co-operative team of talented cooks. Vegan organic food with some cow's milk and honey. The cafe is a part of the main community centre in Glastonbury and, as well as supporting the diverse range of entertainments held in the building, it runs its own events — eg poetry, folk nights, quiz nights, special menu evenings and blues cafe. Licensed.
V ✖ ᴸ✖ (area)

Typical 3 course meal £7 Seats 25
Open 10am–8pm Mon–Sat;
10am–6pm Sun; *if event in main hall — open until midnight*

RAINBOW'S END CAFE
17a High Street, Glastonbury,
Somerset
Tel 01458 833896
Cafe
A warm and welcoming cafe which is brightly decorated, giving a Mediterranean feel. Established for 12 years with a good local trade, including many regular customers. All food is made on the premises and the main chef is vegan, as are most of the staff who are also renowned for their good sense of humour.
V ᴸ✖ (area)
Typical 3 course meal £6.70 Seats 50
+ courtyard area Open
10am–4.30pm Mon–Sun
Easter–Xmas; *closed Sun Jan–Feb*

PORLOCK

LORNA DOONE HOTEL, THE
See page 134.

TAUNTON

HERB GARDEN, THE
24 Upper High Street, Taunton,
Somerset TA1 3PZ
Tel 01823 282884 Fax 01823 353672
Email herbs@herbgarden.co.uk
Website
http://www.herbgarden.co.uk
Cafe Restaurant Take Away
A small cosy vegetarian wholefood

cafe with a rapidly establishing reputation for quality and atmosphere. The majority of the food is vegan. Wines and some beers are organic and vegan.

V Cc ✗

Typical 3 course meal £10 Seats 30
Open 12pm–3pm Tues; 12pm–10pm Wed–Sat
VS members' discount 10%

NUMBER TEN
10 Station Road, Taunton, Somerset TA1 1NH
Tel 01823 256045
Cafe Restaurant Take Away
Fast Food Snacks/Drinks
Established 11 years. Provides a pleasant atmosphere with dedicated kitchen staff, producing fresh food daily. The daily soup, the vegetarian dish (ask to omit cheese) and some cakes are vegan. There is also a vegan filling for jacket potatoes. Counter service.
✗ (upstairs/some areas downstairs)
& (public entrance)
Seats 50 Open 9am–4.30pm
Mon–Sat

WELLS

GOOD EARTH RESTAURANT, THE
4 Priory Road, Wells, Somerset BA5 1SY
Tel 01749 678600
Restaurant Take Away Wholefood Shop
A comfortable and pleasant restaurant in unusual surroundings with conservatory and courtyard garden. Secluded seating areas. Flexible and

welcoming friendly staff. One vegan dish always on offer daily. If vegans ring in advance could do a 3-course take away, otherwise 'pot luck'.
V Cc ✗ (half portion on request) &
(public entrance/dining area)
Seats 80 Open 9.30am–5.30pm
Mon–Sat

SOUTH YORKSHIRE

Places to Eat

SHEFFIELD

CHINSKIS VEGETARIAN RESTAURANT
353 Abbeydale Road, Sheffield, South Yorkshire S7 1FS
Tel 0114 250 1076
Restaurant
The ethos here is to serve food as fresh as possible, which means preparing food daily using fresh vegetables and herbs. There is always at least one vegan option in each course. Bring your own wine. Outside catering available.
V ✗ ✗ & (public entrance/designated parking area/dining area/bar)
Typical 3 course meal £13.50 Seats 30
Open 7pm–11pm Wed–Sun

NIRMAL'S RESTAURANT
189–193 Glossop Road, Sheffield South Yorkshire S10 2GW
Tel 0114 272 4054
Restaurant
Indian

Owners are vegetarian and specialise in vegetarian and vegan cuisine using fresh vegetables and herbs. The restaurant is recommended in Egon Ronay's Good Food Guide and the chief chef has been on TV demonstrating Indian dishes.

♀ ⚑ Cc ✗ ⚐ (public entrance/designated parking area/dining area/bar)
Typical 3 course meal £10.13 Seats 80
Open 12pm–2.30pm Mon–Sat;
6pm–12pm Sun–Thurs; 6pm–1pm Fri & Sat
VS members' discount 10% *Sun & Mon with advance booking*

STAFFORDSHIRE

Places to Eat

STOKE ON TRENT

DYLANS VEGETARIAN RESTAURANT
99 Broad Street, Hanley, Stoke on Trent, Staffordshire ST1 4JQ
Tel 01782 286009   Fax 01785 713066
Restaurant
V Cc ✗
Typical 3 course meal £13.85 Seats 34
Open Mon–Fri 12pm–2pm,
6pm–10.30/11pm; Sat 12pm–11pm
VS members' discount 15%

Please mention the Vegan Travel Guide **when contacting a listed business or advertiser**

SUFFOLK

Places to Stay

CAVENDISH

WESTERN HOUSE
High Street, Cavendish, Suffolk
CO10 8AR
Tel 01787 280550
B&B
Bed and breakfast only. Set in 1 acre of gardens. Owners have a small wholefood shop at the rear of the house.
V
Typical tariff single/double room
£16/£32 Beds 3 Open all year

SAXTEAD

CHURCH COTTAGE
Saxtead, Suffolk IP13 9QR
Tel 01728 724067
B&B Private House
Fast Food Macrobiotic Organic
Situated in a lovely locality half an hour from the coast. A 16th century beamy house with log fires and vegetables available from own organic garden. The property is permaculture-based and would not suit those requiring mod cons.
P 🐕 ⚑ Cc ✗
Typical tariff £15pp Beds 5 Open all year *except Xmas*
Typical 3 course meal £7.50 Seats 10+
open for breakfast & evening meal by arrangement

Places to Eat

BURY ST EDMUNDS

LINDEN TREE, THE
7 Out Northgate, Bury St Edmunds,
Suffolk IP33 1JQ
Tel 01284 754600 Fax 01284 724233
Restaurant Public House
A la Carte Chinese Indian
Italian/Mediterranean
*A large friendly pub with two bars.
Table service for food. Two conserva-
tory non-smoking restaurants.
Specialises in wholesome and home-
made food, large portions and a
speedy service. Large parties catered
for. Garden with children's play area.*
Cc ✖ ✖ ⅗ (access possible with
help)
Typical 3 course meal £12 Seats 120+
Open Mon–Sat 11am–3pm &
5pm–11pm; Sun 12pm–3pm &
6pm–11pm

IPSWICH

MARNO'S
14 St Nicholas Street, Ipswich, Suffolk
IP1 1TJ
Tel 01473 253106 Fax 01473 271094
Email mike.cathrall14@btinternet.com
Cafe Restaurant Take Away
A la Carte Fast Food Organic
Snacks/Drinks
*A regular selection of vegan dishes
and cakes is available. All main dishes
and some cakes are prepared on the
premises. Can cater for special diets —
eg gluten-free or yeast-free. Counter*
*service during the day and waitress
service in the evenings.*
V Cc ✖ ✖ (area) ⅗ (public
entrance/dining area/not toilets)
Typical 3 course meal £8.70 Seats 60
Open 10.30am–3.30pm Mon–Fri;
6pm–9.30pm Thurs–Fri;
10.30am–9.30pm Sat

SURREY

Places to Stay

CAMBERLEY

TEKELS PARK GUEST HOUSE
See **SPECIAL INTEREST**, page 230.

LINGFIELD

CLARIDGE HOUSE
See **SPECIAL INTEREST**, page 229.

Places to Eat

CAMBERLEY

TEKELS PARK GUEST HOUSE
See **SPECIAL INTEREST**, page 230.

CROYDON

HOCKNEY'S
98 High Street, Croydon, Surrey
CR0 1ND
Tel 0181 688 2899
Fax 0181 649 9375
Restaurant Take Away
Around the World Snacks/Drinks

Delicious food prepared from the finest ingredients. An oasis in the heart of Croydon. A perfect place for a drink, a snack or a full meal. Many items are vegan. Party bookings are accepted. Outside catering available.
V Cc ✗ 🍴
Typical 3 course meal £8.10 *(day)/* £12.15 *(eve)* Seats 95 Open 10am–5pm Tues–Sat; 6pm–10pm Fri

RIVERSIDE VEGETARIA, THE
64 High Street, Kingston upon Thames, Surrey KT1 1HN
Tel 0181 546 0609
Restaurant
V 🏛 Cc ✗ 🍴 &. (public entrance/designated parking area/dining area/bar)
Typical 3 course meal £11 Seats 60 Open Mon–Fri 12pm–2.30pm & 5.30pm–11pm; Sat–Sun 12pm–11pm
VS members' discount 10%

KINGSTON UPON THAMES

CAFE BEACON
42a Richmond Road, Kingston upon Thames, Surrey KT2 5EE
Tel 0181 296 9921
Cafe
Chinese Indian Organic
Snacks/Drinks Traditional British
A cafe with a relaxed atmosphere and unusual decor – including furniture made from tree trunks.
V
Open 10am–5pm Mon–Wed; 10am–9pm Thurs–Sat; 12pm–5pm Sun
VS members' discount 10%

RICHMOND

RICHMOND HARVEST
5 The Square, Richmond, Surrey TW9 1DT
Tel 0181 940 1138/0181 948 8584
Restaurant Take Away
V Cc ✗
Typical 3 course meal £8 Seats 40 Open 11.30am–11pm Mon–Sat; 12.30pm–10pm Sun & Bank Hols

THORNTON HEATH

SANTOR MAA'S BHEL POORI HOUSE
848 London Road, Thornton Heath, Surrey CR7 7PA
Tel 0181 665 0626
Restaurant
Chinese Fast Food Indian
South Indian
A unique family-run Indian vegetarian restaurant providing a special touch to the food and atmosphere. Bring your own alcohol to keep your costs down. Families are encouraged. Weekend buffet of £4.95 (adults) or £2.95 (children under 10). Catering for parties and weddings also available.
V Cc 🍴
Typical 3 course meal £7 Seats 40 Open 12pm–9pm Mon–Tues & Thurs–Sun
VS members' discount 10%

TYNE & WEAR

Places to Stay

NEWCASTLE UPON TYNE

DENE HOTEL
38–42 Grosvenor Road, Newcastle
upon Tyne, Tyne & Wear NE2 2RP
Tel 0191 281 1502
Fax 0191 281 8110
Hotel Restaurant
Indian Traditional British
*A family run hotel under the strict
supervision of the proprietor.*
🐾 ♀ 🏊 Cc ✕ ♿ (public
entrance/designated parking
area/one bedroom, bathroom & WC
on same level/dining room/restau-
rant/bar/TV lounge)
Beds 23 Open all year
Typical tariff for 3 course meal £7.50
Seats 35
VS members' discount 10%

Places to Eat

GATESHEAD

**LAST DAYS OF THE RAJ
RESTAURANT**
168 Kells Lane, Low Fell, Gateshead,
Tyne & Wear NE9 5HY
Tel 0191 491 4343 Fax 0191 487 0890
Restaurant
Indian
A la Carte
*The best in first class business ban-
queting and entertaining whatever*
*your need from small, intimate meet-
ings to large, organised parties. A
wide range of traditional and exotic
Indian food from Tandoori, Balti, Thali
or vegetarian.*
Cc ✕ ♿ (public entrance/designated
parking area/dining area)
Seats 100 Open 12pm–2.30pm
Mon–Sat; 6pm–11.30pm Sun;
6pm–12am Bank Hols
VS members' discount 10%

NEWCASTLE UPON TYNE

BOB TROLLOP
36 Sandhill, Quayside, Newcastle
upon Tyne, Tyne & Wear NE1 3JF
Tel 0191 251 1717 Fax 0191 253 4242
Public House
Indian Italian/Mediterranean
Mexican Real Ale Traditional British
*The Back Room at Bob Trollop's is an
authentic 18th century farmhouse on
the banks of the Tyne. The pub serves
a 100% vegetarian menu with plenty
of vegan options. For a menu write to:
Red House Bars Ltd, 1 East Parade,
Whitley Bay, Tyne and Wear NE26
1AW.*
V (menu) Cc ♿ (public entrance/din-
ing area/bar)
Typical 3 course meal £10 Seats 50
Open 11am–11pm Mon–Sat;
12pm–10.30pm Sun

DENE HOTEL
See left.

**RED HERRING WORKERS
CO-OPERATIVE**
4 Studley Terrace, Fenham, Newcastle

upon Tyne, Tyne & Wear
Tel 0191 272 3484
Bakery Cafe Wholefood Shop
Macrobiotic Organic
Everything in the cafe suitable for veg-
ans is clearly marked. Two vegan main
courses plus starters and desserts
available. No alcohol sold but cus-
tomers can bring a bottle (no cork-
age). The shop sells a range of organic
breads. 20% discount for students
holding a current student card.
Outside catering available.
V ✗ ⅏ (area) ᐸ (public
entrance/dining area)
Typical 3 course meal £10 Seats 40
Open 10am–9.45pm *(last orders)*
Tues–Sat

SUPERNATURAL RESTAURANT & WINE BAR

2 Upper Level, Princess Square,
Newcastle upon Tyne, Tyne & Wear
NE1 9ER
Tel 0191 261 2730
Restaurant
The first vegetarian and vegan restau-
rant in the North East. Established in
1976 and still the only vegetarian and
vegan restaurant in town.
V ✗ ⅏ ᐸ (public entrance/desig-
nated parking area/dining area/bar)
Typical 3 course meal £5.50 Seats 75
Open 10.30am–7pm Mon & Sat;
10.30am–7.30pm Tues–Fri
VS members' discount 10% *£3.50+*
order

Please mention the Vegan
Travel Guide when contacting a
listed business or advertiser

WASHINGTON

WILDFOWL & WETLANDS
TRUST, THE
District 15, Washington, Tyne & Wear
NE38 8LE
Tel 0191 416 5454
Fax 0191 416 5801
Cafe Restaurant
Snacks/Drinks
P Cc ✗ ⅏ ᐸ (public entrance/desig-
nated parking area/dining area/bar)
Typical 3 course meal £3.50 Seats 60
Open all year *except Xmas Day*; win-
ter 9.30am–4pm; summer
9.30am–5pm

WARWICKSHIRE

Places to Stay

LEAMINGTON SPA

EATHORPE PARK HOTEL
The Fosse, Eathorpe, nr Royal
Leamington Spa, Warwickshire
CV33 9DQ
Tel 01926 632632 Fax 01926 632481
Email
innvogue@eathorpepark.demon.
co.uk
Website
http://www.eathorpepark.demon.
co.uk
Hotel
A la Carte Continental Ethnic
Snacks/Drinks Traditional British
Exotic
A mid-Victorian manor house sur-

rounded by its own 11 acres. Commanding an elevated position, affording panoramic views across South Warwickshire. Ensuite bedrooms with direct dial telephones, TVs, beverage facilities and hairdryers. Extensive secure parking. 'Bistrotheque', banqueting and conferences rooms.

♀ ☒ Cc ✗ ⊯ ⓖ (public entrance/designated parking area & WC on same level/dining room/restaurant/bar/TV lounge)
Typical tariff single/double room £45/£60 Beds 16 Open all year
Typical 3 course meal £17 Seats 150
Open 12pm–2pm & 6pm–10pm

STRATFORD UPON AVON

MERIDIAN
3 St Gregory's Road, Stratford upon Avon, Warwickshire CV37 6UH
Tel 01789 292356
B&B Guesthouse
Traditional British
A 3 storey Victorian town house just 5 minutes walk along the canal path from the town centre. Situated in a quiet leafy conservation area. A warm friendly welcome awaits. Attention to detail is of the utmost importance. Ensuite, colour TV, tea/coffee making facilities, central heating and on site parking available.
P ★ ☒ ✗ ⊯
Typical tariff single/double room £20.25/£40.45 Beds 4 Open all year

PARKFIELD GUEST HOUSE
3 Broad Walk, Stratford upon Avon,
Warwickshire CV37 6HS
Tel 01789 293313 Fax 01789 293313
B&B Guest House
An elegant Edwardian town house in a quiet location yet only a few minutes walk from theatres and the town centre. Large, comfortable, centrally heated rooms with TV, radio and hot drinks. A wide breakfast choice including vegan and vegetarian. Private car park.
Cc ⊯
Typical tariff single/double room £19/£40 Beds 7 Open all year

ROWAN HOUSE
112 Alcester Road, Stratford upon Avon, Warwickshire CV37 9DP
Tel 01789 205191
B&B
Situated within walking distance of Stratford town centre and within easy reach of all Shakespeare's properties and other places of interest. Friendly and welcoming service with rooms offering hotel and cold water, colour TV, tea/coffee making facilities as well as parking spaces.
⊯
Typical tariff double room £14.18pp
Beds 2 Open all year *except Xmas & New Year*
VS members' discount *5% for first night*

WINTON HOUSE
The Green, Upper Quinton, Stratford upon Avon, Warwickshire CV37 8SX
Tel 01789 720500
Mobile 0831 485483
Email lyong@ibm.net

Website http://www.stratford-upon-avon.co.uk/winton.htm
B&B Self Catering
Traditional British
Historic farmhouse built in 1856 situated in an Area of Outstanding Natural Beauty overlooking Meon Hill. Antique four poster pine bed decorated with handmade quilts and old lace. Ensuite bathroom and tea/coffee making facilities. Private guest lounge. Self catering available in Winton House Cottage nearby.
Typical tariff single/double room £35/£48 Beds 3

Places to Eat

COVENTRY

RYTON ORGANIC GARDENS
Coventry, Warwickshire CV8 3LG
Tel 01203 307142 Fax 01203 639229
Email sfurness@hdra.org.uk
Website http://www.hdra.org.uk
Restaurant
A la Carte Organic Snacks/Drinks Traditional British
Ryton Organic Gardens is run by the Henry Doubleday Research Association, the UK's largest organic organisation. Organic produce is used for all meals. Open for morning coffee, lunches, teas and Saturday night a la carte candlelit dinners. Always anxious to accommodate people requiring special diets.
Cc 🚭
Typical 3 course meal £10 Seats 60
Open 9am–5pm daily; Sat eves

YUM
86 Shakespeare Street, Stone, Coventry, Warwickshire CV2 4JQ
Tel 01203 442711
Cafe Restaurant
Snacks/Drinks World Food
An informal drop in cafe/restaurant. Great for breakfast, lunches and teas. Friendly and cosy.
V Cc 🚭 ♿ (public entrance/designated parking area/dining area/WC)
Typical 3 course meal £10.50 Seats 30
Open 8.30am–8.30pm Mon–Sat; 9.30am–6.30pm Sun

RUGBY

SKYLIGHT CAFE
11–13 Bank Street, Rugby, Warwickshire CV21 2QE
Tel 01788 560701
Cafe Outside Caterer
Chinese French Indian Italian/Mediterranean Mexican Organic Snacks/Drinks Spanish Thai
Situated in the town centre offering a wide selection of cakes, sandwiches and freshly cooked meals. The Vegetarian Society trained chef and proprietor has a huge interest and knowledge of vegetarian and vegan cooking, reflected in the food and regular vegan clientele.
🍴 🚭 ♿ (public entrance/dining area)
Typical 3 course meal £7.50 Seats 50
Open 10am–4pm Mon–Fri; 9.30am–4.30pm Sat
VS members' discount 10% *£5+ orders per person*

SUMMERSAULT
27 High Street, Rugby, Warwickshire
CV21 3BW
Tel 01788 543223
Restaurant
Snacks/Drinks
*Providing vegetarian and some vegan
meals. Egon Ronay recommended.
Retail shop within same establishment
selling freshly ground coffee, special-
ity teas and a range of gift and
designware.*
V Cc ✗ ⓧ ₰ (public entrance/desig-
nated parking area/dining area/bar)
Typical 3 course meal £7 Seats 70
Open 9am–5.30pm Mon–Sat

STRATFORD UPON AVON

STRATFORD HEALTH FOOD CAFE
Unit 1, Greenhill Street, Stratford
upon Avon, Warwickshire CV37 6LF
Tel 01789 415741
Cafe
Snacks/Drinks
*A vegan/vegetarian cafe serving tea,
coffee, etc. Lunch served 11.30am–
2.15pm.*
🏛 Cc ⓧ
Typical 3 course meal £10 Seats 40
Open 9am–4.30pm
VS members' discount 10%

STUDLEY

SUMMER PALACE RESTAURANT
Birmingham Road, Mappleborough
Green, Studley, Warwickshire B80 7DF
Tel 01527 857118 Fax 01527 854770
Restaurant Take Away
Chinese

*Established since 1992 and serving
traditional Cantonese and Peking cuisine. Provides good freshly cooked
food in comfortable surroundings.
Fully licensed and room for about 50
cars. Menu comprises over 150 dishes,
including a substantial vegan selection.*
Cc ⓧ ₰ (public entrance/designated
parking area/dining area/bar)
Typical 3 course meal £18 Seats 90
Open 12pm–2.30pm Mon–Fri;
6pm–11.30pm Mon–Thurs;
6pm–12am Fri–Sat; 6pm–11pm Sun

WEST MIDLANDS
Places to Stay

BIRMINGHAM

LOMBARD ROOM RESTAURANT, THE
180 Lifford Lane, Kings Norton,
Birmingham B30 3NT
Tel 0121 459 5800
Fax 0121 459 8553
Hotel Restaurant
Modern British
*An elegantly converted Victorian
paper mill situated in the suburbs of
Birmingham and only 5 miles from the
city centre. Chef Anthony Morgan
prepares a wide variety of dishes
using only the finest fresh ingredients.
Anthony is always happy to create
memorable dishes for vegetarian and
vegans on request.*
♀ 🏛 Cc ✗ ⓧ ₰(public entrance/
one bedroom, bathroom & WC on

same level/dining room/
restaurant/bar)
Typical tariff single/double room
£95/£105 Beds 9
Typical 3 course meal £23.50 Seats 60
Open 12pm–2pm & 7pm–9.30pm
(last orders) Tues–Fri; 7.30–9.30pm
(last orders) Sat; 12pm–2pm *(last
orders)* Sun

Places to Eat

BIRMINGHAM

2 JAYS RESTAURANT
462 Moseley Road, Moseley,
Birmingham B12 9AN
Restaurant
A la Carte French Indian
Italian/Mediterranean Snacks/Drinks
*First restaurant of its kind to serve tra-
ditional Asian and Italian/French
cuisines in an exquisite and relaxing
atmosphere. Separate menu for children. Also caters for wedding receptions, private parties, etc for up to
200 people. Private functions room
available for up to 100 people.*
Cc ✗ ✤ (area) ♿ (public
entrance/designated parking
area/dining area/bar)
Typical 3 course meal £15 Seats 80
Open 5.30pm–11.30pm
VS members' discount 10%

4 VEG
1a Walford Road, Sparkhill,
Birmingham B11 1NP
Tel 0121 624 4440
Fax 0121 628 4500
Email chauhan@meera.demon.co.uk

Take Away
Indian
*A fast food take away specialising in
vegetarian pizzas. Samosas, onion
bhajias, vegeburgers, jacket potatoes
and fries are also available.*
V

I AM THE KING OF BALTIS
230–232 Ladypool Road, Sparkbrook,
Birmingham B12 8JT
Tel 0121 449 1170
Restaurant Take Away
Indian Kashmiri
Cc ✗ ♿ (public entrance/designated
parking area/dining area/bar)
Typical 3 course meal £6 Seats 42
Open 12pm–12am

JYOTI RESTAURANT
569–571 Stratford Road, Sparkhill,
Birmingham B11 4LS
Tel 0121 766 7199
Restaurant Take Away
Indian Snacks/Drinks Sweet Centre
*Please ask staff which dishes are suit-
able for vegans. Specialises in
Southern Indian food but able to cook
all Indian styles. Sweet centre
attached to restaurant.*
V Cc ✤
Typical 3 course meal £8 Seats 49
Open Tues–Fri 12pm–3pm &
5.30pm–10pm; Sat–Sun
12pm–9.30pm

KHAN BABA BALTI RESTAURANT
632 Bristol Road, Selly Oak,
Birmingham B29 6BQ
0121 471 3844
Restaurant

Indian and English dishes. The flavour is palatable to every kind of constitution. Ideally situated on the main road.
Cc
Seats 65 Open 5pm–late

LOMBARD ROOM RESTAURANT, THE
See page 146.

ONE EARTH SHOP
54 Allison Street, Digbeth,
Birmingham B5 5TH
Tel 0121 632 6909
Shop Take Away
A shop selling wholefoods, packaged foods, cosmetics and household goods. A take away service provides a selection of pasties, flans and cakes.
VEGAN

ROGAN'S VEGETARIAN RESTAURANT
12 College Road, Handsworth Wood,
Birmingham B20 2HX
Tel 0121 515 3906
Restaurant
Tasty, wholesome, homemade food available at reasonable prices.
V 坴 ᐟ�
Typical 3 course meal £7 Seats 20
Open Mon–Sat 12pm–2pm &
5.30pm–9pm

WAREHOUSE CAFE, THE
54 Allison Street, Digbeth,
Birmingham B5 5TH
Tel 0121 633 0261
Fax 0121 643 3122
Cafe Restaurant
A la Carte Organic Snacks/Drinks

World Food
Light airy cafe with a friendly atmosphere. Only 5 minutes from the city centre and New Street Station.
V ✗ ᐟ✗
Typical 3 course meal £10 Seats 40
Open 12pm–9pm *(last orders)*
Mon–Sat; occasional Sun & special events

WILD OATS VEGETARIAN RESTAURANT
5 Raddlebarn Road, Selly Oak,
Birmingham B29 6HJ
Tel 0121 471 2459
Restaurant
Organic
A small friendly restaurant with home cooked food. The largest establishment in Birmingham. Close to Birmingham University. 1–2 vegan options available for starters, main meals and dessert. All freshly made. No alcohol but will open bottle with 50p corkage.
V ᐟ✗ ᐟ & (public entrance/dining area)
Typical 3 course meal £7 Seats 32
Open Tues–Sat 12pm–2pm &
6pm–9pm *(last orders)*

STOURBRIDGE

SPICE OF LYEFE
186 High Street, Lye, Stourbridge,
West Midlands DY9 8JN
Tel 01384 823344
Restaurant Take Away
Indian
The finest Indian restaurant in the Midlands serving the best authentic restaurant and take away meals.

Not licensed.
V 🏤
Open 6pm–12am

WEST SUSSEX

Places to Stay

CHICHESTER

BAYLEAF B&B
16 Whyke Road, Chichester, West
Sussex PO19 2HN
Tel 01243 774330
B&B
*A flint-built Victorian town house
close to the town centre. Some rooms
with ensuite facilities. All rooms provided with tea/coffee and TV. Easy on
street parking. Vegetarian and vegan
guests are very welcome. Prior notice
appreciated but not necessary.*
🏤✗
Typical tariff single/double room
£22/£22pp Beds 6 Open all day for
registered guests

HAMMERWOOD PARK
nr East Grinstead, West Sussex
RH19 3QE
Tel 01342 850594 Fax 01342 850864
Email latrobe@mistral.co.uk
Website
http://www.mistral.co.uk/hammer-
wood/
B&B
A la Carte Chinese Fast Food Indian
Italian/Mediterranean Snacks/Drinks
Traditional British

*Built in 1792 as a Temple of Apollo in
romantic parkland, this was the first
work of Benjamin Latrobe who was
responsible for the Capitol and the
porticos of the White House in
Washington DC. Owned by Led
Zeppelin in the 1970s, it has been
restored by the present owner.*
P 🏤✗
Typical tariff single/double room
£30/£58 Beds 2 Open Easter–Sept
VS members' discount 10%

HORSHAM

PERKINS, MRS PAM
3 Ashleigh Road, Horsham, West
Sussex RH12 2LF
Tel 01403 267264
B&B Private House
Macrobiotic Organic
B&B in spacious home with room
overlooking the garden. Hot and cold
drink facilities in room. Easy access to
Gatwick. Owner vegetarian.
V 🏤✗
Typical tariff single/double room
£15/£30 Beds 1 Open all year *(tele-
phone to confirm)*

SHIPLEY

POND TAIL FARM
nr Shipley, West Grinstead, West
Sussex RH13 8LN
Tel 01403 741019 Fax 01403 741116
Email desm@globalnet.co.uk
Website
http://www.veganvillage.co.uk
B&B Guesthouse
Beautiful period farmhouse and

gardens offering charmingly furnished guest rooms. TV lounge, friendly rescued animals (pigs and ponies) which children can help feed and babysitting service available. Delicious vegan evening meals on request made from locally grown organic vegetables.
V 🐕 🚭
VS members' discount 10%

Places to Eat

BOGNOR REGIS

IN PLACE, THE
6 Endley Road, Bognor Regis, West Sussex PO21 1EU
Tel 01243 869933
Bistro Restaurant
A la Carte Traditional British
A relaxed, stylish restaurant opposite the main post office. Serves breakfast, lunch and dinner. Suitable for parties and/or candlelit meals for two. All food is prepared and cooked to order on the premises from fresh local ingredients. Any specific dietary requirements catered for. Notice preferred to provide vegan meals.
Cc ✗ 🚭 (areas) ♿ (public entrance/designated parking area/dining area/bar)
Typical 3 course meal £13 Seats 50
Open Tues–Sat 10am–2pm & 6.30pm–10pm
VS members' discount 10% *meal*

CHICHESTER

ST MARTINS TEA ROOMS
Chichester, West Sussex PO19 1NP
Tel 01243 786715
Tea Rooms
Organic Traditional British
Situated in a little terraced house in the city centre and typical of Chichester's vernacular architecture with an 18th century facade and mediaeval interior. Uses only healthfoods and as many organic ingredients as possible. No meat served.
🚭
Typical 3 course meal £9.35 Seats 100
Open 9am–6pm Mon–Sat

PLAISTOW

CLEMENTS VEGETARIAN RESTAURANT
Rickmans Lane, Plaistow, West Sussex RH14 0NT
Tel 01403 871246
Restaurant
A family-run business with a sizeable number of vegan customers. Unashamedly upmarket. Dine by candlelight, linen napkins, fine glasses and intimate atmosphere. Vegan organic wines and beers. For that special evening out. Also outside catering for weddings, etc.
V Cc ✗ 🚭 ♿ (public entrance/dining area)
Typical 3 course meal £15 Seats 40
Open 7pm–11pm *(last orders 9pm)* Tues–Sat

SEASONS RESTAURANT
15 Crescent Road, Worthing, West Sussex BN11 1RL
Tel 01903 236011
Cafe Restaurant Take Away

Snacks/Drinks
Established for 8 years and Egon Ronay recommended from the first year. Food freshly cooked each day. Breakfasts, lunches, teas, coffees, cakes and snacks are all available. Prices are very reasonable. Friendly and welcoming to old and young, single or family groups.
V ✕ ⇴ ᕲ (public entrance/dining area)
Typical 2 course meal £5 Seats 37
Open 9am–3pm Mon–Fri; 9am–4pm Sat

WEST YORKSHIRE

Places to Stay

BRADFORD

COURTYARD BY MARRIOTT
The Pastures, Tong Lane, Bradford, West Yorkshire BD4 0RP
Tel 0113 285 4646
Fax 0113 285 3661
Hotel
A la Carte
Located only 10 minutes from Leeds and Bradford city centres. Set in a beautiful green belt area. Accommodating business clients during the week and families at the weekends. All rooms ensuite bathroom, tea/coffee making facilities, hair dryer and telephone. Other facilities include multi gym, public bar, pool room and nearby golf course.
Ϋ ᕲ Cc ✕ ⇴ ᕲ (public

entrance/designated parking area/one bedroom, bathroom & WC on same level/dining room/restaurant/bar/TV lounge)
Typical tariff single/double room £69/£69pp Beds 50 Open all year
Typical 3 course meal £16.50 Seats 65
Open 7am–9.30am breakfast; 12pm–2pm lunch; 7pm–10pm dinner

PENNINGTON MIDLAND HOTEL, THE
Forster Square, Bradford, West Yorkshire BD1 4HU
Tel 01274 735735 Fax 01274 720003
Email sales@penningtonmidland.co.uk
Hotel Night Club Restaurant
A la Carte English European
Snacks/Drinks
Built in 1885 this city centre hotel has been fully restored to its former Victorian glory with glittering chandaliers, ballrooms, spacious bedrooms, conference facilities and a variety of dining and entertaining experiences. Personal service. Free parking.
P ᕲ Ϋ ᕲ Cc ✕ ᕲ (public entrance/restaurant/bar/lounge)
Typical tariff single/double room £65/£75 Beds 91 Open all year
Typical 3 course meal £10.20 Seats 70
Open 11am–11pm Mon–Sun; *closed Sat lunchtimes*

HALIFAX

HEATHLEIGH GUEST HOUSE
124 Skircoat Road, Halifax, West Yorkshire HX1 2RE
Tel 01422 323957
Guesthouse

Traditional British
*Only minutes from the town centre
and offering luxury ensuite accommodation in a lovely Victorian house. All
rooms are centrally heated with
colour TV and tea/coffee making facilities. Private parking available.*
P 🚭 ✻
Typical tariff single/double room
£20/£40 Beds 3

WINDMILL COURT HOTEL
Keighley Road, Ogden, Halifax, West
Yorkshire HX2 8YB
Tel 01422 244941 Fax 01422 240719
Bistro Hotel Restaurant
Self Catering
A la Carte Snacks/Drinks
Traditional British
*A warm welcome awaits guests at this
family-run country house. Beautiful
ensuite rooms and luxury lounges.
Situated in open countryside within
easy reach of the famous Yorkshire
Dales and near Haworth. Good fresh
food beautifully presented.*
P ♀ 🚭 Cc ✻ ⅙ (public entrance/des-
ignated parking area/one bedroom,
bathroom & WC on same level/dining
room/restaurant/bar/TV lounge)
Typical tariff single/double room
£25/£50 Beds 12 Open all year
Typical 3 course meal £10 Seats 80
Open 5pm–9pm Mon–Fri; 12pm–9pm
Sat–Sun
VS members' discount 10%

HAWORTH

ASHMOUNT
Mytholmes Lane, Haworth, West

Yorkshire BD22 8EZ
Tel 01535 645726
B&B Guesthouse
Traditional British
*A large Victorian villa built by Dr
Ingham, the Bronte's family doctor.
Original Gothic features and period
furnishings. Wonderful views of the
Worth Valley and the Moors. Half acre
garden and private parking area. ETB
3 crowns commended.*
🐕 🚭 Cc ⅙
Typical tariff single/double room
£25/£35 Beds 6 Open all year

HEBDEN BRIDGE

BED & BREAKFAST
1 Primrose Terrace, Hebden Bridge,
West Yorkshire HX7 6HN
Tel 01422 844747
B&B
*A small B&B close to the town centre
in an attractive canalside location. Not
exclusively vegetarian but many clients
are vegetarian or vegan.*
Typical tariff single/double room
£14/£28 Beds 2

MYRTLE GROVE
14 Myrtle Grove, Old Lees Road,
Hebden Bridge, West Yorkshire
HX7 8HL
Tel 01422 846078
B&B
A la Carte Chinese Indian
Italian/Mediterranean Organic
Snacks/Fast Food Traditional British
*Comfortable stone cottage set in the
heart of West Yorkshire. Ideal for
walking, touring or just relaxing.*

Wonderful views over the Calder Valley and close to the Pennine and Calderdale Way. Ensuite rooms, tea/coffee making facilities, iron and hair dryer.

Cc ✝✖

Typical tariff single/double room £25/£20pp Beds 2 Open all year

PROSPECT END

8 Prospect Terrace, Savile Road, Hebden Bridge, West Yorkshire HX7 6NA

Tel 01422 843586 Fax 01422 843586

B&B

A Victorian house in a very convenient position on the edge of town. Town centre only 10 minutes walk along canal path. Walkers wecome. Ideal base for exploring the South Pennines. Quiet, private accommodation with direct access to guest rooms. Parking outside house. ETB 2 crown commended.

✖ ⚿ (one bedroom/bathroom & WC on same level)

Typical tariff single/double room £21/£36 Beds 2 Open all year

ROYD WELL

35 Royd Terrace, Hebden Bridge, West Yorkshire HX7 7BT

Tel 01422 845304

B&B

A small, friendly stone terraced house built in 1850 situated in the centre of town. Catering mainly for walkers. Guests receive a warm welcome and individual service. Arrangements are homely. Breakfast is served in the kitchen. Lock up available for bikes.

P ✝ ♿

Typical tariff single/double room £15/£30 Beds 2 Open all year

ILKLEY

ARCHWAY COTTAGE

24–26 Skipton Road, Ilkley, West Yorkshire LS29 9EP

Tel 01943 603399

B&B

A warm friendly guesthouse only 5 minutes from the town centre, Moors and Dales. Well appointed rooms offering TV, tea/coffee and vanity facilities in all rooms. Provides a cook to order breakfast and has no problem accommodating vegans, vegetarians or any other dietary requirements.

✝ ♿

Typical tariff single/double room £20/£33 Beds 4 Open all year

KEIGHLEY

NEWSHOLME MANOR RESTAURANT

Slaymaker Lane, Slack Lane, Oakworth, Keighley, West Yorkshire

Tel 01535 642964

Hotel Restaurant

A la Carte French Italian/Mediterranean Snacks/Drinks Spanish Traditional British

Established for 25 years, a family-run country manor set in 2 acres of gardens. Magnificent views. Celebrated chef. Ensuite bedrooms. Civil weddings, wedding receptions, parties, dinner/dances and bar meals available. Open for coffee, lunches and evening meals.

♀ 🏠 Cc ✗ ⚑ ♿ (public entrance/designated parking area/dining room/restaurant/bar/TV lounge)
Typical tariff single/double room £25/£40 Beds 4
Typical 3 course meal £7.95 lunch; £12.95 dinner Seats 80 Open Mon–Sun lunchtime

LEEDS

BEE GEE'S GUEST HOUSE
18 Moor Allertoin Drive, off Street Lane, Moortown, Leeds West Yorkshire LS17 6RZ
Tel 0113 293 5469
Fax 0113 275 3300
Mobile 0589 069478
B&B Guest House
Betty and Bernard Gibbs wecome you to their homely guest house close to Roundhay Park but situated in a residential area north of Leeds. Convenient to Harrogate, Otley, Ilkley, Skipton, Leeds and Bradford Airport yet only 3 miles to Leeds city centre. Own keys on arrival. Come as a guest, leave as a friend.
P 🏠 ⚑
Typical tariff single/double room £22/£38 Beds 4

BOUNDARY HOTEL, THE
42 Cardigan Road, Headingley, Leeds, West Yorkshire LS6 3AG
Tel 0113 275 7700
Fax 0113 275 7700
Hotel
Snacks/Drinks Traditional British
A small comfortable hotel. Personal service by either owners or their managers with an accent on a friendly welcome and excellent home cooking.
🐾 ♀ 🏠 Cc
Typical tariff single/double room £26/£40 Beds 17 Open all year
Typical 3 course meal £8.50 Seats 19
Open 7am–10.30pm

HIGHBANK HOTEL, THE
83 Harehills Lane, Chapel Allerton, Leeds, West Yorkshire LS7 4HA
Tel 0113 2622164 Fax 0113 237 4436
Hotel
A la Carte Fast Food Indian Mexican
Convenient, comfortable and quietly located. Only minutes from the city centre, St James and Chapel Allerton. Secure car park, satellite TV and direct dial telephones. 3 crown commended. Late key available.
P ♀ 🏠 Cc ✗ ⚑ (areas) ♿ (public entrance/designated parking area/dining area/bar)
Typical tariff single/double room £21/£37.25 Beds 21 Open all year 7am–12am
Typical 3 course meal £8.95 Seats 54
VS members' discount 5%

Places to Eat

BRADFORD

BOMBAY BRASSERIE
1 Simes Street, Bradford, West Yorkshire BD1 3RB
Tel 01274 737564 Fax 01274 370515
Restaurant
Indian

A large selection of vegetarian dishes available. Vegans welcome.
Cc
Seats 120 Open 12pm–2pm & 6pm–12am

COCOBANA RESTAURANT & CLUB
47–49 Cheapside, Bradford, West Yorkshire BD1 4HP
Tel 01274 739441
Restaurant Night Club
A la Carte Caribbean
Caribbean restaurant with disco.
VEGAN ♀ ☖ Cc ౬ (public entrance/designated parking area/dining area/bar)
Typical 3 course meal £14 Seats 40
Open 6.30pm–12am Thurs–Sat; 6.30pm–2am Fri & Sat

PENNINGTON MIDLAND HOTEL, THE
See page 151.

SOUTH SQUARE VEGETARIAN RESTAURANT
South Square, Thornton Road, Thornton , Bradford, West Yorkshire BD13 3LD
Tel 01274 834928
Cafe
Organic
Located in an old 19th century courtyard of cottages. Owned by organisation for people with learning difficulties. A craft complex which includes a cafe, shops and a gallery. Relaxed casual atmosphere, waitress service, home cooked food made to order — including vegan soup, salads, main courses and cakes. Not licensed.
V ✗ ⮲ ౬ (public entrance/dining

area)
Typical 3 course meal £6.50 Seats 28
Open 12.30am–4.30pm Tues–Sat; 12pm–4pm Sun; open until 8pm on 1st Fri in month — *telephone to confirm*
VS members' discount 10%

LEEDS

BEANO WHOLEFOODS
36 New Briggate, Leeds, West Yorkshire LS1 6NU
Tel 0113 243 5737
Shop Take Away
Macrobiotic Organic Snacks/Drinks
A busy worker's co-operative established in 1976 and situated by the Grand Theatre. A wide range of vegan foods available including the largest selection of vegan sandwiches in Leeds. Chilled and frozen vegan foods and a large range of vegan/ eco-friendly toiletries and cleaning products.
V ౬ (public entrance)
Open 9am–5pm Mon–Tues; 9.30am–5pm Weds; 9am–5.30pm Thurs–Fri; 9am–5pm Sat
VS members' discount 10% £8+ purchases

STRAWBERRY FIELDS BISTRO & BAR
159 Woodhouse Lane, Leeds, West Yorkshire LS2 3ED
Tel 0113 243 1515
Fax 0131 243 1515
Bistro Wine Bar
Italian/Mediterranean Mexican
A small family-run bistro, established for 17 years. The owners have been

vegetarian for the past 10 years. All vegetarian meals are marked in green on the menu and a separate vegan menu is available on request.
Cc ✖ ᴸᵂ❌ (areas)
Typical 3 course meal £9.50 Seats 45 Open 11.45–2pm *(last orders)* Mon–Fri; 6pm–10.30pm *(last orders in bistro)* Mon–Sat

TAFF

85 Kirkgate, Leeds, West Yorkshire LS2 7DJ
Tel 0113 246 0889
Fax 0113 246 0889
Sandwich Bar Take Away
Fast Food Snacks/Drinks
V ᴸᵂ❌
Open 7.45am–4pm Mon–Fri; 8.45am–5pm Sat

OTLEY

CURLEW CAFE, THE
11–13 Crossgate, Otley, West Yorkshire LS21 1AA
Tel 01943 464351
Bistro Cafe
A small cosy cafe bistro. Friendly staff serve tasty fresh vegetarian and vegan food. Menu changed weekly. Everything homemade. Bookings essential for the evenings.
V ✖ ᴸᵂ❌ (room) ᶜᵏ (WC)
Typical 3 course meal £6.95 *(day)* £12.15 *(eve)* Seats 28 Open 11am–4pm & 7pm–9pm Sat; 12pm–5pm Sun; 11am–3pm Tues–Thurs; 11am–3pm & 7pm–9pm Fri

PONTEFRACT

ROTI RESTAURANT
North Baileygate, Pontefract, West Yorkshire WF8 1ES
Tel 01977 703915 Fax 01977 600005
Restaurant Take Away
A la Carte Indian
The most exclusive authentic Asian restaurant in Yorkshire. The only Asian restaurant in Yorkshire where you can see your food being prepared and cooked in an open plan kitchen. Everything is cooked fresh to order. Fully licensed. Join the Roti Restaurant Dinner Club free.
Cc ✖ ᴸᵂ❌ ᶜᵏ (public entrance/desig-nated parking area/dining area/bar)
Typical 3 course meal £10–£15 Seats 100 Open 5pm–12am Mon–Sun

SHIPLEY

SALTS DINER
Salts Mill, Shipley, West Yorkshire BD18 3LB
Tel 01274 531163 Fax 01274 531187
Email post@saltsmill.demon.co.uk
Website http://www.clanvis.com/loc/holy.htm
Restaurant
A la Carte Snacks/Drinks
Traditional British
A diner situated in an historic mill which is a listed building. Contains 3 art galleries devoted to David Hockney and a number of high quality shops.
✖ ᴸᵂ❌ ᶜᵏ (public entrance/designated parking area/dining area)
Typical 3 course meal £10 Seats 350 Open 10am–6pm

WATERWAY'S BISTRO

The Courtyard, Shipley Wharf, Wharf
Street, Shipley, West Yorkshire
BD17 7DW
Tel 01274 585383
Mobile 0976 158737
Bistro
Italian/Mediterranean Mexican
Snacks/Drinks
*A continental theme to this bistro.
Alfresco dining area overlooking the
Leeds/Liverpool Canal. Catering for
vegans and vegetarians with plenty of
unusual and exciting dishes to suit all
tastes. Call as a stranger, leave as a
friend. Booking advised for Thurs–Sat
and for parties of more than 6.*
Cc ✖
Typical 3 course meal £10 Seats 28
Open 10am–2pm Mon;
10am–10.30pm Tues–Fri;
11am–10.30pm Sat; 12pm–4pm Sun
VS members' discount 10%

WILTSHIRE

Places to Stay

SALISBURY

OLD CHEQUERS COTTAGE

17 Guilder Lane, Salisbury, Wiltshire
SP1 1HW
Tel 01722 325335
B&B
Traditional British
*A 600-year-old cosy medieval cottage
with beams and inglenook. Situated 3
minutes from town centre. Excellent*

*breakfast choices, including vegetar-
ian, vegan, coeliac and gluten-free.
West Country Tourist Board listing
highly commended.*
✖
Typical tariff double room £36 Beds 1
Open all year
VS members' discount *£28 room only
with refreshment tray*

STRATFORD LODGE

4 Park Lane, Salisbury, Wiltshire
SP1 3NP
Tel 01722 325177 Fax 01722 328177
Guesthouse
Traditional British
*Charming Victorian house. All bed-
rooms ensuite. Breakfast includes
mushrooms on toast, fruit compote,
fruit salad, muesli and other cereals.*
P 🏛 (5 yrs+) Cc ✖ ✖ ⅋ (public
entrance/one bedroom, bathroom &
WC on same level/dining
room/restaurant/bar/TV lounge)
Typical tariff single/double room
£37.50/£57.50 Beds 8 Open all year
except Xmas
Typical 3 course meal £15.50 Seats 20

Places to Eat

MARLBOROUGH

STONES RESTAURANT

Avebury, Marlborough, Wiltshire
SN8 1RF
Tel 01672 539514 Fax 01672 539683
Email stones@vebury.demon.co.uk
Restaurant
Chinese French Indian
Italian/Mediterranean Japanese

Lebanese Mexican Organic Spanish Thai

An established restaurant with an international reputation for quality food and service. All food is freshly prepared, where possible using local and organic ingredients. Much of the produce comes from own gardens in Avebury. Always vegan cakes and usually vegan salads available. Prefer 1 day prior notice to produce dishes for vegans.

V Cc ✗ ⤇ 🅰 (public entrance/dining area/bar)
Typical 3 course meal £12 Seats 80 inside; 100 outside Open 10am–6pm Easter–Oct; rest of winter weekends only 10am–5pm; *closed Jan*

SALISBURY

CHUTNEY'S
37 Estcourt Road, Salisbury, Wiltshire SP1 3AS
Tel 01722 504456 Fax 01722 504456
Take Away
Indian Mediterranean
This Indian take away specialises in vegetarian and Mediterranean food, using freshly bought vegetables. Food is prepared without the use of any artificial colourings "as it would be back home in India".
🅰 Cc
Open 12am–2pm & 5pm–12pm
VS members' discount 10% *£10+ orders*

SALISBURY HEALTHFOODS
15 Queen Street, Salisbury, Wiltshire SP1 1EY

Tel 01722 335965 Fax 01722 412519
Health Food Store
Take Away Wholefood
Health food store with over 5500 lines. Many organic vegetarian and vegan foods. Mail order service available with credit cards.
V Cc
Open 9am–5.30pm Mon–Sat
VS members' discount 10%

WORCESTERSHIRE

Places to Stay

DROITWICH

TYTCHNEY GABLES
Boreley, Ombersley, nr Droitwich, Worcestershire WR9 OHZ
Tel 01905 620185
B&B Private House
A 16th century Medieval Hall House situated in a quiet country lane overlooking the Severn Valley and the Malvern Hills. Ideal for touring the Heart of England and City of Worcester. Inglenook log fires, central heating, lounge with TV for guests. Garden available for guests to use.
🐕 🅰 ⤇
Typical tariff single/double room £15/£30 Beds 3 Open all year

KIDDERMINSTER

OLD BAKE HOUSE, THE
46–47 High Street, Cleobury

Mortimer, nr Kidderminster,
Worcestershire DY14 8DQ
Tel 01299 270193
B&B
Indian Italian/Mediterranean
Snacks/Drinks Traditional British
*A grade two listed town house
providing evening meals by prior
arrangement for vegetarians and
vegans.*
P 🐾 🏛
Typical tariff single/double room
£18/£36 Beds 2 Open normal
working hours
Typical 3 course meal £10 Seats 4
Open by prior arrangement

Places to Eat

GREAT MALVERN

ST ANN'S WELL CAFE
St Ann's Road, Great Malvern,
Worcestershire WR14 4RF
Tel 01684 560285
Cafe
Snacks/Drinks
*A small cafe situated on the side of
the Malvern Hills approximately 300ft
above the town. A rural position with
no other buildings close by. Access is
by foot with a restriction on wheeled
vehicles in the area. Situated at the
north end of the hills (which run for
11 miles) this makes an excellent area
for a walking.*
V 🏛✕
Typical 3 course meal £6.15 Seats 20
Open summer 10am–6pm; winter
weekends 10am–dusk

VS members' discount 10%

WORCESTER

KING CHARLES II RESTAURANT
King Charles House, 29 New Street,
Worcester WR1 2DP
Tel 01905 22449 Fax 01905 723746
Restaurant
A la Carte French
Italian/Mediterranean
Traditional British
*Set in an oak panelled restaurant in
the house where King Charles
escaped his enemies during the Civil
War. See the dungeon. Lovely open
fires in the winter, silver service wait-
ressing, lace tablecloths and crystal
glasses. Friendly ambience offering
gorgeous food.*
P Cc
Typical 3 course meal £9.95 lunch;
£25 eve Seats 60 Open 12pm–2pm
& 6.30pm–9.30pm Mon–Sat

Wales

Wales

CARMARTHENSHIRE

Places to Eat

ST CLEARS

OLD MILL CAFE/RESTAURANT, THE
Tenby Road, Llanddowror, St Clears,
Carmarthenshire SA33 4HR
Tel 01994 230836
Cafe Restaurant
Fast Food Indian
Italian/Mediterranean Snacks/Drinks
Traditional British
*A delightful country cafe/restaurant
on the A477 trunk road, mid way
between the market town of
Carmarthen and the popular seaside
resort of Tenby and Saunderfoot. Set
in woodland with a large car park and
outdoor eating facilities.*
Cc ✖
Typical 3 course meal £5 cafe; £10
restaurant Seats 30 cafe; 30 restau-
rant Open cafe 7am–5pm Mon–Sun;
restaurant 7.30am–11.30pm
Thurs–Sat
VS members' discount 5% *10+ parties*

CLWYD

Places to Stay

BODELWYDDAN

FAENOL FAWR
Bodelwyddan, St Asaph, Denbighshire
LL18 5UN

Tel 01745 591691 Fax 01745 591183
Country Hotel Restaurant
A la Carte
*One of the most historical and inter-
esting buildings in North Wales. It consists of an elegant restaurant,
conference facilities, private
dining/dancing areas for parties etc,
and leisure facilities — including a
swimming pool, sauna, steam room
and gym.*
P 🐾 ♀ 🏊 Cc ♿ (public entrance/des-
ignated parking area/one bedroom,
bathroom & WC on same level/dining
room/restaurant/bar/TV lounge)
Typical tariff single/double room
£49.50/£65.50 Beds 25 Open all year
VS members' discount 10%

MOLD

BRON AFON
Maes Bodlonfa, Mold, Clwyd CH7 1DR
Tel 01352 753671
B&B
*Welsh speaking vegan home. Central
for touring. Breakfast includes cereal,
fruit, toast, etc.*
VEGAN 🏊 🥬
Typical tariff single/double room
£13/£22 Beds 2 Open all year

Places to Eat

BODELWYDDAN

FAENOL FAWR
See left.

DENBIGHSHIRE

Places to Stay

LLANGOLLEN

GUEST HOUSE GWYNFA
Llanarmon DC, nr Llangollen,
Denbighshire LL20 7LF
Tel 01691 6002287
Guesthouse
Traditional British
*Small quality guesthouse. Ideal for
country lovers and peaceful relax-
ation. Superb location in beautiful
village within the spectacular Ceiriog
Valley on the edge of the Berwyn
Mountains. Guided hillwalking and
map/compass courses also available.*
P 查 ✻✗
Typical tariff single/double room
£17/£34 Beds 3 Open Feb–Nov

DYFED

Places to Stay

ABERYSTWYTH

BARN HOUSE, THE
See **SPECIAL INTEREST**, page 231.

GLYN-GARTH GUEST HOUSE
South Road, Aberystwyth, Ceredigion,
Dyfed SY23 1JS
Tel 01970 615050
Guesthouse

Traditional British
*Delightful guesthouse only a few
yards from the sea front and run by
the very friendly Evans family for over
40 years. Immaculately maintained.
Fresh and bright decor with pretty,
modern well equipped rooms.
Comfortable lounge. CTV and tea/
coffee making facilities in all rooms.
RAC high acclaimed and WTB high
commended.*
P ✻✗
Typical tariff single/double room
£19/£38 Beds 10

YSTRAD MEURIG

HILLSCAPE WALKING HOLIDAYS
See **SPECIAL INTEREST**, page 231.

Places to Eat

ABERYSTWYTH

Y GRAIG WHOLEFOOD CAFE
34 Pier Street, Aberystwyth, Dyfed
SY23 2LN
Tel 01970 611606
Cafe Restaurant
Organic Wholefood
*An alternative community cafe estab-
lished in 1980 and attracting a wide
range of customers from families and
university students to tourists and
alternative politically aware citizens.
Aberystwyth has a higher proportion
of vegans than many places. Easy to
find near the pier. Many vegan dishes
available each day.*
✗ ✻✗ ♿ (public entrance/dining

area)
Typical 3 course meal £8 Seats 26
Open 9.30am–6pm Mon–Sat; occasional eves

CEREDIGION

ANCIENT RAIN VEGETARIAN EATERY
13 Cambrian Place, Ceredigion,
Aberystwyth, Dyfed SY23 1NT
Tel 01970 612363
Eatery
Organic Snacks/Drinks
*Beautiful relaxing surroundings with
water feature. Soothing background
music and a friendly helpful service.
Customers call it their 'sanctuary'
and 'oasis' to escape the hustle and
bustle. All dishes are homemade and
cooked fresh to order. Extra virgin
olive oil, fresh vegetable juices and
freshly ground coffee. Bring your
own wine.*
V ✖
Typical 3 course meal £10–£12 Seats
26 Open 10am–5pm Mon–Sat; *parties catered for at anytime*

LLANDEILO

FANNYS RESTAURANT
3 King Street, Llandeilo, Dyfed
SA19 6AA
Tel 01558 822908
Cafe Restaurant Take Away
A la Carte Snacks/Drinks
Traditional British
*Situated in a Grade 2 listed building,
tea rooms are combined with bistro-
style lunches. The food is prepared
daily with as much local and organic*

produce as possible. Tasty vegetarian
and vegan choices.
Cc ✖
Typical 3 course meal £7–£20 Seats
40–50 Open 10am–5pm Tues–Sat;
7pm–9pm Thurs–Sat; 12pm–2pm Sun

GWENT

Places to Stay

NEWPORT

CHAPEL GUEST HOUSE
Church Road, St Brides, Wentloog, nr
Newport, Gwent NP1 9SN
Tel 01633 681018 Fax 01633 270470
B&B
*TV and beverage trays in all rooms. TV
lounge and dining room.*
🐾 🏛 Cc ✖ ♿ (public entrance/designated parking area/one bedroom,
bathroom & WC on same level/dining
room/restaurant/TV lounge)
Typical tariff single/double room
£20/£38 Beds 3 Open all year

WEST USK LIGHTHOUSE
St Brides, Wentloog, nr Newport,
Gwent NP1 9SF
Tel 01633 810126
B&B
*175-year-old grade II listed converted
lighthouse with wedge-shaped rooms.
Situated near Newport and Cardiff
and overlooking the Severn Estuary.
All rooms are ensuite and include
waterbed and 4 poster bed. Relaxing
and romantic. Friendly hosts. Flotation*

tank and complementary therapies available. Definitely different!
🏠 Cc 🗙

Typical tariff single/double room £45/£75 Beds 3 Open all year

GWYNEDD

Places to Stay

CAERNARFON

GRAIANFRYN
Penisarwaun, Caernarfon, Gwynedd
LL55 3NH
Tel 01286 871007
Email a.crawshaw@bangor.ac.uk
Website
http://www.ndirect.co.uk/~graian
fryn
Guesthouse
Around the World Wholefood
Luxurious accommodation in comfortable Victorian ex-farmhouse. Ideally situated on the edge of Snowdonia between mountains and sea. Magnificent countryside for walking and exploring. Exciting imaginative cuisine using fresh (organic where possible) ingredients.
V 🐾 🏠 🗙

Typical tariff single/double room £18/£36 Beds 3 Open all year
Typical 3 course meal £13 Seats 8

DOLGELLAU

BONTDDU HALL HOTEL
Bontddu, nr Dolgellau, Gwynedd

LL42 2UF
Tel 01341 430661 Fax 01341 430284
Hotel Restaurant
French Traditional British
Historic country house hotel situated in Southern Snowdonia National Park. Three star hotel. Two rosettes from the AA for quality cuisine. 1997 award for courtesy and care. Merit award from the RAC for hospitality, comfort and restaurant. Menu changes daily.
P ⅄ 🏠 Cc 🗙 🗙 ♿ (public entrance/designated parking area/one bedroom, bathroom & WC on same level/dining room/restaurant/bar/TV lounge)
Typical tariff single/double room £62.50/£100 Beds 20
Typical 3 course meal £23.50 Seats 60

MAENTWROG

OLD RECTORY HOTEL, THE
Maentwrog, Gwynedd LL41 4HN
Tel 01766 590305 Fax 01766 590305
Hotel Restaurant
Italian/Mediterranean
Built 1745–1801, this hotel was originally the Dower House of the Oakley family who were local slate miners. Amidst 3 acres of riverside gardens. All rooms are ensuite with TVs and beverage facilities. Informal and peaceful atmosphere. Dogs welcome in annex. Owner vegan.
P 🐾 ⅄ 🏠 Cc 🗙
Typical tariff single/double room £25/£38 Beds 10
Typical 3 course meal £11.95 Seats 50
Open seasonal

PENTIR

RAINBOW COURT
Village Square, Pentil, nr Bangor,
Gwynedd LL57 4UY
Tel 01248 353099 Fax 01248 353099
Email rainbow@marketsite.co.uk
Website
http://www.marketsite.co.uk/rainbow
B&B Restaurant
A la Carte French
Italian/Mediterranean Snacks/Drinks
*It is advisable to provide advance
notice for long stays so the best of
menus can be arranged. Bike hire,
golf bookings available and access to
all other sports.*
🏛 Cc ✕ ⅙✖
Typical tariff single/double room
from £16/£19 Beds 3 Open 1 Jan–
23 Dec
Typical 3 course meal from £9.50
Seats 24+ Open *(coffi shop)*
9.30am–5pm Mon–Sat; *(restaurant)*
6.30pm–8.30pm *(last orders)*
Mon–Sat — except Tues eve; *(restaurant)* 4.30pm–6.30pm Sun

TALSARNAU

TREMEIFION VEGETARIAN HOTEL
Soar Road, Talsarnau, Gwynedd
LL47 6UH
Tel 01766 770491 Fax 01766 771272
Email tremeifion@mcmail.com
Website
http://www.tremeifion.mcmail.com
Guesthouse
Organic
*Situated in 3 acres of gardens with
views across the estuary. All prices*
*include B&B and evening meal.
Licensed with vegetarian and vegan
wines available. Choice of evening
meal. Wide selection of books in the
spacious lounge.*
V 🐾 🏛 ✕ ⅙✖
Typical tariff double room £44pp incl
evening meal Beds 5 Open all year
Typical 3 course meal £16 Seats
10–12

Places to Eat

DOLGELLAU

BONTDDU HALL HOTEL
See page 167.

MAENTWROG

OLD RECTORY HOTEL, THE
See page 167.

PENTIR

RAINBOW COURT
See left.

PORTHMADOG

VEGONIA WHOLEFOODS
49 High Street, Porthmadog,
Gwynedd LL49 9LR
Tel 01766 515195
Wholefood Shop
Organic Snacks/Drinks
*Over 1000 vegan products for sale —
including dried, chilled/frozen and
convenience foods, snacks, hot and
cold drinks, organic gluten-free and
diabetic goods, household products,*

toiletries, cosmetics, natural remedies, essential oils, flower remedies, supplements, books, posters and leaflets. Proprietors are vegan.
VEGAN
Open 9am–5pm Mon–Sat

MONMOUTHSHIRE

Places to Stay

ABERGAVENNY

PENTRE HOUSE
Brecon Road, Abergavenny, Monmouthshire NP7 7EW
Tel 01873 853435 Fax 01873 853435
B&B Guesthouse
Snacks/Drinks Traditional British
Small, pretty country house set in 1 acre of award winning gardens. Many interesting plants and colourful containers. Comfortably furnished. Excellent home cooking. River Usk and Sugar Loaf Mountain within walking distance. WTA high commended.
🐕 🏠 ✕ ✳ (bedrooms) ♿ (public entrance/designated parking area/dining room/restaurant/TV lounge)
Typical tariff single/double room £18/£32 Beds 3 Open Jan–Dec
Typical 3 course meal £10 Seats 6
Open 6.30pm–8.30pm

CHEPSTOW

OLD RECTORY, THE
Tintern, nr Chepstow,

Monmouthshire NP6 6SG
Tel 01291 689519 Fax 0374 570395
Guesthouse
19th century former rectory overlooking the beautiful River Wye. Comfortable accommodation in well-appointed rooms. Log fires and own spring water. Good cooking and a warm welcome assured. Evening meals available by prior arrangement. Close to Tintern Abbey, Monmouth, Chepstow and Forest of Dean.
🐕 (dogs) 🏠 ✳
Typical tariff single/double room from £22/£34 Beds 4 Open all year except Xmas & New Year

PEMBROKESHIRE

Places to Stay

HAVERFORDWEST

HILTON MILL
Roch, Haverfordwest, Pembrokeshire SA62 6AE
Tel 01437 710744 Fax 01437 710744
Self Catering
Owned by vegetarians, this watermill is set in a beautiful 6 acre valley nature reserve within the Pembrokeshire Coast National Park. Two immaculate self-catering apartments with one double bedroom in each. Grade 5 Tourist Board. No pets due to resident cats and ducks.
✳
Open Easter–end Sept

**OLD COURT HOUSE VEGETARIAN
GUEST HOUSE, THE**
See **SPECIAL INTEREST**, page 231.

TENBY

FOURCROFT HOTEL
North Beach, Tenby, Pembrokeshire
SA70 8AP
Tel 01834 842886 Fax 01834 842888
Email fowerfr@celtic.co.uk
Website
http://www.walledtowns.com/4croft
Hotel
A la Carte French Snacks/Drinks
Traditional British
*Family-run seaside hotel overlooking
Tenby's old fishing harbour and
Carmarthen Bay. Spectacular cliff top
gardens leading down to the famous
Blue Flag Beach. Swimming pool,
sauna, spa pool, table tennis, football,
snooker, pool, short mat bowls and
giant chess. 3 star AA/RAC and 4
crowns WTB.*
🐾 ♀ 🏊 Cc ✗ 🏊 (areas) ♿ (public
entrance/dining room/
restaurant/bar/TV lounge)
Typical tariff single/double room
£29.39/£58.78 Beds 46 Open all year
Typical 3 course meal £18 Seats 100
Open 7.30am–9.30am;
12pm–2.30pm; 7pm–8.30pm

Places to Eat

HAVERFORDWEST

**CAROLINE'S WHOLEFOODS &
TAKE AWAY**
Unit 17, Riverside Market,

Haverfordwest, Pembrokeshire
SA61 2AN
Tel 01437 765490 Fax 01437 765490
Sandwich Bar Take Away
Wholefood Store
Fast Food Indian
Italian/Mediterranean Organic
Snacks/Drinks Traditional British
*All food prepared on the premises by
the vegan proprietor. Hot and cold
food available. Sandwiches, rolls and
bakery products incorporated into a
well stocked wholefood store.*
V 🏊 ♿ (public entrance/designated
parking area)
Open 8am–5.15pm Mon–Sat
VS members' discount 10%

TENBY

**PLANTAGENET HOUSE &
QUAY ROOM**
Quay Hill, Tenby, Pembrokeshire
SA70 7BX
Tel 01834 842350/845148
Fax 01834 843915
Cafe Restaurant Take Away
Tea Rooms
A la Carte French
Italian/Mediterranean Snacks/Drinks
Traditional British
*Tenby's oldest house near the har-
bour with a stunning 12th/13th
century medieval Flemish chimney in
which you can dine. Internationally
renowned and recommended by
WTB. Visited by President Jimmy
Carter. Coffee bar/bar downstairs and
the main restaurant with beams and
open fires upstairs.*
Cc ✗ ♿ (public entrance/designated

parking area/dining area/bar)
Typical 3 course meal £12 Seats 80
Open 9am–12.30am Mar–Nov;
Fri–Sun Nov–Mar; Xmas & New Year

POWYS

Places to Stay

BRECON

BEACONS, THE
16 Bridge Street, Brecon, Powys
LD3 8AH
Tel 01874 623339 Fax 01874 623339
Guesthouse Restaurant
Modern European
*Recently restored Georgian house
with standard ensuite and luxury
period rooms. Fine cuisine by award-
winning chef who is happy to cater
for any requirements. Situated close
to the centre of this small historic
market town with its cathedral, castle,
river and canal marina. Private car
park. Motorbike & bicycle lock-up.*
🏇 ♀ 🕏 Cc ✗ ⅍ (except bar) ⅍
(public entrance/one bedroom,
bathroom & WC on same level/dining
room/restaurant/TV lounge)
Open all year
Typical 3 course meal £16.95 Seats 42
Open 6.30pm–9pm Tues–Fri

BULL'S HEAD, THE
86 The Struet, Brecon, Powys LD3 7LS
Tel 01874 622044
B&B Public House

Snacks/Drinks Traditional British
*An edge of town pub with a commu-
nity feel. The home of Brecon Folk
Club, which meets the first Saturday
of the month for music and fun! A
vegetarian menu available with meals
suitable for vegans.*
♀ 🕏
Typical tariff single/double room
£12/£24 Beds 2 Open all year
Typical bar meal £8 Open Mon–Sat
12pm–3pm & 6.30pm–11pm; Sun
12pm–3pm & 7pm–10.30pm

BUILTH WELLS

BICYCLE BEANO
See **SPECIAL INTEREST** page 231.

HEAD FOR THE HILLS
See **SPECIAL INTEREST** page 232.

**TRERICKET MILL VEGETARIAN
GUEST HOUSE**
Erwood, Builth Wells, Powys LD2 3TQ
Tel 01982 560312
Bunkhouse Camping Guesthouse
*Situated in a former water mill which
was previously used for grinding corn.
Now sympathetically restored.
Overlooking the River Wye and set in
an old cider orchard beside the mill
stream. Wholesome vegetarian/vegan
breakfast. Evening meals also
available.*
V
Typical tariff single/double room
£24.50/£39 Beds 5 Open all year
except Xmas
VS members' discount 10% *2 nights+*

Wales

LLANBRYNMAIR

BARLINGS BARN
Llanbrynmair, Powys SY19 7DY
Tel 01650 521479 Fax 01650 521520
Email barlbarn@zetnet.co.uk
Website
http://www.telecentres.com/
business/newtownbiz/baringsbarn/
index.htm
Self Catering
*Two rose covered self-catering
Barnlets available for 8–12 or 2–4
people. Situated in a secluded location surrounded by gardens and a
stream nearby. Sandy beaches 30 minutes' drive. Snowdonia National Park
nearby. Heated outdoor swimming
pool, sauna, sunbed and squash court
available for use. Vegetarian owner.*
P 🐐 (prior arrangement) ♿
Typical tariff £165–£735
VS members' discount 5% *low season*

CYFEILIOG GUEST HOUSE
Bont Dolgadfan, Llanbrynmair, Powys
SY19 7BB
Tel 01650 521231
Guesthouse Restaurant
Italian/Mediterranean
Traditional British
*A traditional Welsh village riverside
guest house. A relaxed informal
atmosphere. All meals cooked at
home using home-grown vegetables,
fruit and herbs. A small licensed
restaurant facility for non-residents.
Ideal base for walking, cycling and
exploring the villages and small towns
of mid Wales. Set in wonderful countryside.*

🍷 ♿ ✗ 🐾
Typical tariff single/double room
£18/£36 Beds 3 Open all year
Typical 3 course meal £8.50 Seats 12
Open evenings *if booked by 10am on
day*

MACHYNLLETH

GWALIA
Tel 01650 511377
B&B Self Catering
*A peaceful and remote small farm
with goats, hens and sheep. Beautiful
views of Dyfi Valley and Snowdonia
National Park with Machynlleth and
Centre for Alternative Technology
nearby. Excellent for walking and
birdwatching. Lake available for swimming. Wholefood home cooked meals
using own organic vegetables and
fruit.*
V 🐾 ♿ 🐾
Typical tariff single/double room
£15/£30 Beds 2 Open all year

TYGLYN GUEST HOUSE
Eglwysfach, Machynlleth, Powys
SY20 8SX
Tel 01654 781348
Guesthouse
*A small friendly guesthouse run by
husband and wife. Comfortable sitting
room for guests' use including an
open fire and TV. Close to beautiful
walking country, the excellent Ynyshir
RSPB Reserve in the Dovey Valley and
the Centre for Alternative Technology.
Bicycles available.*
P (preferably) 🐾 ♿ 🐾
Typical tariff single/double room

£16/£32 Beds 5 Open all year

MONTGOMERY

DRAGON HOTEL
Montgomery, Powys SY15 6PA
Tel 01686 668359 Fax 01686 668359
Email
dragon_michaels@compuserve.com
Website
http://www.hub.co.uk/nickrs/hooool.
html
Hotel
A la Carte Snacks/Drinks
*Indoor heated pool available for use.
No notice required for vegetarians but
would prefer notice for vegan guests.*
P 🐕 ♀ 🏊 Cc ✕
Typical tariff single/double room
£42/£72 Beds 15
Typical 3 course meal £17.25 Seats 42
Open 12pm–2pm & 7pm–9pm

Places to Eat

BRECON

BULL'S HEAD, THE
See page 171.

OAK, THE
12 The Bulwary, Brecon, Powys
LD3 7AD
Tel 01874 625501
Bistro Cafe Restaurant Tea Rooms
Around the World Traditional British
*A traditional English/European
restaurant set in a 1640s dining room
in the heart of the Brecon Beacons.
A beautiful place to stop and eat.
Menus are changed quarterly with at*

*least 6 vegetarian options. Vegans
are easily catered for. Reservations
recommended.*
🐕 (in tea garden) 🏊 Cc ✕ ♿ (public
entrance/dining area)
Typical 3 course meal £13.25 Seats 32
Open 10am–10pm Mon–Sun

LLANDRINDOD WELLS

HERB GARDEN CAFE, THE
Spa Road, Llandrindod Wells, Powys
LD1 5EY
Tel 01597 824737
Cafe
Continental Organic
*Wholefood cafe in a small mid-Wales
spa town. Specialising in homemade
food using locally grown and organic
produce as much as possible. Vegan
options available daily — including
snack items, soups, cakes and a
pudding.*
V ✕ 🐾 ♿ (public entrance/dining
area)
Typical 3 course meal £7.50 Seats 40
Open 9.30am–5.30pm Mon–Fri;
9.30am–4.00pm Sat

MACHYNLLETH

CELTICA
Y Plas, Machynlleth, Powys SY20 8ER
Tel 01654 702702 Fax 01654 703604
Email bryn@celtica.wales.com
Web site
http://www.celtica.wales.com
Tea Rooms Tourist Attraction
Snacks/Drinks Traditional British
*A unique heritage centre presenting
the history and culture of the Celtic*

people. Located in a restored mansion, the centre includes a tea room which serves morning coffee, lunches and afternoon teas.
Cc ✕ ⧉ ♿ (public entrance/designated parking area/dining area) Typical 3 course meal £8 Seats 50 Open 10am–6pm

CENTRE FOR ALTERNATIVE TECHNOLOGY
Machynlleth, Powys SY20 9AZ
Tel 01654 702400 Fax 01654 702782
Email cat@catinfo.demon.co.uk
Website http://www.cat.org.uk/
Cafe Tourist Attraction
Snacks/Drinks Wholefood
Catering is an integral part of the visitor experience at CAT, which demonstrates lifestyle and technological choices for sustainability and quality of life. Customers of the cafe and shop not using the rest of the site don't pay the entrance fee.
V Cc ✕ ⧉ ♿ (public entrance/designated parking area/dining area) Typical tariff for 3 course meal £8.25 Seats 60 Open 10am–5pm Mar–Oct; 11am–4pm Nov–Feb

QUARRY SHOP & CAFE
13–23 Maengwyn Street, Machynlleth, Powys SY20 8EB
Tel 01654 702624 Fax 01654 702624
Cafe Sandwich Bar Take Away
Organic Shop Snacks/Drinks
Wholefoods
Owned by the Centre for Alternative Technology, a wholefood vegetarian cafe and supplies shop. Always vegan choices available in the cafe which

offers snacks, drinks, main meals and cakes. The shop contains a huge range of wholefoods and organic supplies, remedies and fair trade products.
V ⧉
Typical 3 course meal £6.50 Seats 50 Open 9am–4.30pm Mon–Sat; *Sun in summer*
VS members' discount 10% *wholefood shop*

SOUTH GLAMORGAN
Places to Stay

CARDIFF

ANGEL HOTEL
Castle Street, Cardiff, South Glamorgan CF1 2QZ
Tel 01222 232633 Fax 01222 396212
Email angel@paramount-hotels.co.uk
Website http:///www.paramount-hotels.co.uk
Hotel
A la Carte French Snacks/Drinks
Table d'Hote Traditional British
A traditional RAC 4 star hotel in the heart of Cardiff city centre. Excellent location opposite Cardiff Castle and Cardiff Arms Park. Convenient for all city amenities — including Victorian shopping arcades and major department stores. All special dietary requirements catered for at Restaurant Castell.
P ♙ ♖ Cc ✕ ⧉ ♿ (public entrance/ designated parking area/dining room/restaurant/bar/TV lounge)

Typical tariff single/double room
£92/£105 Beds 103 Open all year
Typical 3 course meal £17.50 Seats 70
Open 11am–5pm & 6.30pm–9.30pm

UNIVERSITY OF WALES INSTITUTE
Conference Services, Cyncoed Road,
Cardiff, South Glamorgan CF2 6XD
Tel 01222 506181/2
Fax 01222 506912
Email conferenceservices@uwic.ac.uk
B&B Self Catering University Venue
*Accommodation from one of Wales'
top academic establishments. Facilities
for any number of people for formal
business conferences, educational
trips, sports events or just bed and
breakfast. Tennis, badminton and
squash courts, indoor pool, fitness
suite and newsagents. Dining facilities
for up to 300 with all dietary preferences catered for.*
P ♀ ✤ Cc ↳✖
Typical tariff single room £17.50 Beds
1000 Open all year
VS members' discount on application
for groups

Places to Eat

CARDIFF

CELTIC CAULDRON
47–49 Castle Arcade, Castle Street,
Cardiff, South Glamorgan CF1
Tel 01222 387185 Fax 01222 708853
Cafe Restaurant Sandwich Bar
Fast Food Snacks/Drinks
Traditional Welsh
*Situated opposite the castle at the
entrance to one of central Cardiff's*

*charming arcades. Laverr bread, lus-
cious lentil soup and vegetable curry
are some of the dishes available. 6–8
dishes on the menu purely for vegans.*
✖ ↳✤ ☗ (public entrance/designated
parking area/dining area/bar)
Typical 3 course meal £7.50 Seats 65
Open 8.30am–6pm Mon–Sat winter;
9.30am–4pm Sun winter;
8.30am–9pm Mon–Sat summer;
9.30am–4pm Sun summer
VS members' discount 5%

SSKILLETSS AT MORGANS
635 Newport Road, Cardiff, South
Glamorgan CF3 8DB
Tel 01222 779911
Public House Restaurant
A la Carte
*A country pub and restaurant in the
heart of Cardiff city. The restaurant
provides an 'all you can eat' menu
with a good selection for all the family, including a large salad bar which is
changed daily. The pub has a terraced
garden and adventure play area.*
♀ ✤ Cc ✖ ↳✤ ☗ (public
entrance/dining area/bar)
Typical 3 course meal £6.50 Seats 70
Open *(restaurant)* 12pm–2pm &
6pm–9.30pm Mon–Sat; 12pm–4pm
Sun; *(bar)* 12pm–11pm

PENARTH

**TOMLINS VEGETARIAN
RESTAURANT**
46 Plassey Street, Penarth, South
Glamorgan CF64 1EL
Tel 01222 706644
Restaurant

A la Carte

An exclusively vegetarian restaurant whose aim is to provide a choice for vegetarians and vegans, as well as giving them security in the knowledge that everything, including the wine, has the V symbol approval. Customers are encouraged to enjoy, come back and tell others.

V Cc ✕ ⠞

Typical 3 course meal £14.50 Seats 40
Open 7pm–10.30pm Wed–Sat;
11am–3pm Sat

WEST GLAMORGAN

Places to Stay

SWANSEA

KEN & JAN'S B&B

89–93 Alexandra Road, Garseinon,
Swansea, West Glamorgan SA4 4NU
Tel 01792 897940
B&B
Traditional British

A family-run guesthouse situated close to Swansea and the beautiful Gower. A Victorian style lounge with wood fire, two kitchens, laundry facilities, family rooms, ensuite rooms and large car park at the rear. Close to shops, restaurants, pubs, etc.

🐕 ♨ ♿ (public entrance/one bedroom, bathroom & WC on same
level/dining room)
Typical tariff single/double room
£15/£30 Beds 21 Open all year
VS members' discount 10%

Scotland

ABERDEENSHIRE

Places to Stay

ABOYNE

BIRSE LODGE HOTEL
Charleston Road, Aboyne,
Aberdeenshire AB34 5EL
Tel 013398 86253
Fax 013398 87796
Email
birse_lodgehotel@compuserve.com
Website http://www.royal-
deeside.org.uk/birse.htm
Hotel
A la Carte Snacks/Drinks
Traditional British
*Built in 1896 as Dower House for
Huntly Estates, this is a small, family-
run hotel blending traditional
standards of hospitality with modern
comforts. Ideally situated on the Royal
Deeside for Yorkshire.*
P ⚥ 🛏 Cc ♿ (public entrance/desig-
nated parking area/one bedroom,
bathroom & WC on same level/dining
room/restaurant/bar/TV lounge)
Typical tariff single/double room
£39/£40 Beds 12 Open all year
Typical 3 course meal £18 Seats 40
Open Mon–Sun 12pm–2pm &
6pm–9pm
VS members' discount 10% food

CORNHILL

CASTLE OF PARK
Cornhill, Aberdeenshire AB45 2AX
Tel 01466 751667
Fax 01466 751667
Hotel Restaurant
Self Catering
A la Carte Traditional Scottish *(with
modern approach)*
*Peacefully set amongst park and
woodland, this historic castle offers
guests private suites, catered house
parties and self catering. A restaurant
and gallery are open to non-
residents and painting holidays and
gallery hire are also offered. Murder
mysteries, weddings and celebrations
a speciality.*
P ⚥ 🛏 Cc ✗ ⟐ ♿ (public
entrance/designated parking
area/dining area/bar)
Typical tariff single/double room
£27–£40/£54–£80 Beds 7
Open all year
Typical 3 course meal £13 Seats 16
Open *advanced bookings*
**VS members' discount 10% per
couple** — *subject to availability and
not specials*

SAUCHEN

WESTER DALHERRICK
Sauchen, Aberdeenshire AB51 7RP
Tel 01330 833450
B&B
*An exclusively vegetarian and vegan
B&B in a peaceful, rural setting.
Serving home baked bread and
organic vegetables in season. Evening
meal by arrangement.*
V 🛏 (12 yrs+)
Typical tariff double room from £15
Beds 2 Open all year

Places to Eat

ABERDEEN

OWLIES BRASSERIE
Littlejohn Street, Aberdeen AB10 1FF
Tel 01224 649267 Fax 01224 590342
Restaurant
A la Carte French
Serves an imaginative vegetarian and vegan menu at affordable prices. Set in relaxed brasserie-style surroundings. Ideal for special occasions for large groups, as well as intimate dinners and family outings.
Cc ✗ ⅘ (areas)
Typical 3 course meal £12 Seats 130
Open Mon–Sat 12pm–2.30pm & 6pm–10pm *(last orders)*

STAGE DOOR RESTAURANT, THE
26 North Silver Street, Aberdeen AB10 1RL
Tel 01224 646111 Fax 01224 634466
Restaurant
A la Carte Continental French Italian/Mediterranean
Pre-theatre suppers and an a la carte dinner menu. Private room available for a maximum of 16 people.
P Cc ✗
Typical 3 course meal £20 Seats 125
Open 11.30am–3pm & 5.30pm–12am Mon–Sat; 5.30pm–11pm Sun

CORNHILL

CASTLE OF PARK
See page 180.

HUNTLY

BORVE BREWERY
Ruthven, Huntly, Aberdeenshire AB54 4SG
Tel 01466 760343
Brewery
Family run brewery.
VEGAN Cc ⅘ (public entrance/designated parking area)
Open 11am–11pm

ANGUS

Places to Stay

GLENESK HOTEL
High Street, Edzell, Angus DD9 7TF
Tel 01356 648319 Fax 01356 647333
Hotel
Traditional British
A traditional family-run county house hotel. Situated in the heart of Angus. Catering thoughtfully for vegans. Large conferencing facilities for up to 200 people. Leisure club with swimming pool, gym, sauna and whirlpool spa. Extensive car parking.
P 🐾 ♀ ♨ Cc ✗
Typical tariff single/double room £50/£82 Beds 25 Open all year except 1st week Jan
Typical 5 course meal £16 Seats 60
Open 7.30pm–8.45pm *(restaurant last orders)*; 7.30pm–9.30pm *(bar suppers)*

ARGYLLSHIRE

Places to Stay

ISLE OF BUTE

NEW FARM
Mount Stuart, Isle of Bute, Argyllshire
PA20 9NA
Tel 01700 831646 Fax 01700 831646
Farmhouse B&B Restaurant
Traditional Scottish
Set on a 1000 acres farm on the beautiful Island of Bute in Argyll. Carole bakes fresh bread every day and uses fresh herbs and vegetables gathered from the kitchen garden for meals. She is highly recommended in The Taste of Scotland, *the Scottish guide to good eating.*
P ☰ ✕ ⅙ (areas) ♿ (public entrance/designated parking area/one bedroom, bathroom & WC on same level/dining room/restaurant)
Typical tariff single/double room
from £17.80/£35 Beds 3 Open all
year; *booking essential*
VS members' discount 10%

ISLE OF IONA

ST COLUMBA HOTEL
Isle of Iona, Argyllshire PA76 6SL
Tel 01681 700304 Fax 01681 700688
Hotel
A friendly, peaceful hotel near Iona Abbey. Serves home cooking. Superb views over the Sound of Iona. An
ideal setting for a relaxing holiday for young and old.
P 🐕 ☰ Cc ♿ (one bedroom/bathroom & WC on same level/dining room)
Typical tariff single/double room
£51/£47pp Beds 27 Open Apr–Oct

ISLE OF MULL

BRUACH MHOR
Fionnphort, Isle of Mull, Argyllshire
PA66 6BL
Tel 01681 700276 Fax 01681 700276
B&B Private House
A comfortable, modernised croft-house offering traditional vegetarian and vegan B&B and dinner. Half a mile from the ferries to Iona and Staffa. Uses home-grown organic vegetables whenever possible. Lovely area for walking, with fine coastal scenery. Peaceful and secluded sandy beaches.
☰ ✕ (beds & dining room) ♿ (one bedroom, bathroom & WC on same level/dining room/lounge)
Typical tariff single/double room
£15/£30 Beds 4 Open Jan–Dec
except Xmas & New Year

Places to Eat

ISLE OF BUTE

NEW FARM
See left.

AYRSHIRE

Places to Stay

GIRVAN

GLENDRISSAIG GUEST HOUSE
Newton Stewart Road, Girvan,
Ayrshire KA26 0HJ
Tel 01465 714631
B&B Guesthouse
Organic Traditional British
*Wonderful location for guesthouse,
catering for vegans and vegetarians.
Spacious ensuite rooms. Ideal for
walks, golf, cycling and touring.*
� ⅍✕
Typical tariff single/double room
£25/£20pp Beds 3 Open Apr–Oct
Typical 3 course meal £12
VS members' discount 5% *4 nights+*

BERWICKSHIRE

Places to Stay

DUNS

ALLANTAN INN
Allantan, By Duns, Berwickshire
TD11 3JZ
Tel 01890 818260 Fax 01361 882014
Website http://www.s-h-
systems.co.uk/66scot.html#Duns
Hotel Inn
A la Carte Snacks/Drinks
Table d'Hote Traditional British

*A pretty inn in the heart of a conserva-
tion village, once the home of the the
real Blackadder family. There is a beer
garden and families are welcome.
Comfortable rooms with ensuite facilities. Vegan guests are requested to
make themselves known when booking so the vegan menu can be
extended. 3 crown commended.*
⅍ ⅌ 🐾 ☚ Cc ⅍✕ (accommodation &
restaurant)
Typical tariff single/double room
£34–£76 Beds 5 Open all year
Typical 3 course meal £13.95 Seats 18
restaurant; 50 bar Open Mon–Thurs
12pm–2.30pm & 6pm–11pm; Fri
12pm–2.30pm & 6pm–1am; Sat
12pm–1am; Sun 12pm–12am

Places to Eat

DUNS

ALLANTAN INN
See left.

BORDERS

Places to Stay

COLDINGHAM

**WHEATEARS COUNTRY
VEGETARIAN GUEST HOUSE**
Lumsdaine, Coldingham, Scottish
Borders TD14 5UA
Tel 018907 71375 Fax 018907 71375
Guesthouse
Bangladeshi Chinese Indian

Italian/Mediterranean Organic
Sri Lankan Thai Traditional British
*A warm welcome is guaranteed in this
guesthouse set in 1¹/₂ acres of wildlife
garden. TVs and hospitality trays in all
rooms. Bike hire, video and book
library, pick up service from stations.
Evening meals also open to non-residents but booking is essential. All
dishes are homemade using local and
homegrown produce when possible.*
V ⁕
Typical tariff single/double room
£30/£20pp Beds 3 Open Feb–Nov
Typical 3 course meal £14 Seats 6
Open eves Feb–Nov
VS members' discount 5% *off-peak*

PEEBLES

GREY GABLES
Springwood Road, Peebles, Scottish
Borders EH45 9HB
Tel 01721 721252
B&B Private House
Organic Traditional British
*Old coach house in quiet part of town
offering excellent accommodation.
Vegetarian and vegan food available.*
⛩ ⁕
Typical tariff single/double room
£17.50/£17.50pp Beds 2 Open all
year

Places to Eat

COLDINGHAM

**WHEATEARS COUNTRY
VEGETARIAN GUEST HOUSE**
See page 183.

DUMFRIES

Places to Stay

DUMFRIES

CAIRNDALE HOTEL & LEISURE CLUB
English Street, Dumfries DG1 2DF
Tel 01387 254111 Fax 01387 250555
**Cafe Hotel Leisure Club Restaurant
Sandwich Bar**
A la Carte French
Italian/Mediterranean Snacks/Drinks
Traditional British
*Ideally located for discovering local
area steeped in history. Beautiful
countryside and coastline. 24 hour
reception including night porter. Pool,
sauna, steam room, gym, sunbeds
and toning tables available. Room ser-
vice menu. STB 5 crowns commended.
AA/RAC 3 stars. Vegans "Absolutely
welcome. No problem".*
P 🐕 (prior notice) ⚲ ⛩ Cc ✕ ⁕
(some rooms) ♿ (public entrance/one
bedroom, bathroom & WC on same
level/dining room/restaurnat/bar)
Typical tariff single/double room
£79.50/£99.50 Beds 786
Open all year
Typical 3 course meal £17 Seats 160
Open hours vary seasonally for 2
restaurants; 8am–10.30pm 3 cafe
bars

Places to Eat

NEW ABBEY

NEW ABBEY
26 Main Street, New Abbey, Dumfries
Tel 01387 850377 Fax 01848 200536
Cafe Restaurant
Snacks/Drinks Traditional British
*A family-run restaurant/coffee shop
with all meals prepared on the
premises using mostly local produce.
Terrace overlooks Sweetheart Abbey.
Large public car park to the rear. Egon
Ronay recommended and member of
the Tea Council.*
✗ Cc ♨ ♿ (public entrance/toilet/
designated parking area/dining space
– although not designated)
Typical 3 course meal £7.50 Seats 56
Open 10am–5.30pm, all week from
Easter–Oct; weekends Nov–Dec

EDINBURGH
Places to Stay

CAMERON TOLL GUEST HOUSE
299 Dalkeith Road, Edinburgh
EH16 5JX
Tel 0131 667 2950
Fax 0131 662 1987
Email camerontoll@msn.com
Guesthouse
*Friendly family-run guest house.
Rooms have own shower, toilet,
colour TV, tea and coffee making
facilities. Comfortable lounge and
plenty of tourist information. Situated
10 minutes' drive/bus ride to centre
of Edinburgh on A7. Varied Scottish
breakfast and evening meals plus
packed lunches.*
P 🛏 Cc
Typical single/double room
£25–£33/£20–£29 Open Jan–Dec

DUKES OF WINDSOR STREET
17 Windsor Street, Edinburgh
EH7 5LA
Tel 0131 556 6046
Fax 0131 556 6046
B&B
*Beautifully restored Georgian town
house in a quiet, central location.
Close to main shopping areas, theatre
and historic venues. On street parking.
Commended by the Scottish Tourist
Board.*
🛏 Cc
Typical tariff single/double room
£27/£55.75 Beds 10 Open check in
1pm–5pm

ECOSSE INTERNATIONAL
15 McDonald Road, Edinburgh
EH7 4LX
Tel 0131 556 4967
Fax 0131 556 7394
Guesthouse
Continental Traditional British
*A luxury guesthouse with a warm,
friendly and homely atmosphere.
Personally run by the owner. All
rooms ensuite with tea/coffee making
facilities and courtesy whisky.
Centrally located and an ideal base for
day trips to the Highlands, Loch Ness,
Trossachs and Gleneagles.*

P 率 ⅍ ⅍ (public entrance/desig-
nated parking area/one bedroom,
bathroom & WC on same level/dining
room/restaurant/bar/TV lounge)
Typical tariff single/double room
£35/£35pp Beds 5 Open Dec–Jan

HERALD HOUSE HOTEL
70 Grove Street, Edinburgh EH3 8AP
Tel 0131 228 2323
Fax 0131 228 3101
Email admin@herald-house.u-net.com
Hotel
A la Carte French
Italian/Mediterranean Snacks/Drinks
Traditional British
🐕 (prior arrangement) ⅍ 率 Cc ✕
⅍ ⅍ (public entrance/one bed-
room, bathroom & WC on same
level/dining room/restaurant/bar)
Typical tariff single/double room
£57/£98 Beds 45 Open all year
Typical 3 course meal £13.95 Seats 12
& 24 Open 7.30am–9.30am;
6.30pm–9pm

No 1 BED & BREAKFAST
1 Gayfield Place, Edinburgh
EH7 4AB
Tel 0131 557 4752
B&B
*Situated on the top floor of a classical
Georgian Edinburgh building near the
Playhouse in the city centre. Free on
street parking nearby. Vegan owner.
Good vegetarian- and vegan-friendly
restaurants nearby.*
V ⅍
Typical tariff single/double room
£20/£40 Beds 4 Open all year

SIX ST MARY'S PLACE GUESTHOUSE
Raeburn Place, Stockbridge,
Edinburgh EH4 1JD
Tel 0131 332 8965
Fax 0131 624 7060
Email ECT_Social_Firms/smpl.htm
Website http://www.ourworld.
compuserve.com/homepages/
Guesthouse
*A superior guesthouse situated in a
beautifully restored Georgian town
house. Dining conservatory,
delightful garden and antique
furniture throughout. Only 5 minutes
walk from the celebrated Royal
Botanic Gardens. STB 2 crown
commended.*
V 率 Cc ✕ ⅍
Typical tariff single/double room
£28/£56 Beds 8 Open 24 hours
Typical 3 course meal £12 Seats 12
Open all year

LIEBERMAN, SUE
39 Gilmour Road, Edinburgh
EH16 5NS
Tel 0131 662 9769
Fax 0131 662 9769
Email suelieberman-
mayfield@virgin.net
Private House
*Elegant Edwardian ground floor flat
with upper level in secluded part of
Edinburgh. With easy access to city
centre and 2 miles from Princes
Street. Informal atmosphere and
welcoming environment with a
home-from-home feel. Resident cats.*
V ⅍
Typical tariff double room £40 Beds 1
Open flexible

Places to Eat

ANN PURNA VEGETARIAN RESTAURANT
45 St Patrick Square, Edinburgh
EH8 9ET
Tel 0131 662 1807
Restaurant
A la Carte Indian
Ann Purna means goddess of food and drink. A culmination of first class vegetables cooked in delightfully spiced sauces. Dishes suitable for vegetarians and vegans. Served with Indian beers and fine wines. Complemented by a clean, fresh and brightly decorated dining area.
V Cc ⊯ & (public entrance)
Typical 3 course meal £11 Seats 60
Open *reservations necessary — mention vegan diet to increase menu choice*

BAKED POTATO SHOP, THE
56 Cockburn Street, Edinburgh
EH1 1PB
Tel 0131 225 7572
Take Away
Fast Food Snacks/Drinks
Small intimate fast food outlet. Friendly and helpful staff on hand offering a refreshing pit stop. Primarily sells baked potatoes with a vast range of fillings and salads, many using homemade vegan mayonnaise. Also a selection of wholemeal rolls, pitta breads, vegan savouries, soup, freshly squeezed juices and cakes.
V ✗ ⊯
Seats 6 Open 9am–9pm Mon–Sun;

9am–11pm Sat & Sun; *late opening during Edinburgh Festival*
VS members' discount 20%

CORNERSTONE CAFE
Church of St John the Evangelist,
Princes Street, Edinburgh EH2 4BJ
Tel 0131 229 0212
Cafe Wine Bar
Chinese Indian Snacks/Drinks
Traditional British
Mostly vegetarian food. Situated on a terrace in a graveyard with views of the castle. Everything cooked on the premises. Licensed.
🏛 ⊯ & (public entrance/designated parking area/dining area/bar)
Typical tariff for 3 course meal £4.50
Seats 74 Open 9.30am–4.30pm
Mon–Sat

ELEPHANT HOUSE, THE
21 George IV Bridge, Edinburgh
EH1 1EP
Tel 0131 220 5355
Fax 0131 220 4272
Gourmet Coffee House
Fast Food Snacks/Drinks
Traditional British
A gourmet coffee house situated in the centre of the old town. Very friendly atmosphere and flexible attitude. Gorgeous vegan cakes available.
Cc ✗ ⊯ (area) & (public entrance/dining area/toilet)
Typical 3 course meal £6 Seats 70
Open 8am–10pm Mon–Fri; 8am–8pm
Sat–Sun

ENGINE SHED, THE
19 St Leonard's Lane, Edinburgh

EH8 9SD
Tel 0131 662 0040
Fax 0131 667 5319
Cafe
Organic Snacks/Drinks
*A training centre for adults with
learning disabilities, providing a
work setting where people can learn
practical skills. Four production units
have been established — including a
bakery, cafe, outside catering and
food processing. All vegetables used
in the cafe are organic or
biodynamic.*
V ✗ ⚬ ♿ (public entrance/desig-
nated parking area)
Typical 3 course meal £5.50 Seats 50
Open 10.30am–3.30pm Mon–Thurs;
10.30am–2.30pm Fri; 10.30am–4pm
Sat; 11am–4pm Sun

HENDERSON'S SALAD TABLE
94 Hanover Street, Edinburgh
EH2 1DR
Tel 0131 225 2131
Fax 0131 220 3542
Email hend94@aol.com
Bistro Restaurant Shop
*Edinburgh's original vegetarian cafe
and restaurant. Established in 1965 by
Janet Henderson and still owned and
managed by the same family. Menu
changes continuously throughout the
day. Live music nightly in the wine
bar. Cosmopolitan atmosphere
enjoyed by a diverse range of
customers.*
V Cc ✗ ⚬
Typical 3 course meal £9.50 Seats 160
Open 8am–10.45pm Mon–Sat; bistro
12pm–6pm Sun

ISABELS CAFE
83 Clerk Street, Edinburgh EH8 9SG
Tel 0131 662 4014
Cafe Take Away
Fast Food Snacks/Drinks
*Situated underneath Natures Gate, a
longstanding healthfood shop in
Edinburgh. Provides a range of deli-
cious and inexpensive homemade veg-
etarian and vegan meals and snacks in
relaxed surroundings. Menu is roughly
75% vegan.*
V ✗ ⚬
Typical 3 course meal £6.75 Seats 24
Open 11.30am–6.30pm Mon–Sat

KALPNA RESTAURANT
2–3 St Patrick Square, Edinburgh
Tel 0131 667 9890
Restaurant
A la Carte Indian/Gujarati
Snacks/Drinks
Good choice of vegan dishes.
V ⚬
Typical 3 course meal £7.50–£13.50
Open 12pm–2pm Mon–Fri;
5.30pm–11pm Mon–Sat
VS members' discount 5%

SURUCHI RESTAURANT
14a Nicholson Street, Edinburgh
EH8 9DH
Tel 0131 556 6583
Fax 0131 622 7227
Restaurant Take Away
Indian
*Cuisine from all the major culinary
regions of modern day India — from
Crispy Pancakes Stuffed with Spicy
Potatoes (a speciality from the South),
to Mild Mushroom Curry from the*

North. All tastes catered for.
Cc ✗
Typical 3 course meal £10.15 Seats 80
Open 12pm–2pm Mon–Sat;
1pm–3pm Sun
VS members' discount 10%

SUSIE'S DINER
51–53 West Nicholson Street,
Edinburgh EH8 9DB
Tel 0131 667 8729
Email susies@ednet.co.uk
Cafe
Catering for a diverse range of people with special theme nights — including belly dancing, singers, guitarists and exhibitions of the work of local artists. Probably the most laid back place in Edinburgh. Easy to find next to the Pear Tree Pub.
V ✗ ⁕ (areas) ♿ (public entrance/dining area)
Typical 3 course meal £7 Seats 58
Open 9am–8pm *(last orders)* Mon;
9am–9pm *(last orders)* Tues–Sat;
9am–12pm *snacks & drinks*

GLASGOW

Places to Stay

ADELAIDES
209 Bath Street, Glasgow G2 4HZ
Tel 0141 248 4970
Fax 0141 226 4247
Guesthouse
A re-developed church building comprising a guesthouse, cafe, nursery and auditoreum in the heart

of the city centre. An ideal base for exploring this revitalised city. Ensuite is available and all rooms are comfortably furnished with tea/coffee facilities and colour TVs. Prior notice will ensure choice for vegans.
🏠 (family room available) Cc ⁕
Typical tariff single/double room £29/£42.50 Beds 8 Open all year *except Xmas & New Year*

Places to Eat

13TH NOTE
50–60 King Street, Glasgow G1 4JH
Tel 0141 553 1638
Fax 0141 552 5797
Cafe/Bar
Large cafe/bar with dining area. Live music and basement area for private hire. Large club premises within 6 minutes walk. Look out for 8am opening for substantial vegan breakfasts. All food is vegan and cow's milk is served in coffee only on request.
✗ ♿ (public entrance/dining area/bar)
Typical 3 course meal £8 Seats 80
Open 12pm–11.45pm Mon–Sat;
12.30pm–11.45pm Sun
VS members' discount 10% *food*

ADELAIDES
See left.

ASHA VEGETARIAN RESTAURANT
141 Elderslie Street, Glasgow G3 7AW
Tel 0141 221 7144
Restaurant
A la Carte Indian Wholemeal
Fully licensed restaurant with house

BAR CAFE VENUE
50-60 King Street
Glasgow G1 5QT
0141 553 1638

Come along to The 13th Note and
experience our delicious home-cooking.
There is a 10% discount on food bill for all
Vegan Society members.
The 13th Note cafe is virtually
animal/dairy free and is therefore suitable
for both vegans and vegetarians.

Opening hrs: Noon–11.45pm
Food served noon-7pm

specialities for vegans. Pre-theatre 4-course menu available every day. 10% discount on all carryouts (not set meals).

V ♀ 🏃 Cc ✕ ⇻

Typical 3 course meal £7 Seats 34
Open Mon–Thurs 12pm–2pm &
5.30pm–11.30pm; Fri–Sat 12pm–2pm
& 5.30pm–12am; Sun 5pm–11.30pm

TRON THEATRE
63 Trongate, Glasgow G1 5HB
Tel 0141 552 3748
Fax 0141 552 6657
Website http://www.tron.co.uk
**Cafe Public House Restaurant
Theatre**
International
Situated in part of Tron Theatre complex, incorporating a 272 seat converted Adam Church dating back to 1795. Original vaulted ceiling church hall. A warm and informal atmosphere. Prior notice to cater for vegans at busy times or if large booking.
Cc ✕ ⇻ ♿ (public entrance/dining area/bar)
Seats 65 Open 10am–12am
Mon–Sat; 10.30am–11pm Sun

FIFE

Places to Stay

FALKLAND

COVENANTER HOTEL
The Square, Falkland, Fife KY15 7BU
Tel 01337 857224 Fax 01337 857163

**Bistro Cocktail Bar Hotel
Restaurant Self Catering**
A la Carte Snacks/Drinks
Traditional Scottish
A family-run hotel situated in the historic village of Falkland. Only 25 minutes from Forth Bridge and St Andrews. The family has run the hotel for 18 years and has expanded the business to include self catering cottages in the village. Special diets catered for, with prior notice for a more varied menu. A warm welcome is assured.
♀ 🏃 Cc ⇻ (dining room/back section of bistro)
Typical tariff single/double room
£39/£48 Beds 5 Open Tues–Sun
all year
Typical 3 course meal £10–£17.50
Seats 36 dining room; 50 bistro Open
Tues–Sun 12pm–2pm & 6pm–9.30pm

Places to Eat

FALKLAND

COVENANTER HOTEL
See left.

HIGHLANDS

Places to Stay

FORT WILLIAM

LODGE ON THE LOCH, THE
Onich, Fort William, Scottish
Highlands PH33 6RY

Tel 01855 821237 Fax 01855 821238
Email
reservations@mysteryworld.co.uk
Website
http://www.freedomglen.co.uk
Hotel Restaurant
Traditional Scottish
Renowned for its spellbinding blend of gentle elegance, exacting standards and delightful, informal atmosphere. Enjoy the 'taste of Scotland' cuisine, an extensive wine list, crackling log fires and the elegant cocktail bar. Benefit from complimentary membership of Pool & Leisure Club at sister hotel.
🐕 ♀ 🌣 Cc ✗ 🍴 ♿ (public entrance/designated parking area/one bedroom, bathroom & WC on same level/dining room/restaurant/bar/TV lounge)
Typical tariff single/double room £81/£162 Beds 19 Open all year *except Jan*
Typical 3 course meal £29.50 Seats 50

SUTHERLAND

SUMUNDAR VILLA
Harbour Road, Brora, Sutherland, Scottish Highlands KW9 6QF
Tel 01408 621717 Fax 01408 621717
B&B
A la Carte Chinese Fast Food Indian Snacks/Drinks Traditional British
Comfortable family home situated at the mouth of the River Brora looking on to the North Sea. Seals in the river only 20 yards from the window. Miles of golden sandy beaches, a fossil beach, a seal colony and wonderful

unspoilt views. Good freshly made home cooking. A little corner of heaven.
V 🌣 Cc ✗ 🍴 ♿ (public entrance/designated parking area/dining area)
Typical tariff double room from £15 Beds 2 Open all year *except Xmas & New Year*

WESTER ROSS

GLEN FRUGART
3 Castle Terrace, Ullapool, Wester Ross, Scottish Highlands IV26 2XD
Tel 01854 612409
B&B Private House
Family home with single, standard twin and double ensuite centrally heated rooms. Centrally located but peaceful with magnificent views to Summer Isles. Pleasant garden, parking and delicious breakfasts — including fruits and homemade jams. Some German and French spoken.
V 🐕 🍴 ♿ (public entrance/designated parking area/one bedroom, bathroom & WC on same level/dining room)
Typical tariff single/double room £16–£17/£17pp Beds 3 Open mid April–Sept; *other times by arrangement*

TAIGH NA MARA
The Shore, Ardindrean, Lochbroom, nr Ullapool, Wester Ross, Scottish Highlands
Tel 01854 655282 Fax 01854 655292
Email mara@lochness.co.uk
Website

http://www.lochness.co.uk/mara
Guesthouse
Organic Traditional Scottish
*Secluded idyllic lochside home of
Jackie & Tony, authors of Rainbows
and Wellies, a Scottish vegan cook-
book, and Scotland the Green, a cru-
elty-free travel guide to Scotland.
Planning on closing the guesthouse
soon so this could be the last chance
to visit this award winning establish-
ment "with lots of something you
can't quite put your finger on."*
VEGAN Cc ⁜✕
Typical tariff double room £66 for 2
people incl eve meal Beds 3
Open all year
Typical 3 course meal £15 Seats 6
Open by appointment
VS members' discount 5% *off season*

Places to Eat

KYLE OF LOCHALSH

**SEAGREEN RESTAURANT &
BOOKSHOP**
Plockton Road, Kyle of Lochalsh,
Wester Ross, Scottish Highlands
IV40 8DA
Tel 01599 534388
Cafe Restaurant Take Away
*A la Carte Modern Scottish Organic
Situated in Kyle's old village school
which has been renovated to provide a
relaxed, spacious and friendly meeting
place to have a cup of coffee or deli-
cious meal. A sunny terrace with magi-
cal views over the sea to the islands of
Skye and Raasay. All food is prepared
and cooked on the premises.*

Cc ✕ ⁜✕ ᵬ (public entrance with
ramp/dining area)
Open winter 10.30am–5pm
Mon–Sun; summer 10am–9pm
Mon–Sun; *closed Jan–Easter*

INVERNESS-SHIRE
Places to Stay

CARR-BRIDGE

PINES COUNTRY HOUSE, THE
Duthil, Carr-Bridge, Inverness-Shire
PH23 3ND
Tel 01479 841220
Guesthouse
Traditional British
*A family-run guest house situated 2
miles from Carr-Bridge. Situated in 2
acres and surrounded by a pine forest.
It faces south with uninterrupted
views of the Spey Valley. Clean com-
fortable rooms with ensuite facilities,
central heating, TV, radio and tea/
coffee making facilities.*
P ⤙ ⚥ ✕ ⁜✕
Typical tariff single/double room
£19.50/£17pp Beds 4 Open Jan–Dec
Typical 3 course meal £8 Seats 8

FORT WILLIAM

RHU MHOR GUEST HOUSE
Alma Road, Fort William, Inverness-
Shire PH33 6BP
Tel 01397 702213
Guest House

Built in 1925, an old fashioned guest-house set in one acre of steep wild garden above Loch Linnhe and the hills of Loch Eil. 10 minutes walk from the town centre. If given advance notice is happy to cater for most diets. Dinner must be pre-booked. Owners vegetarian.

P 🐾 🏛 Cc

Typical tariff double room £40 Beds 7 Open Easter–Oct

FOYERS

CRAIGDARREN HOUSE HOTEL

Foyers, South Loch Ness Side, Inverness-Shire IV1 2XU
Tel 01456 486400 Fax 01453 486444
Hotel
A la Carte French Italian/Mediterranean Traditional British
Situated high above Loch Ness and enjoying panoramic views. STB 4 crown highly commended. A spacious drawing room, magnificent conservatory where guests can sit and enjoy the views. To the rear is a cosy lounge bar. A family business. Son is chef and is happy to discuss meal requirements for vegans.
♀ Cc ᴾ✹ (some rooms) ♿ (public entrance/designated parking area/dining area/bar)
Typical single/double room £65/£110 Beds 15 Open 13 Feb–3 Jan
Typical 3 course meal £24.50 Seats 30

ISLE OF SKYE

DONMAR

43 Bernisdale, Isle of Skye, Inverness-Shire IV51 9NS
Tel 01470 532204 Fax 01470 532204
B&B
Traditional British
A traditional croft house in a quiet area surrounded by sheep. 7 miles from Portree and 15 miles from Dunvegan. Views of Cuillin and Storr Mountains. Tea and coffee making facilities. Ensuite available. Log fire in lounge. Family rooms with reductions for children. Awarded 2 stars by the Scottish Tourist Board.
P 🐾 🏛 ✕ ᴾ✹ (lounge)
Typical tariff single/double room £18/£18pp Beds 3 Open all year
Typical 3 course meal £9 Seats 6
VS members' discount 10% *B&B*

TABLES HOTEL, THE

Dunvegan, Isle of Skye, Inverness-Shire IV55 8WA
Tel 01470 521404 Fax 01470 521404
Hotel Restaurant
Snacks/Drinks Traditional British
A small, relaxed and friendly hotel overlooking Loch Dunvegan and MacLeods table mountains. Close to Dunvegan Castle. Excellent touring or walking base. Books, maps and guides available to help you get around. Bike hire and TV lounge. Advance notice appreciated but not essential. Vegan wines and beers available. Cannot guarantee animal-free toiletries.
♀ 🏛 Cc ✕ ᴾ✹ (bedrooms & restaurant)
Typical tariff single/double room £30/£27pp Beds 5 Open all year — *mostly by arrangement*
Typical 3 course meal £16.50 Seats 24

Open 8am–8pm Mar–Oct
VS members' discount 10% *spring & autumn*

WHITEWAVE ACTIVITIES
See **SPECIAL INTEREST** page 232.

INVERGARRY

GLENDALE VEGETARIAN GUESTHOUSE
Mandally Road, Invergarry, Inverness-Shire PH35 4HP
Tel 01809 501282
Guesthouse
Situated in 1 acre of gardens. Spectacular scenery and good flat walking area and access to 3000' mountains, Caledonian Canal and Great Glen Water Park. No need for car as good bus service and on cycle path. Quiet and safe for children. Friendly and relaxed. TV lounge, open fire and games provided.
V 🐾 🏊 ✗ ⭐ (dining area) ⅍ (bungalow)
Typical tariff £18 for single/£16pp for 2+ Beds 5 Open all year
Typical 3 course meal £10 Seats 14
Open 6.30pm–8.30pm all year for residents *(non-residents when not busy — telephone to confirm)*

INVERNESS

GLEN MHOR HOTEL & RESTAURANT
9–12 Ness Bank, Inverness, Inverness-Shire IV2 4SG
Tel 01463 234308   Fax 01463 713170
Bistro Hotel Restaurant
A la Carte International Modern

Taste of Scotland Traditional Scottish
A traditional style hotel with ensuite standard and executive rooms. 4 crown commended by Scottish Tourist Board. Beautiful riverside location near all amenities. Ideal base for touring Scottish Highlands. Vegan food always available but prior notice will allow a choice.
🖵 🏊 Cc ✗ ⅍ (public entrance/designated parking area/one bedroom, bathroom & WC on same level/dining room/restaurant/bar/TV lounge)
Typical tariff single/double room £58/£72 Beds 30
Typical 3 course meal bistro £15; restaurant £24 Seats bistro 65; restaurant 50 Open bistro 12pm–2pm, 5pm–9.30pm (10.30pm Fri & Sat); restaurant 6pm–9pm — Sats only in winter

NEWTONMORE

ARDNABRUACH
Glen Road, Newtonmore, Inverness-shire PH20 1DZ
Tel 01540 673339
B&B
A family home for 100 years. Traditional friendly Highland hospitality in a beautiful and peaceful setting overlooking village.
P 🐾 (by arrangement) ⭐
Typical tariff single/double room £14/£29 Beds 3 Open all year

---

Please mention the Vegan Travel Guide **when contacting a listed business or advertiser**

Scotland

Places to Eat

ISLE OF SKYE

TABLES HOTEL, THE
See page 196.

WHITEWAVE ACTIVITIES
See **SPECIAL INTEREST**, page 232.

INVERGARRY

**GLENDALE VEGETARIAN
GUEST HOUSE**
See page 197.

INVERNESS

**DICKENS INTERNATIONAL
RESTAURANT**
77–79 Church Street, Inverness,
Inverness-Shire IV1 1ES
Tel 01463 713111 Fax 01463 713111
Restaurant
A la Carte Chinese French
Traditional British
*An international restaurant catering
for various tastes. Established in 1979
and situated in the centre of town
with easy access and parking on road.
Renee Mackintosh designed tables
and chairs. Good food and good service.*
♀ ⇥ 🍸 Cc ✕ ♿ (public
entrance/designated parking
area/dining area/bar)
Typical 3 course meal £5.95 lunch;
£9.10 dinner Seats 50–60 Open
12pm–2pm & 5.30pm–11pm

GLEN MHOR HOTEL & RESTAURANT
See page 197.

LAIRG

ACHINS BOOKSHOP & COFFEESHOP
Inverkirkaig, Lochinver, By Lairg,
Inverness-Shire IV27 4LS
Tel 01572 844262 Fax 01571 844262
Cafe
Snacks Drinks Fast Food
*Small coffeeshop attached to a book-
shop and craftshop in a very remote
location.*
Cc ⇥
Seats 28 Open 10am–5pm Mon–Fri
Easter–Oct

KIRKCUDBRIGHTSHIRE

Places to Stay

CASTLE DOUGLAS

ROSSAN, THE
Auchencairn, Castle Douglas,
Kirkcudbrightshire DG7 1QR
Tel 01556 640269
Website http://www.world-
traveler.com/scotland/rossan.html
B&B Guesthouse Private House
*An early Victorian ex-Manse on the
Eastern edge of Auchencairn in over
one acre of grounds. Situated
between the Screel Hills and the sea
overlooking Auchencairn Bay and
Heston Island. Special diets a forte
with vegetarian, vegan and gluten-
free meals always available. Owner is*

vegetarian and coeliac.

🐕 (dogs) 🚱

Typical tariff £14pp B&B Beds 3 family *(max 6 people)*

MORAYSHIRE

Places to Stay

FORRES

NEPTUNE HOUSE & VERDANT RESTAURANT
22/24 Tolbooth Street, Forres,
Morayshire IV36 0PH
Tel 01309 674387 Fax 01309 674387
B&B Restaurant Self Catering
Organic Snacks/Drinks
Neptune House and Verdant Restaurant comprise a 17th century modernised Scottish town house and licensed restaurant. Offers a fine selection of organic wines and monastic beers. Neptune Cottage sleeps 6 and is a completely self-contained self-catering cottage located next to Neptune House.
V 🐕 🏛 Cc ✗ ♿ (Designated parking area/one bedroom, bathroom & WC on same level/dining room/restaurant/bar/TV lounge)
Typical tariff single/double room £18.50/£32 Beds 5 Open all year
Typical 3 course meal £10 Seats 20
Open 9am–4pm Mon–Sat

Places to Eat

FORRES

NEPTUNE HOUSE & VERDANT RESTAURANT
See left.

PERTHSHIRE

Places to stay

PITLOCHRY

GLENRANNOCH HOUSE
Kinloch Rannoch, By Pitlochry,
Perthshire PH16 5QA
Tel 01882 632307
Guesthouse
Organic (where possible)
Situated at the eastern end of Loch Rannoch in Highland Perthshire. A relaxing haven with spectacular scenery and wildlife. Log fires, books, games, peace and quiet always available. Home baked breads a speciality. In season, meals are prepared based on own organic produce from the garden.
V 🐕 🏛 Cc 🚱
Typical tariff single/double room £20/£36 Beds 3
Typical 3 course meal £14 Seats 10
VS members' discount 5% *B&B*

Please mention the Vegan
Travel Guide **when contacting a listed business or advertiser**

ROSS-SHIRE

Places to Stay

ISLE OF RAASAY

RAASAY OUTDOOR CENTRE
See **SPECIAL INTEREST**, page 232.

KINLOCHEWE

ALLTAN DOMHAIN
2 Cromasaig, Kinlochewe, Ross-Shire
IV22 2PE
Tel 01445 760297
B&B
Beautifully located next to the Beinn Eighe National Nature Reserve, amidst stunning scenery. Superb area for walking, climbing, photography and wildlife. Accessible by public transport. Cycle store, map loan and drying facilities.
P ⁵⁄ₓ
Typical tariff single/double room
£16/£32 Beds 3 Open all year

KYLE OF LOCHALSH

CULAG
Carr Brae, Dornie, Kyle of Lochalsh,
Ross-Shire IV40 8HA
Tel 01599 555341
Website
http://dspace.dial.pipex.com/jneath/
bandb.htm
B&B
Modern bungalow set amongst native broadleaved woodland. Spectacular
views of mountains and sea lochs. Peaceful, secluded location only 9 miles from Kyle of Lochalsh. Excellent area for hillworkers, geologists and naturalists.
V 표 ᵇ⁄ₓ
Typical tariff double room £16pp
Beds 2

NIGG BY TAIN

NIGGFERRY HOTEL
Nigg by Tain, Ross-Shire
Tel 01862 851440
Hotel Restaurant
A la Carte Snacks/Drinks
Newly renovated (opening Easter 1998). Family-run business using local produce for vegetarian and vegan menu.
🐕 표 Cc ✕ 또 & (public entrance/designated parking area/one bedroom, bathroom & WC on same level/dining room/restaurant/bar/TV lounge)
Typical tariff single/double room
£25/£20.25pp Beds 10
Seats 40

ULLAPOOL

CEILIDH PLACE, THE
14 West Argyle Street, Ullapool, Ross-shire IV26 2TY
Tel 01854 612103 Fax 01854 612886
Email jean@ceilidh.demon.co.uk
Bunkhouse Cafe Hotel
Public House Restaurant
A la Carte Snacks/Drinks
Traditional British
The Ceilidh Place is deemed to be an

arts centre with bedrooms. As far as you can get in style from a chain hotel with an exhibition area, regular entertainment and bookshop. Relax with a book, a drink, great food and good company.

♀ ⋔ ⛉ Cc ✗ ⤙✕ (dining room) ♿ (public entrance/designated parking area/dining area/bar)

Typical tariff single/double room £55/£110 hotel; £14/£20 bunkhouse
Beds 13 hotel; 11 bunkhouse
Typical tariff 3 course meal £18 Seats 50+ Open 8am–9pm
VS members' discount 5%food

Places to Eat

ISLE OF RAASAY

RAASAY OUTDOOR CENTRE
See page 232.

NIGG BY TAIN

NIGGFERRY HOTEL
See page 200.

ULLAPOOL

CEILIDH PLACE, THE
See page 200.

ORKNEY ISLES

Places to Stay

EVIE

WOODWICK HOUSE
Evie, Orkney, Orkney Isles KW17 2PQ
Tel 01856 751330 Fax 01856 751383
B&B Guesthouse Restaurant
Traditional British
Overlooking the Island of Gairsay and set in its own grounds with lawns, bluebell woodland, a burn cascading down to the sea, private bay and wonderful views. One of the most sheltered parts of Orkney. Available for small conferences, retreats, workshops, concerts, lectures, etc. Candlelight dinners in a warm and peaceful environment.

P ⋔ ♀ ⛉ ⤙✕ (bedrooms & dining room) ♿ (public entrance/designated parking area/one bedroom, bathroom & WC on same level/dining room/restaurant/bar/TV lounge)

Typical tariff single/double room from £30/£22pp Beds 8
Open all year
Typical 3 course meal £16.50 Seats 20
Open 7.30pm onwards

Places to Eat

EVIE

WOODWICK HOUSE
See above.

SHETLAND ISLES

Places to Stay

YELL

BAYANNE HOUSE
Sellafirth, Yell, Shetland, Shetland
Isles ZE2 9DG
Tel 01957 744219 Fax 01957 744219
Email liz.gott@zetnet.co.uk
B&B
Organic
This 5 acre croft is ideally suited to the nature lover. Otter watching, walking and unspoilt solitude on offer. The house is situated on the beach, 1 mile from the ferry terminal to Unst and Fetlar. Designated an Environmentally Sensitive Area.
P 🏠 ✕ 🍽️
Typical tariff double room £20 Open all day
Typical 3 course meal £10 Seats 4
Open 7pm–9pm *(meals)*

STRATHCLYDE

Places to Stay

ISLE OF ARRAN

DENARD
Glencloy Road, Brodick, Isle of Arran,
Strathclyde KA27 8DA
Tel 01770 302475 Fax 01770 302475
B&B
A la Carte Snacks/Drinks

Friendly, helpful family-run house catering for vegetarians and vegans. Good sized rooms with coffee making, TV, etc. Good sized garden. Situated in the main village in a quiet area with easy access to walks and other activities. Both proprietors are interested in crafts.
V 🍽️
Typical tariff single/double room
£18/£18pp Beds 2 Open April
onwards

WESTERN ISLES

Places to Stay

ISLE OF BARRA

ISLE OF BARRA HOTEL
Tangasdale Beach, Isle of Barra,
Western Isles HS9 5XW
Tel 01871 810383 Fax 01871 810385
Email barrahotel@aol.com
Hotel Public House Restaurant
Snacks/Drinks Traditional British
A family-run modern hotel overlooking a beautiful wide sandy bay washed by the Atlantic ocean. The dining room faces west and enjoys spectacular sunsets over the sea. All rooms have hospitality trays and ensuite facilities. Sandy beach and rocky beach on site.
P 🐾 🍷 🏠 Cc 🍽️ (dining
room/lounge) ♿ (access via fire
doors/one bedroom, bathroom & WC
on same level/dining room/restaurant/bar/TV lounge)

Typical tariff single/double room
£56.50/£52.50 *(bed, breakfast &
dinner)* Beds 30 Open end Apr–
early Oct
Typical 3 course meal £16.50 Seats 72
Open restaurant 7pm–8.30pm; bar
meals 6pm–9pm
VS members' discount 5%

ISLE OF HARRIS

SORREL COTTAGE
2 Glen, Leverburgh (An T-ob), Isle of
Harris, Western Isles HS5 3TY
Tel 01859 520319
B&B
Chinese Italian/Mediterranean
Organic
*A comfortably converted croft house
situated in South Harris only 1¹/₂ miles
from North Uist and Harris Car Ferry
(Leverburgh to Otternish). A great
place for beaches, walking and bird
watching. Has been catering for vege-
tarians and vegans for the past 8
years. Evening meals available*
P ⚓ ⚒
Typical tariff single/double room
£20/£18pp Beds 3
Typical 3 course meal £10–£12

ISLE OF LEWIS

WILLOWS VEGETARIAN
GUEST HOUSE, THE
19 Tolstachaolais, Isle of Lewis,
Western Isles HS2 9DW
Tel 01851 621321
Guesthouse
Indian Italian/Mediterranean
Mexican Traditional British

*An old lochside crofthouse in beauti-
ful surroundings near Callanish stones.
A wonderful place to retreat and walk
with mountains, wildlife, sealife and
empty sandy beaches. Private living
and bathroom. Excellent cooking.
Vegans are nurtured and well under-
stood by vegetarian hosts. Warm,
friendly welcome. Vegetarian Society
Food & Drink Guild members. STB 2
crowns commended.*
V ⚒ ✗
Typical tariff single/double room
£20/£18pp Beds 1 Open all year
except Xmas & New Year
Typical 3 course meal £12 Seats 2–3

Places to Eat

ISLE OF BARRA

ISLE OF BARRA HOTEL
See page 202.

Northern Ireland

COUNTY ANTRIM

Places to Stay

BUSHMILLS

AHIMSA
243 Whitepark Road, Bushmills,
County Antrim BT57 8SP
Tel 012657 31383
Guesthouse
*Traditional cottage, tastefully mod-
ernised with its own organic garden.
Yoga, reflexology and meals for non-
residents available on request. Very
close to the Giants Causeway and suit-
able for walking, birdwatching, etc.*
V 🐕 🏠 🍴✕
Typical tariff double room £15 Beds 2
Open all year
Typical tariff 3 course meal £10 Seats
8 Open by arrangement

Places to Eat

BELFAST

GIGOLO'S RESTAURANT
23 Donegall Pass, Belfast, County
Antrim BT1
Tel 01232 246900
Restaurant
Italian Organic
*A typical traditional Italian restaurant.
All the food is freshly prepared and
caters for all tastes. Excellent atmos-
phere which is only surpassed by the
unique cuisine. Licensed.*
🍷 🏠 Cc ✕ 🍴✕ (areas) ♿ (public

entrance/designated parking
area/dining area/bar)
Typical 3 course meal £15 Seats 80
Open 5pm–11pm Mon–Sat
VS members' discount 15%

BUSHMILLS

AHIMSA
See left.

COUNTY DOWN
Places to Stay

BALLYNAHINCH

BUSHYMEAD COUNTRY HOUSE
86 Drumaness Road, Ballynahinch,
County Down BT24 8LT
Tel 01238 561171 Fax 01238 561171
B&B
*Award winning country home set in
the heart of Down. A base camp for
exploring County Down's many tourist
and historical attractions. All rooms
decorated with period-style furnishings, TV and hospitality tray. Guest
lounge, gardens, play area. Beside bus
stop. Vegetarian and vegan breakfasts
served with a few hours prior notice.*
P 🏠 Cc 🍴✕
Typical single/double room
£16–£18/£32–£36 Beds 8

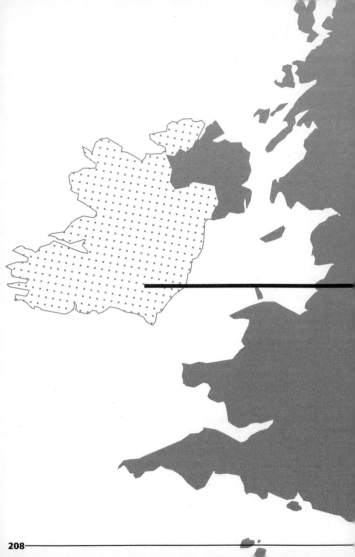

Southern
Ireland

COUNTY CAVAN

Places to Stay

BALLINAGH

ILSE KIEBLER BAVARIA HOUSE
Garrymore, Ballinagh, County Cavan
Tel 00 353 49 37452
B&B
Continental Macrobiotic Organic
A unique atmosphere with colourful gardens. Ideal place to relax. Discover historic and famous sites. Golf, swimming, boating and cycling all available. Superb food served with own organic vegetables. English/German spoken.
V 🐾 🎿 ⊯✖
Typical tariff single/double room
£20/£30 Beds 3 Open Apr–Oct

COUNTY CLARE

Places to Stay

LISDOONVARNA

BURREN HAVEN
St Brendan's Road, Lisdoonvarna, County Clare
Tel 00 353 65 74366
Website http://www.family-homes.ie
B&B
Traditional British/Irish
A family-run B&B central to the Burren area in the west of Ireland. A splendid area for touring. A magnificent choice of breakfast menu. Vegetarians, vegans and animals welcome. Non-vegetarians also welcome.
🐾 🎿 Cc ⊯✖ ♿ (public entrance/designated parking area/one bedroom, bathroom & WC on same level/dining room/TV lounge)
Typical tariff single/double room
£13/£13pp Beds 4 Open Apr–Oct
VS members' discount 5%

Places to Eat

LAHINCH

BARRTRA SEAFOOD RESTAURANT
Barrtra, Lahinch, County Clare
Tel 00 353 5 81280
Restaurant
A family-run business using organically grown vegetables when possible and fresh herbs from own garden. Vegetarian dishes always feature on the menu and a comprehensive wine list includes organic wines.
🎿 ✖ ⊯✖ ♿ (public entrance/dining area)
Seats 30 Open 12.30pm–2.30pm
Tues–Sat June–Aug; 6pm–10pm
Mon–Sat Feb–Oct; *other times by arrangement*

COUNTY CORK

Places to Stay

BANTRY

TRAWNAMADREE
Ballylickey, Bantry, County Cork
Tel 00 353 27 66146
Self Catering
Situated in a peaceful and beautifully wooded setting in West Cork. The accommodation is a single storey terrace. Each apartment is ensuite with private entrance and cooking facilities. Linen and towels are provided. Vegan wholefoods, homegrown organic vegetables and homebaked bread are available.
VEGAN 표 ㅎ (public entrance/designated parking area/one bedroom, bathroom & WC on same level/dining room)
Typical tariff small/family flat £95/£120 single/double bedsit £55/£75 Open all year *with prior notice out of season*

DUNMANWAY

SHIPLAKE MOUNTAIN HOSTEL
Shiplake, Dunmanway County Cork
Tel 00 353 23 45750
Fax 00 353 23 45750
Hostel
French Italian/Mediterranean Organic
A charming farmhouse nestling on the side of a mountain looking onto Nowen Hill and its beautiful surroundings. An independent holiday hostel accommodating young and old alike. Families and groups welcome. Offering a variety of delicious vegetarian and vegan meals. Bike hire available plus free pick up from Dunmanway.
V 표 ✕ ✖
Typical tariff single/double room £10/£15 or £6.50 *(dorm)* Beds 4
Open all year
Typical 3 course meal £7.50 Open 12pm–11pm; *meal advance booking compulsory for non-residents*
VS members' discount 10%

SKIBBEREEN

LISS ARD LAKE LODGE
Skibbereen, County Cork
Tel 00 353 28 40000
Fax 00 353 28 40001
Email Lissardlalohotel@tinet.ie
Hotel
Eurasian Macrobiotic Organic
Luxurious contemporary living of the healthiest kind. Dishes are concocted and flavours are revealed without any regard to meat or dairy products. This dazzling, thrilling, soul-satisfying food should set the template for Irish vegetarian and vegan cookery in the future. Complimentary welcome drink.
Cc ㅎ (public entrance/dining area)
Typical tariff single/double room £135/£180 Beds 10 Open 15 Jan–14 Jan
Typical 4 course meal £3 Seats 20
Open 7pm–9pm; *closed Tues*

TIMOLEAGUE

LETTERCOLLUM HOUSE
Timoleague, County Cork
Tel 00 353 23 46251
Fax 00 353 23 46270
Email conmc@iol.ie
Website http://www.clon.ie/
letterco/html
Guesthouse Restaurant
A la Carte French Organic
*Victorian manor house overlooking
Courtmacsherry Bay. Modern vibrant
cooking using organic produce from
own garden and the locality in an
essential French style with ethnic influ-
ences. All rooms are ensuite with
direct-dial telephones.*
P Cc ✕ ㅊ (public entrance/WC/din-
ing room/restaurant)
Typical tariff single/double room
£26/£40 Beds 9
Typical 3 course meal £20 Seats 40
Open 7.30pm–9.30pm & 1pm–
3pm Sun

Places to Eat

BALLYDEHOB

HUDSON'S WHOLEFOODS
Main Street, Ballydehob, County Cork
Tel 00 353 28 37211
Fax 00 353 28 37211
Email hudsons@indigo.ie
Take Away Wholefood Shop
Macrobiotic Organic Snacks/Drinks
*A wholefood shop selling a wide
range of organic grains, rice, bread
and vegetables. Frozen vegetarian
and vegan meals, environmentally*
*friendly and non-animal tested house-
hold cleaners, washing powders and
shampoos. Take away home baked
vegetarian and vegan pasties, snacks,
etc.*
V
Open 10am–6pm Mon–Sat; *closed
1.30pm–2.30pm Sept–May*

CLONALEILLY

**FIONNUELA'S LITTLE ITALIAN
RESTAURANT**
30 Ashe Street, Clonaleilly,
County Cork
Tel 00 353 23 343355
Restaurant
Italian/Mediterranean
*An intimate candlelit restaurant with
home cooked food. Nice atmosphere.
Two separate private dining rooms for
20 people.*
Cc ✕ ➹ ㅊ (public entrance/dining
area)
Typical 3 course meal £12.50 Seats 40
Open 5pm–9.30pm Mon–Sun; *all year
except 24–26 Dec*

CORK

CAFE PARADISO
16 Lancaster Quay, Western Road,
Cork, County Cork
Tel 00 353 21 277939
Restaurant
Italian Japanese Organic Spanish
*Booking in advance is essential. This is
not a wholefood restaurant – it uses
organic white flour and chocolate!
Customers are encouraged to try the
strong Italian roast coffee and explore*

the interesting wine list.
V Cc ✕ ♿ (public entrance/dining area)
Typical tariff 3 course meal £9 Seats 40 Open Tues–Sat 12.30pm–3pm & 6.30pm–10.30pm

EWE ART RETREAT, THE
See **SPECIAL INTEREST**, page 233

DUNMANWAY

SHIPLAKE MOUNTAIN HOSTEL
See page 211.

TIMOLEAGUE

LETTERCOLLUM HOUSE
see page 212.

COUNTY DUBLIN
Places to Eat

BLACKROCK

AYUMI-YA JAPANESE RESTAURANT
Newpark Centre, Newtownpark Avenue, Blackrock, County Dublin
Tel 00 353 1 283 1767
Fax 00 353 1 288 0478
Restaurant
A la Carte Japanese
Established in 1983, this was the first ever Japanese restaurant in Ireland. A traditional Japanese restaurant with a wide ranging menu, including a full selection for vegetarian and vegan customers. Menu items suitable for
vegans include tofu, tempura (without egg or wheat batter) and various noodle dishes.
Cc ✕ ㄨ ♿ (public entrance/designated parking area/dining area/bar)
Typical 3 course meal IR£15.20 Seats 60 Open 6pm–11pm Mon–Sat; 5.30pm–9.30pm Sun

DUBLIN

101 TALBOT RESTAURANT
101 Talbot Street, Dublin 1, County Dublin
Restaurant
Italian/Mediterranean
A busy licensed restaurant. Waiter service upstairs. Specialises in freshly cooked food with a large pasta menu. 35% vegetarian menu. Full bar.
Cc ㄨ (area)
Typical 3 course meal £9 lunch; £12 dinner Seats 80 Open 10am–11pm Tues–Sat

BLAZING SALADS
25c Powerscourt, Town House, Dublin 2, County Dublin
Tel 00 353 1 67 19552
Restaurant
Macrobiotic Organic
Specialising in wholefood/vegetarian cooking, this restaurant has a good range of main meals, soups and desserts which are sugar, yeast, dairy and wheat free. Everything is prepared with the best ingredients on the premises.
V ㄨ (designated area)
Typical tariff for 3 course meal £7.25 Seats 45 Open 9am–6pm Mon–Sat

OLD DUBLIN RESTAURANT
90–91 Francis Street, Dublin 8,
County Dublin
Tel 00 353 45 42028
Fax 00 353 45 41406
Restaurant
Russian Scandinavian
*Located in the heart of mediaeval
Dublin. The chef, Eamonn Walsh, uses
only the finest fresh ingredients. The
restaurant also has two private dining
rooms available.*
Cc ✗ ✖ ⅄ (public entrance/dining
area/bar)
Typical 3 course meal £23.60 Seats 60
Open 12.30pm–2.15pm Mon–Fri;
6pm–11pm Mon–Sat; *closed Sun &
Bank Hols*

PEACOCK ALLEY
47 South William Street, Dublin 2,
County Dublin
Tel 00 353 1 677 0708
Fax 00 353 1 671 8854
Restaurant
Italian/Mediterranean New World
*One of Dublin's finest restaurants,
owned by chef Conrad Gallagher who
creates unique Mediterranean and
New World style food.*
P Cc
Typical 3 course meal £25.30 Seats 75
Open Mon–Sun 12pm–2.30pm &
6pm–11.30pm

RAJDOOT TANDOORI
26–28 Clarendon Street, Westbury
Centre, Dublin 2, County Dublin
Tel 00 353 679 4280
Fax 00 353 679 4274
Restaurant

Indian
*Award winning North Indian gourmet
cuisine with exotic ambience.
Specialises in tandoori (charcoal clay
oven) cooking and subtle North
Indian curries. Branches in Bristol,
Birmingham, Manchester and
Fuengirole. Happy hour from Monday
to Thursday 6.30pm–7.30pm where
customers can receive a 25% discount.*
Cc ✖
Typical 3 course meal £15 Seats 92
Open Mon–Sat 12pm–2.30pm &
6.30pm–11.30pm

TOSCA RESTAURANT
20 Suffolk Street, Dublin 2,
County Dublin
Tel 00 353 1 679 6744
Fax 00 353 1 679 6744
Restaurant
Italian/Mediterranean
Southern European
*Management is very willing to discuss
the dietary needs of customers and
the chefs are very willing to adapt
dishes to suit. A large proportion of
the menu is vegetarian and a signifi-
cant number of dishes suitable for
vegans, which are clearly marked.*
Cc ✗ ✖ ⅄ (public entrance/dining
area/not toilets)
Typical 3 course meal £15 Seats 80
Open Mon–Sun 12pm–3.30pm,
3.30pm–5.30pm & 5.30pm–12am

WELL FED CAFE
6 Crow Street, Dublin, County Dublin
Tel 00 353 1 677 2234
Restaurant Self Service
Macrobiotic Organic

A relaxed, laid back atmosphere in a Covent Garden style development. 2 out of 5 of the dishes on the menu each day are vegan. The soup is always vegan and there is a vegan dessert available. Soya milk is provided and vegan margarine is always used. Not licensed and no corkage fees.
V ✗ ✻ (area) ♿ (public entrance/dining area)
Typical 3 course meal £5 Seats 70
Open 12pm–9pm Mon–Sat

WINDING STAIR BOOKSHOP & CAFE, THE
40 Lower Ormond Quay, Dublin 1, County Dublin
Tel 00 353 1 873 3292
Fax 00 353 1 873 3292
Bookshop Cafe Sandwich Bar
Snacks/Drinks
A bookshop stocking over 30 000 new, secondhand and antiquarian titles. Located on 4 floors of a large building overlooking the Ha'penny Bridge on the River Liffey.
Cc
Seats 50 Open 10am–6.30pm Mon–Sat; open Sun in season

STILLORGAN

CHINA-SICHUAN RESTAURANT
4 Lower Kilmacud Road, Stilorgan, County Dublin
Tel 00 353 28 84817
Fax 00 353 28 80882
Restaurant
Chinese Sichuan
Authenticity is the key word at this modest Chinese restaurant situated 5 miles south of Dublin City centre. Established in 1986 this is the first Sichuan restaurant in Ireland and the UK. Oriental Restaurant of the Year in Ireland in 1996.
Typical 3 course meal £18 Seats 50
Open 12.30pm–2.30pm Mon–Fri; 1pm–2.30pm Sun & Bank Hols; 6pm–11pm Mon–Sun & Bank Hols; closed Good Fri & Xmas

COUNTY GALWAY

Places to Stay

INCHABY GORT

INSE BUI HOUSE
Lough Cutra Drive, Inchabey Gort, County Galway
Tel 00 353 91 632509
B&B
A delightful renovated farmhouse in the foothills of the Sliabh Aughty Mountains. Organic flower and vegetable gardens. Breathtaking views of Burren region, lakes, woodlands and castles. Ensuite rooms with TV, tea and coffee making facilities.
P 㤠
Typical tariff double room £16.20pp sharing Beds 3

LOUGHREA

CARTRON HOUSE FARM
Ballinakill, Kylebrack, Loughrea,
County Galway
Tel 00 353 509 45211
Guesthouse Self Catering
Indian Italian/Mediterranean
Macrobiotic Organic
Traditional British/Irish
*A family-owned and run guesthouse
in rural Ireland offering home-grown
food in a friendly atmosphere. Central
for touring the West and 35 miles
from Galway City. Guests can relax
around the house or visit local pubs
with live Irish music.*
🐓 🏊 ✕ ⛄ (public entrance/desig-
nated parking area/one bedroom,
bathroom & WC on same level/dining
room/TV lounge)
Typical tariff single/double room
£13/£26 Beds 7 Open all year
Typical 3 course meal £10 Seats 16

Places to Eat

MOYCULLEN

DRIMONG HOUSE
Moycullen, County Galway
Tel 00 353 91 555115
Fax 00 353 91 555836
Restaurant
*One of Ireland's foremost restaurants.
Set in lakeland Moycullen only 15 min-
utes from Galway. Owner-run estab-
lishment offering interesting good
value fare.*
P Cc ✕

Typical 3 course meal £20 Seats 50
Open 6.30pm–10.30pm Mon–Sun

COUNTY KERRY

Places to Stay

CASTLEMAINE

PHOENIX, THE
Shanahill East, nr Boolteens,
Castlemaine, County Kerry
Tel 00 353 66 66284
**Cafe Camping Hostel Restaurant
Self Catering**
Indian Italian/Mediterranean
Lebanese Macrobiotic Organic
*Resting under the Slieve Mish
Mountains on the Dingle Peninsula.
Family-run with a relaxed atmosphere.
Renowned for its cuisine — including
vegan lunches and dinners, soya milk
cappuccino and soya shakes. Lounge
with open log fire, library, extensive
gardens, camping facilities and studio
for workshops. Free pick up from
Castlemaine.*
V 🐓 (not bedrooms) 🏊 ✕ ⟡ ⛄
(restaurant)
Typical tariff £8 hostel; £11.50pp dou-
ble room Beds 5 Open Apr–Nov;
Nov–Mar — bookings
Typical 3 course meal £16 or £11.50
for residents Seats 12–16

DINGLE

MOUNTAIN ROAD B&B, THE
Deerpark, Lispole, Dingle,

County Kerry
Tel 00 353 66 51149
Website http://www.holistic.ie/
veguide
B&B
*Situated on the scenic 'Dingle Way'
walking route. All rooms ensuite.
Though quiet and secluded, it is close
to shops, a Post Office and other
amenities. The proprietor is a well
known musician and can point people
in the direction of the best traditional
Irish music sessions in Dingle and
beyond.*
🐟
Typical tariff single/double room
£20/£15pp Beds 4

Places to Eat

CASTLEMAINE

PHOENIX, THE
See page 216.

DINGLE

SMEARE DUBHA
The Wood, Dingle, County Kerry
Tel 00 353 66 51465
Restaurant
*Established in 1992 this is a friendly
family-run restaurant in a small village
overlooking Dingle Bay. Friendly
atmosphere. Easy to find. Home made
food available with 1–2 vegan options
for each course. Prefers notice when
catering for vegans to ensure choice.
Candlelit meals using local pottery.*
V ✗ ➽ ♿ (public entrance/desig-
nated parking area/dining area)
Typical 3 course meal £13 Seats 16
Open 6pm–10pm Mon–Sun & *Bank
Hols in summer*

KILLARNEY

A TASTE OF EDEN
7 Bridewell Lane, New Street,
Killarney, County Kerry
Tel 00 353 64 33083
Restaurant Wine Bar
Indian International
Italian/Mediterranean Mexican
*Situated opposite Dunnes Stores
down one of Killarney's most pic-
turesque lane ways. Utterly scrump-
tious food, home made wines, good
music and enchanting atmosphere.
Specialises in international cuisine
using only the finest ingredients.
Menu changes constantly. Banqueting
evenings .*
V Cc ✗ ➽ ♿ (public entrance/desig-
nated parking area/bar)
Typical 3 course meal £13 Seats 22
Open 12.30pm–3.30pm Wed–Fri;
6.30pm–10pm Tues–Sun

TRALEE

BRATS
18 Milk Market Lane, Tralee,
County Kerry
Restaurant
Macrobiotic Organic
V ➽ ♿ (public entrance/dining area)
Open 12.30pm–3pm Mon–Sat

ROOTS VEGETARIAN CAFE
76 Boherbue, Tralee, County Kerry

Tel 00 353 66 22665
Cafe Restaurant
Italian/Mediterranean Organic
Snacks/Drinks Traditional British
*Situated on the right hand side as you
approach the town centre of Tralee. A
small, very friendly restaurant with
good wholesome food, cooked freshly
on the premises every day. As far as
possible organic locally-grown vegetables are used.*
v ✗
Typical 3 course meal £7.20 Seats 17
Open 11am–3.30pm Mon–Sat

COUNTY LIMERICK
Places to Stay

KILMALLOCK

CUSSEN'S COTTAGE
Ballygrennan, Bulgaden, Kilmallock,
County Limerick
Tel 00 353 63 98926
Guesthouse
Chinese Indian
Italian/Mediterranean Organic
Macrobiotic
*Converted labourer's cottage.
Extensive organic garden, excellent
vegetarian and vegan cooking. A
good base for seeing the south west
of Ireland. A day's travelling to Mizen
in the south or Galway in the north.
Mountain walking, golf and bike hire
available.*
V 🐓 🎋 ➳
Typical tariff single/double room

£15/£12pp Beds 3 Open all year
Typical 3 course meal £8 *(incl tea/coffee)* Seats 10 Open all year by
arrangement

COUNTY MAYO
Places to Eat

WESTPORT

QUAY COTTAGE
The Harbour, Westport, County Mayo
Tel 00 353 98 26412 Fax 00 353 98
28120
Restaurant
A la Carte Organic
Delightful harbourside cottage restaurant with a nautical theme throughout.
Cc ✗ ➳
Typical 3 course meal £15.20 Seats 80
Open all year from 6pm Mon–Sun;
closed Xmas

COUNTY SLIGO
Places to Stay

COLLOONEY

**GLEBE HOUSE RESTAURANT &
ACCOMMODATION**
Collooney, County Sligo
Tel 00 353 71 67787
Fax 00 353 71 67787
Email glebehse@iol.ie

Guesthouse Restaurant
Modern Irish
*A restored Georgian Country House
set in 7 acres of its own grounds.
Fruit, vegetables and herbs from own
walled garden. Famous for its individually prepared dishes, comfortable
surroundings and friendly service. All
cooking is done on the premises
under the award winning chef Brad
Torrades.*
🏛 Cc ♿ (public entrance/designated
parking area/one bedroom, bathroom & WC on same level/dining
room/restaurant/bar)
Typical tariff single/double room
£25.29/£20.25pp Beds 4 Open
Mon–Sun summer; *winter — telephone for details*
Typical 3 course meal £17 Seats 45
Open *as above*
VS members' discount 10% *request
on booking*

GRANGE

KARUNA FLAME
See **SPECIAL INTEREST**, page 233.

TONAPHUBBLE

SARU B&B
Tonaphubble, Sligo, County Sligo
Tel 00 353 71 70518
B&B
Macrobiotic Organic
*Relax in comfortable artistic surround-
ings and be pampered. B&B situated
only 2k south of Sligo town and of
the scenic route to Lough Gill and
Holy Well. Maureen is a qualified*
*wholefood cookery demonstrator
who specialises in catering for guests
with special dietary requirements.*
V Cc ⚑
Typical tariff single/double room
£23/£18pp Beds 3

Places to Eat

SLIGO

**WINDING STAIR BOOKSHOP &
CAFE, THE**
Hyde Bridge House, Sligo,
County Sligo
Tel 00 353 71 41244
Fax 00 353 71 41299
Bookshop Cafe Sandwich Bar
Snacks/Drinks
*A bookshop stocking over 10 000
new, secondhand and antiquarian
titles. Located on 2 floors.*
Cc
Seats 30 Open 10am–6.30pm
Mon–Sat; *Sun in season*

COUNTY TIPPERARY

Places to Stay

CASHEL

CASHEL PALACE HOTEL
Main Street, Cashel County Tipperary
Tel 00 353 62 62707
Fax 00 353 62 61521
Email reception@cashel-palace.ie
Website http://www.cashel-palace.ie
Hotel Restaurant

A la Carte
Situated in an historic building next to the Rock of Cashel.
P ⚥ 菜 Cc
Typical tariff single/double room £105/£155 Beds 13 Open all year
Restaurant seats 60

COUNTY WATERFORD

Places to Eat

CHEEKPOINT

McALPINE SUIR INN
Cheekpoint, County Waterford
Tel 00 353 51 382224
Email cheekpoint@tinet.ie
Restaurant
A 17th century riverside inn only 7 miles from Waterford. Two or three vegan dishes on menu.
Cc ✕ ⥢ (area) 🔗 (public entrance/designated parking area/dining area/bar)
Typical 3 course meal £12 Seats 35
Open Tues–Sat 6pm–9.45pm & 6pm–11.30pm; also Mon Jul–Aug

WATERFORD

HARICOTS WHOLEFOOD RESTAURANT
11 U'Connell Street, Waterford, County Waterford
Tel 00 353 51 841299
Bistro Cafe Restaurant Take Away Wine Bar
A la Carte French Indian

Italian/Mediterranean Macrobiotic Mexican Organic Snacks/Drinks Thai Wholefoods
An efficient, reasonably-priced and friendly service. A healthy home baked menu using no artificial additives, colourings or preservatives. Serving starters, soups, main courses, beverages and wholemeal snacks throughout the day.
✕
Typical 3 course meal £7.50 Seats 34
Open 9am–8pm *(last orders)* Mon–Fri; 9am–5.45pm *(last orders)* Sat
VS members' discount 10%

COUNTY WICKLOW

Places to Stay

DONARD

CHRYSALIS
See **SPECIAL INTEREST**, page 233.

GLENDALOUGH

GLENDALOUGH RIVER HOUSE
Glendalough, County Wicklow
Tel 00 353 404 45577
B&B
A two storey stone built house located in the Garden of Ireland and on the Wicklow Way, which is ideal for hill walking. Spacious ensuite rooms with beautiful views.
菜 Cc ⥢
Typical tariff double room from £40
Beds 4 Open Easter weekend–31 Oct

RATHDRUM

HOLLY FARM
Rathdrum, County Wicklow
Tel 00 353 404 46912
Fax 00 353 404 46912
B&B
Mexican Organic Traditional British
Superbly located overlooking the Wicklow Mountains and rolling countryside. Breathtaking views. Secluded, picturesque, peaceful and relaxing. Wonderful food. Glendalough, Avondale, Avoca (Ballykissangel) and Clara Lara nearby. Painting holidays/weekends available.
☖ Cc ⤳✕
Typical tariff single/double room £20/£17.50pp Beds 4 Open all year

OLD FARMHOUSE, THE
Greenane, nr Rathdrum,
County Wicklow
Tel 00 353 404 46676
Fax 00 353 404 46676
B&B
Macrobiotic Organic
Traditional British
Set amongst the beautiful mountainous scenery of County Wicklow. Large organic fruit, vegetable and herb gardens provide fresh produce for homemade 'farmhouse' cuisine. Peaceful and secluded. Groups and families welcome. Loveable resident donkey.
☖ Cc ✕ ⤳✕
Typical tariff single/double room £16/£15pp Beds 10 Open Feb–Nov
Typical 3 course meal £14 Seats 16
Open *bookings only*

Places to Eat

BRAY

ESCAPE VEGETARIAN RESTAURANT
1 Albert Avenue, Seafront, Bray,
County Wicklow
Tel 00 353 28 66755
Email jjackson@indigo.ie
Bistro Cafe Coffee House Patisserie Restaurant
Snacks/Drinks Take Away
One of the main features of this restaurant is the menu which changes daily. All main dishes are the same price. Bring your own wine and beer. Corkage 75p per person. Doubles as an art gallery and gift shop.
V ☖ Cc ⤳✕
Typical 3 course meal £11.45 Seats 60
Open 10am–11.30pm Mon–Sun

Channel
Islands

GUERNSEY
Places to Stay

ST PETER PORT

**OLD GOVERNMENT HOUSE
HOTEL, THE**
PO Box 47, Anne's Place, St Peter
Port, Guernsey GU1 4AZ
Tel 01481 724921 Fax 01481 724429
Email ogh@guernsey.net
Hotel
A la Carte Table d'Hote
Italian/Mediterranean Snacks/Drinks
Traditional British
*Centrally located in the heart of St
Peter Port. The ideal hotel for a won-
derful holiday, catering for a large
choice of menu. Every menu has a veg-
etarian option and the chefs are more
than happy to cater for most require-
ments.*
P 🐕 (small dogs) 🏧 ♀ Cc ✕ 🍽✕
Typical tariff single/double room
£70/£105 Beds 68 Open all year
Typical 3 course meal £15 Seats 180
Open 12pm–2.30pm &
6.30pm–9.15pm

Save animals from the carving knife

Viva! the campaigning vegetarian and vegan charity, is determined to stop the mindless slaughter of millions of farm animals. We launch regular, hard-hitting campaigns and have a huge commitment to youth education. *Viva!* is sowing the seeds of a more compassionate tomorrow.

- *Viva!* offers a wealth of information on going, being and staying vegan including:

- *Viva! Guides*, written by experts and celebrities on all aspects of a vegan diet from easy nutrition and delicious recipes to animal rights and practical tips.

- *Viva! Books for Life*, featuring 100 titles from bringing up children to bringing down the meat industry.

- *Viva! Catalogue*, with vegan wines, hand-made chocs, T-shirts, cards, pens, mugs and much more.

- *Viva!* books – *The Silent Ark* (for adults) and *The Livewire Guide to Going, Being & Staying Veggie* (for teenagers). Written by *Viva!*'s director and covering all the issues – everything you need to argue your beliefs with confidence and attitude!

Add your voice to ours and join the fight for life.

Please send your name and address for a free pack to:

Viva! **(Dept. AFS),
12 Queen Square,
Brighton BN1 3FD
Tel: 01273 777688**

Viva!

Special
Interest

ENGLAND

BERKSHIRE

LIONEL BRADFORD TENNIS & SWIMMING ACADEMY
Thicket Meadows North, Newlands Drive, Maidenhead, Berkshire SL6 4LL
Tel 01628 629744
Guesthouse
At the rear of the property is a full size international tennis court and tennis coaching is available from the owners who are LTA coaches. Tennis memorabilia and extensive library with books on sport and health is on show. Tourists welcome.
V 🐾
Typical tariff single/double room £25/£40 Open all year
VS members' discount 10%

CUMBRIA

FERNHILL VEGETARIAN COUNTRY HOUSE
Witherslack, nr Grange Over Sands, Cumbria LA11 6RX
Tel 015395 52237 Fax 015395 52237
Email fernhillv@aol.com
B&B Country House Private House
Organic
A Victorian house with a warm, luxurious and informal atmosphere. Open fires in the sitting room and dining room. Own organic produce used for meals. Dinner menu discussed with guests each day. Retreats organised with range of complementary therapies, wonderful food and guided walks.
V 🐾 (well behaved dogs) 🏊 🚭
Typical tariff single/double room £24/£46.52 Beds 3 Open all year
Typical 3 course meal £16 Seats 10
(occasionally non-residents)
VS members' discount 5% *2 nights;*
10% *3 nights+*

DORSET

KINGCOMBE CENTRE, THE
Lower Kingcombe, Toller Porcorum, Dorchester, Dorset DT2 0EQ
Tel 01300 320684
Residential Study Centre
French Organic Traditional British
A small residential study centre in West Dorset surrounded by 500 acres of superb unspoilt nature reserve. Offering a wide range of courses for adults and children in natural history, conservation and the arts. Non-residents are welcome to join in all activities and meals except breakfast.
P 🐾 (negotiable) 🍸 🏊 ✕ 🚭
(indoors) ♿ (public entrance/designated parking area/one bedroom, bathroom & WC on same level/dining room)
Typical tariff single/double room £16/£30 Beds 11 Open all year
Typical 3 course meal £10 Seats 30
Open evening meals 7.30pm

MONKTON WYLD SCHOOL
Monkton Wyld Court, Charmouth, Bridport, Dorset DT6 6DQ
Tel 01299 560342 Fax 01297 560395
Email monktonwyldcourt@btinternet.com

Website
http://www.btinternet.com/~monkton/
Holistic Education Centre
Organic
Run by a resident community of around 20 adults and children. All or part of the centre can be hired for groups. Runs a programme of courses and workshops. Situated in a large stone-built rectory and out-buildings with 11 acres of grounds in a secluded valley.
V 本 ♨✖
Typical tariff £30pp Beds 35
Open all year

KENT

ROYDON HALL
Roydon, off Seven Mile Lane,
East Peckham, nr Tonbridge, Kent
TN12 5NH
Tel 01622 812121 Fax 01622 813959
**B&B Centre for Transcendental Meditation Guesthouse Private House
Restaurant Self Catering**
Ayur Vedic Organic Snacks/Drinks
A 16th century Tudor manor house with guesthouse facilities available for the general public throughout the year. Meals available on request. The building is also used to teach courses on Transcendental Meditation and associated self development programmes.
V 本 Cc ✖ ♨✖ ઠ (public entrance/bathroom & WC on same level/dining room/restaurant)
Typical tariff single/double room £21.46/£40.55 Beds 25 Open all year

Typical 3 course meal £6 Seats 40
Open 7am–10pm

SOMERSET

SHAMBHALA HEALING CENTRE
Coursing Batch, Glastonbury, Somerset BA6 8BH
Tel 01458 831797 Fax 01458 834751
Email isisandargon@shambhala.co.uk
Website
http://www.shambhala.co.uk/shambhala/
**Centre for Spiritual Growth
& Healing Guesthouse**
Organic Snacks/Drinks
A peaceful place to unwind and relax. Beautiful rooms, personal attention and opportunities for spiritual growth and healing. Situated on a sacred site on the slopes of the Tor with fabulous views of the Vale of Avalon. Sauna, jacuzzi, massage, channelling and healing available.
V 本 Cc ✖ ♨✖
Typical tariff single/double room £27.50/£30 Beds 5 Open all year
Typical 3 course meal £9.50 Seats 12
Open by arrangement
VS members' discount 5%

SURREY

CLARIDGE HOUSE
Dormans Road, Lingfield, Surrey
RH7 6QH
Tel 01342 832150
Retreat Centre
A Quaker centre owned by the Friends Fellowship of Healing. Standing in 2 acres of gardens, the house

house contains two lounges and a Quiet Room. Claridge House is available to anyone seeking healing, rest, renewal or recreation for a few days or a few weeks. Courses and workshops available.

V ♦ ♿ (public entrance/designated parking area/one bedroom, bathroom & WC on same level/dining room/lounge)
Typical tariff single/double room £38/£34pp Beds 12 Open all year

TEKELS PARK GUEST HOUSE
Tekels Park, Camberley, Surrey
GU15 2LF
Tel 01276 23159
B&B Centre for Spiritual Courses
Guesthouse

Set in 50 acres on a private estate and including meadow and woodland. A perfect setting for a relaxing break. Dealing mainly in conferences of a spiritual nature. Individuals are also welcome for accommodation or meals.
V ♨ Cc ♦
Typical tariff single/double room
£25.50/£45 Beds 24
Typical 3 course meal £6.50 Seats 50
Open *advance bookings*
VS members' discount 10% *accommodation*

Claridge House

Centre for Healing, Rest & Renewal

Dormansland, Lingfield, Surrey RH7 6QH
Telephone 01342 832150
Wardens: John and Rosalind Smith

Managed by Friends Fellowship of Healing, Claridge House is situated in a peaceful south-east corner of Surrey, easily reached by train from London. Set in beautiful gardens and offering a relaxing and tranquil atmosphere.

Guests are welcome throughout the year on our special mid-week breaks at very reasonable prices. Full-board vegan/vegetarian accommodation.

We also have an exceptionally wide range of courses based on health and healing themes, all led by qualified instructors. For a full list of events please request our Courses leaflet from our Wardens.

We look forward to hearing from you

Registered charity no 228102

WALES

DYFED

BARN HOUSE, THE
Llanon, Aberystwyth, Ceredigion,
Dyfed SY23 5LZ
Tel 01974 202581
**Aromatherapy & Reflexology Centre
B&B**
Aromatherapy and reflexology available in an idyllic converted barn situated in one acre of private woodland and beautiful gardens. Offering lovely views of Cardigan Bay. Just 50 yards off the A487 main coastal road. 4 miles from Aberaeron and 12 miles from Aberystwyth. Proprietor is a fully qualified massage practitioner.
P 🐾 🏠 🍽️ ♿ (public entrance/designated parking area/one bedroom, bathroom & WC on same level/dining room/TV lounge)
Typical tariff single/double room
£18/£36 Beds 4 Open all year

HILLSCAPE WALKING HOLIDAYS
Blaen y Ddol, Pontrhydygroes, Ystrad
Meurig, Ceredigion, Dyfed SY25 6DS
Tel 01974 282640
Email hills@globalnet.co.uk
Website http://www.users/global-net.co.uk/~hills
Adventure Guesthouse
A family-run business catering exclusively for walkers with 40 self-guided routes, many starting straight from the guesthouse. Walks range from 5–18 miles and each has an accurate route description and an OS map. All meals are home cooked and often home grown with a wholefood bias.
P 🍽️
Typical tariff single/double room
£32/£32pp Beds 4 Open Mar–Nov

PEMBROKESHIRE

OLD COURT HOUSE VEGETARIAN GUEST HOUSE, THE
Trefin, nr Haverfordwest,
Pembrokeshire SA62 5AX
Tel 01348 837095
Adventure Guesthouse
A cosy cottage just 5 minutes walk from the Pembrokeshire coastal path. Offers a warm welcome, ensuite accommodation, an open fire and delicious vegetarian/vegan food freshly prepared by Lynne, a Cordon Vert chef. Walking, climbing and cycling holidays available.
V 🍽️
Typical tariff single/double room
£18.50/£18.50pp Beds 3 Open
Jan–Dec
VS members' discount 5% *not school hols*

POWYS

BICYCLE BEANO
Erwood, Builth Wells, Powys LD2 3PQ
Tel 01982 560471
Email bicycle@beano.kc3Ltd.co.uk
Website
http://www.kc3.co.uk/beano
Cycling Holidays
Cycling holidays in Wales and Welsh Borders. Sociable, non-macho cycling

for 10–30 people. Weeks and weekends with venues varies from camping to a 3-Crown hotel, a Georgian watermill, Victorian Country House or an ex-stately home. Detailed routes with short-cuts and longer detours plus mechanic/guides available.

V 🏠 ♨ ♿ (public entrance/one bedroom, bathroom & WC on same level/dining room/lounge at West Coast venue)
Typical week £260–£340 Open May–Sep
VEGAN 🐕 🏠

HEAD FOR THE HILLS
Garth, Builth, Powys LD4 4AT
Tel 01591 620388
Adventure
Walking trips through exceptional landscapes in England and Wales. Crew travel ahead with luggage and an ingenious camp which is erected in a wild place. Celebrated cuisine is prepared while the party is guided on a magical route. Relaxed pace, personal tents and an emphasis on attuning to the rhythm of nature.
V
Typical tariff £36 per day *(up to 12 people with individual tents)*

SCOTLAND

INVERNESS-SHIRE

WHITEWAVE ACTIVITIES
19 Linicro, Kilmuir, Isle of Skye, Inverness-Shire IV51 9YN
Tel 01470 542414
Adventure B&B Cafe
A la Carte Snacks/Drinks
More than just an outdoor centre — a cross between an outdoor centre, an inn, a ceilidh place and a family home. A small establishment catering for all and will happily cater for vegans. Bike hire, kites, kayaking, windsurfing, music, walking and exploring available.
🐕 ♀ 🏠 ♨ ♿ (public entrance/designated parking area/one bedroom, bathroom & WC on same level/dining room/restaurant/bar)
Typical tariff single/double room £16/£16pp Beds 4 Open all year
Typical 3 course meal £12 Seats 15

ROSS-SHIRE

RAASAY OUTDOOR CENTRE
Raasay House, Isle of Raasay, by Kyle, Ross-shire IV40 8PB
Tel 01478 660266 Fax 01478 660200
Adventure Cafe Camping
Outdoor Centre Restaurant
French Indian Italian/Mediterranean
Mexican Spanish Thai
Traditional British
Based in a 250-year-old Georgian mansion and set in its own grounds. Offers families, individuals, groups and unaccompanied children accommodation, holidays and specialist courses with qualified instruction. Windsurfing, sailing, kayaking, rock climing, abseiling, walking and mountain biking.
🐕 ♀ 🏠 Cc ✗ ♿ (public entrance/restaurant/bar)

Typical tariff single/double room
£28/£28pp Beds 11 Open Mar–Oct
Typical 3 course meal £17.30 Seats 16
Open 10am–11pm Mar–Oct
VS members' discount 5%

SOUTHERN IRELAND

COUNTY CORK

EWE ART RETREAT, THE
Goleen, West Cork, County Cork
Tel 00 353 28 35492
Fax 00 353 28 35492
Activity Retreat Self Catering
French Italian/Mediterranean Irish
*Set amongst green hills and flowering
gardens with wonderful Atlantic
views. A creative centre offering pottery and other courses to all from
beginner to professional. Colourful
galleries, sculpture gardens and terraced waterfalls. Ideal place to
unwind. A tranquil homely atmosphere.*
🏛 ❧
Typical tariff £180/week 2 self catering cottages & 2 lodges Open Easter–end Oct

COUNTY SLIGO

KARUNA FLAME
Celtic Farm, Derry Road, Grange,
County Sligo
Tel 00 353 71 63337
**B&B Holistic Health Centre Hostel
Organic Farm Self Catering**
Indian Organic Traditional British

*Nestled between Ben Bulben Moun-
tain and the Atlantic Ocean. An ideal
base for relaxation and retreats as
well as historical sightseeing. Available
for groups and individuals. Massage,
aromatherapy, reflexology, quantum
colour therapy, steam therapy and
seaweed bath also available.*
P 🏛 ✗
Typical tariff from £6–£9pp Beds 6
Open all year

COUNTY WICKLOW

CHRYSALIS
Donard, County Wicklow
Tel 00 353 45 404713
Website
http://www.holistic.ie/chrysalis
Holistic Centre Self Catering
*Specialises in residential courses cover-
ing many aspects of personal growth
and spirituality. Offers vegan and veg-
etarian catering for weekend courses
and midweek self-catering in wooden
Scandinavian chalet. Sauna available.*
V Cc ❧
Typical tariff single room £15 or self-
catering £15/day Beds 9

ANNUAL EVENTS

**BRITISH MACROBIOTIC
SUMMER CAMP**
191 Hartington Road, Brighton, East
Sussex BN2 3PA
Tel 01273 279439 Fax 01273 279439
Macrobiotic
Vegan

An impressive mix of educational workshops and activities. The Camp is usually held in England (1996–98: Sussex). Accommodation typically consists of a choice between private rooms, camping and dormitory-style. (1998) Prices start at £99 for adults to £69 for children for 5 days.

VEGAN CAMP
30 Dinsdale Avenue, King's Estate, Wallsend, Tyneside NE28 9JD
Tel 0191 262 8844
Typically a 2-week (summer) camp for vegans of all ages, held in England, Scotland or Wales. Activities (optional) may include: walking, sing-songs, fun sports, trips and communal meals.
VEGAN

VEGAN SUMMER GATHERING
10B Windsor Square, Exmouth, Devon EX8 1JU
An opportunity to meet other vegans, share and develop ideas, and make contacts and friends. This week-long event generally takes place in England. Accommodation is typically self-catering.
VEGAN

MULTIPLE OUTLET

PIZZA PIAZZA
30 Barwell Business Park, Leatherhead Road, Chessington, Surrey KT9 2NY
Tel 0181 397 3330
Fax 0181 974 1298
Restaurants

Italian/Mediterranean
Pizza bases are suitable for vegans and can be topped to customer requirements.
🕱
Typical 3 course meal £10 Seats approx 100

TOUR OPERATORS

HF HOLIDAYS
Imperial House, Edgware Road, London NW9 5AL
Tel 0181 905 9558
Fax 0181 205 0506
Tour Operator
Traditional British
Guided walking and special interest holidays at 19 locations throughout Britain. Stay at country house hotels with full board accommodation. Caters for vegetarians, vegans and other special diets. Locations include Loch Leven, Pitlochry, Arran, Alnmouth, Derwentwater, Conistonwater, Sedbergh, Whitby, Malhamdale, Conwy, Dovedale, Brecon, Bourton on the Water, Selworthy, St Ives, Lyme Regis, Thurlestone Sands, Freshwater Bay and Abingworth.
♀ 🕱 Cc ♿
Typical tariff single/double room £32/£32pp Open Feb–Nov & Xmas/New Year

VEGIVENTURES
Castle Cottage, Castle Acre, Norfolk PE32 2AJ

Tel 01760 755888 Fax 01760 755888
Tour Operator
*VegiVentures operates holidays in
Britain and abroad with great vegetarian and vegan food. Founded in 1989
by Swiss-trained chef Nigel Walker, it
organises holidays annually in Peru,
Bali, Crete and the Lake District. Also
organises house parties and creativity
weekends. Groups are small and
friendly. The holidays are environ-
ment-oriented.*
V

USEFUL CONTACTS

BRITISH UNIVERSITIES ACCOMMODATION CONSORTIUM LTD
University Park
Nottingham
NG7 2RD
Tel 0115 950 4571
Fax 0115 942 2505
Email carole.formon@nottingham.ac.uk

British Universities open their doors for conferences, exhibitions and groups. There are 67 venues throughout England, Scotland, Wales and Northern Ireland. Professional chefs are able to meet the most demanding requirements of conference and exhibition organisers, whether for a large group or a small intimate lunch. Bed and breakfast, self catering and activity/study courses are also available.

FREEWHEELERS
25 Low Friar Street
Newcastle
NE1 5UE
Tel 0191 222 0090
Email freewheelers@freewheelers.co.uk
Website http://www.freewheelers.co.uk/freewheelers/

Tired of spending too much cash just getting there? Sick of seeing 80% of cars carrying just one person? If you want to travel with likeminded people going your way, get to it with Freewheelers lift-share club, for journeys wholly or partly on these routes: Glasgow, Edinburgh, Newcastle, Leeds, Manchester, Sheffield, Nottingham, Birmingham, Bristol, London and Exeter. Lifts to and from the continent are also arranged but are more common in the summer. Full security procedures in place.

> Vegan food must not contain any animal product,
> by-product or derivative

such as:

• **animal-derived additives** — *(see ADDITIVES, page 238)* • **animal milks** — eg cow's, goat's, sheep • **animal milk derivatives** — casein, caseinates, lactates, lactic acid, lactose • **bee products** — bee pollen, beeswax, honey, propolis, royal jelly • **dairy products and by-products** — butter, cheese, whey, yoghurt • **eggs** — eg hen's, quail, duck, ostrich • **egg derivatives** — eg albumen, lecithin, lutein • **items obtained directly from the slaughter of animals** — fish (including anchovies), game and their derivatives (eg meat/fish extracts and stocks), poultry, meat • **marine animal products** — caviar(e), fishmeal, isinglass, marine oils and extracts (eg fish oils, shark oil (squalene or squalane), seal oil, whale oil), roe, seal meat, shellfish, whale meat • **miscellaneous** — carmine/carminic acid, cochineal, crushed snails or insects, shellac, some vitamins (eg D$_3$) and *any carriers, processing aids or release agents (see NOTE, below) containing/comprising substances of animal origin* • **slaughter by-products** — animal fats (eg dripping, lard, suet, tallow), amino acids, aspic, bone, bone meal, fatty acid derivatives, gelatin(e), glycerin(e)/glycerol, oleoic oil, oleostearin, pepsin, proteins (eg elastin, keratin, reticulin), rennet, stearates, stearic acid, stearin(e)

Vegetable, mineral or plant/mineral-derived synthetic forms of the substances above are acceptable, as are microbiologically-fermented substances of plant origin.

NOTE

Carriers — gelatin(e) may be used to carry beta-carotene and D$_2$
Processing aids — lactose is often used to fix flavour in crisps
Release agents — may be used to prevent confectionery and baked goods adhering to manufacturing equipment

ADDITIVES

ANIMAL-DERIVED ADDITIVES

• **E120** cochineal • **E542** edible bone phosphate • **E631** sodium 5'-inosinate • **E901** beeswax • **E904** shellac • **calcium mesoinositol hexaphosphate** • **lactose** • **sperm oil** • **spermaceti**

POSSIBLY ANIMAL-DERIVED

• **E101** riboflavin, lactoflavin, vitamin B$_{12}$ • **E101a** riboflavin 5'-phosphate • **E153** *(believed animal-free version only may be used in food)* carbon black, vegetable carbon • **E161(b)** lutein • **E161(g)** canthaxanthin • **E236** formic acid • **E237** sodium formate • **E238** calcium formate • **E270** lactic acid • **E322** lecithin • **E325** sodium lactate • **E326** potassium lactate • **E327** calcium lactate • **E422** glycerol (glycerine) • **E430** *(believed to be no longer permitted in food)* polyoxyethylene (8) stearate, polyoxyl (8) stearate • **E431** polyoxyethylene (40) stearate, polyoxyl (40) stearate • **E432** polyoxyethylene sorbitan monolaurate, polysorbate 20, tween 20 • **E433** polyoxyethylene sorbitan mono-oleate, polysorbate 80, tween 80 • **E434** polyoxyethylene sorbitan monopalmitate, polysorbate 40, tween 40 • **E435** polyoxyethylene sorbitan monostearate, polysorbate 60, tween 60 • **E436** polyoxyethylene sorbitan tristearate, polysorbate 65, tween 65 • **E470(a)** sodium, potassium and calcium salts of fatty acids • **E470(b)** magnesium salts of fatty acids • **E471** glycerides of fatty acids, glyceryl monostearate, glyceryl distearate • **E472(a)** acetic acid esters of glycerides of fatty acids, acetoglycerides, glycerol esters • **E472(b)** lactic acid esters of glycerides of fatty acids, lactylated glycerides, lactoglycerides • **E472(c)** citric acid esters of glycerides of fatty acids • **E472(d)** — tartaric acid esters of glycerides of fatty acids • **E472(e)** mono and diacetyltartaric acid esters of glycerides of fatty acids **E472(f)** mixed acetic and tartaric acid esters of mono- and di-glycerides of fatty acids • **E473** sucrose esters of fatty acids • **E474** sucroglycerides • **E475** polyglycerol esters of fatty acids • **E476** polyglycerol esters of polycondensed fatty acids of castor oil, polyglycerol polyricinoleate; polyglycerol esters of dimerised fatty acids of soya bean oil • **E477** propylene glycol esters of fatty acids; propane-1,2-diol esters of fatty acids • **E478** lactylated fatty acid esters of glycerol and propane-1,2-diol • **E479(b)** thermally oxidised soya bean oil interacted with mono- and di-glycerides of fatty acids • **E481** sodium stearoyl-2-lactylate • **E482** calcium stearoyl-2-lactylate • **E483** stearyl tartrate • **E491** sorbitan monostearate • **E492** sorbitan tristearate, span 65 • **E493** sorbitan monolaurate, span 20 • **E494** sorbitan

mono-oleate, span 80 • **E495** sorbitan monopalmitate, span 40 •
E570 fatty acids (including myristic, stearic, palmitic and oleic), butyl
stearate • **E572** magnesium salts of fatty acids (including magnesium
stearate); calcium stearate • **E585** ferrous lactate • **E627** guanosine
5'-disodium phosphate, sodium guanylate, disodium guanylate •
E635 sodium 5'-ribonucleotide • **E640** glycine and its sodium salt •
E920 L-cysteine hydrochloride • **E1518** glyceryl mono-, di- and tri-
acetate (triacetin) • **calcium hepatonate • calcium phytate •
diacetin, glyceryl • leucine • monoacetin • oxystearin •** and **any
unspecified flavourings**

GUIDELINES FOR FEEDING & ACCOMMODATING VEGANS

Vegans — of which there an estimated ¼ million in the UK — avoid eating meat, fish, poultry, animal milks, honey and all animal by-products and derivatives. Most go further and use only non-food products which are free of animal ingredients and animal testing.

Abhorrence of the cruel practices inherent in dairy, livestock and poultry farming is probably the single most common reason for the adoption of veganism, but many people are drawn to it for health, ecological, resource and spiritual reasons.

WHAT DO VEGANS EAT?

Vegans eat only plant foods and usually select foods from the following groups on a regular basis:
- *Cereals* — eg rice, wheat (bread, pasta, bulgar, cous cous), barley, millet
- *Pulses* — eg beans, peas, lentils
- *Nuts & seeds*
- *Vegetables*
- *Fruits*

A rapidly expanding range of processed vegan foods — including soya milks, 'cheeses', 'ice cream' and 'yoghurts'; convenience meals; meat substitutes — is available in health/wholefood shops and an increasing number of supermarkets. For a summary of what vegans avoid eating, see **VEGAN FOOD CRITERIA**, page 237.

VEGAN MENU IDEAS

BREAKFAST

Cereal Muesli, porridge oats or some well-known brands — eg Kellogg's Optima, Frosties, Choco Krispies, Common Sense Oat Bran Flakes.

Soya/Rice/Oat/Pea milk Most are suitable for vegans. Sold in health/wholefood shops and supermarkets.

Toast Most breads are vegan. Some brands — especially those sold in health/wholefood shops may contain milk or honey (used to activate the yeast instead of sugar). Some bagels are suitable — eg the New York Bagel Co range.

Margarine Most are not suitable for vegans. All supermarkets sell at least one vegan-friendly brand. All Granose and Vitaquell margarines (available in health/wholefood shops) are vegan.

Jam Most are suitable. Beware of lemon curd which contains egg.

Peanut and other nut butters Most are suitable.

Yeast extracts Most are suitable — eg Marmite.

Other ideas: Vegan sausages, fried mushrooms & green tomatoes, baked beans, scrambled tofu, houmous, fresh fruit salad, freshly sliced tomatoes or tempeh slices.

LUNCH/DINNER

Starter

Melon, stuffed vegetables, tofu or vegetable pâté, soup (beware of stocks containing milk derivatives), dips, salad (with vegan dressing), corn on the cob (with vegan margarine), deep fried vegetables (using vegetable oil), marinated vegetables.

Main Course

Any dish can be 'veganised' — eg spaghetti bolognese, lasagne, pizza, casserole, curry, shepherd's pie, burgers, pies, risotto, flans, quiches.

Vegetables can be presented in a variety of ways.

Soya products — eg tofu, milk and cream — can be used instead of meat, cow's milk and (dairy) cream.

Other suitable processed foods could include: gravy, sauces, pickles, vegan mayonnaise, nut meats, hard and soft 'cheese' and mock meat slices.

SNACKS

Fresh fruit; dried fruit; nuts; vegetable 'fingers' (eg carrots or courgettes) with dips, crackers, crisps, oatcakes, crispbreads (eg Ryvitas); biscuits; sandwiches or rolls with a variety of fillings; vegan sausage rolls, somosas or spring rolls.

BEVERAGES

Most mineral waters, fruit juices and fizzy drinks are vegan — but some (orange-coloured) may contain gelatine, which won't appear on the ingredients.

Most readily-available alcoholic drinks are *not* suitable for vegans. Beers and wines are predominantly clarified with isinglass.

Coffee and tea are animal-free and may be served with or without non-dairy milk. Coffee substitutes are popular — eg Barleycup or Caro. Some vegans prefer herbal tea instead of the ordinary cuppa.

AND LASTLY, A FEW IMPORTANT POINTS . . .

Ensure any processed/packaged foods are vegan. If in doubt, consult the *Animal-Free Shopper (see opposite)* or ring the manufacturer.

• Make sure pastries, sauces and gravies do not contain animal fats or margarines contain milk products
• Ensure non-vegans foods are not fried in the same oil as vegan food
• Quorn contains egg and is therefore not acceptable
• Agar agar or Gelozone can be used instead of gelatine to make jellies and moulds
• Vegans *usually* prefer conservatively cooked or raw vegetables, and wholemeal (rather than white) pasta or breads
• HP Baked Beans contain skimmed milk powder
• Sharwood's Puppadums contain shellac (not on the ingredients listing)
• Dried banana chips may have been dipped in honey
• Vitamin D is commonly D_3 (from lanolin) rather than the vegan D_2
• Flavourings may be held in an animal-derived carrier — eg lactose
• Additives and E numbers may not be vegan
• Do not use the same utensils for serving vegan and non-vegan food
• Do not call out 'Who's the vegan?' in a loud voice!
• *Accommodation only:* Many vegans will expect to be provided with non-wool blankets, quilts and pillows without feathers, and toiletries (eg soap) which do not contain animal ingredients *and* have not been animal-tested

Don't forget that by being able to cater for vegans you will automatically be catering for vegetarians and the dairy intolerant!

RESOURCES

The Animal-Free Shopper

The *Animal-Free Shopper* is an indispensable shopping guide listing vegan foods, drink (including alcohol), toiletries, household products and so on. Copies are available directly from the Vegan Society for £5.90 (p&p incl).

Vegan Catering

Further information on catering for vegans, including recipes, can be found in *Vegan Catering — an Information Pack for Caterers*. Available from the Vegan Society for £1.95 (p&p incl).

Vegan Cookbooks

For details of vegan cookbooks ring *01424 427393* and ask for a merchandise catalogue.

Produced by

THE
Vegan
SOCIETY

Donald Watson House
7 Battle Road
St Leonards-on-Sea
East Sussex
TN37 7AA

Tel 01424 427393
Fax 01424 717064
e-mail info@vegansociety.com.

INDEX

Red Triangle Cafe *Lancs* 75
Regency Guest House *Norfolk* 110
Rhu Mhor Guest House
 Inverness-Shire 195
Richmond Harvest *Surrey* 141
Riverside Vegetaria, The *Surrey* 141
Robinson, Mr & Mrs
 Northumberland 113
Rogan's Vegetarian Restaurant
 W Midlands 148
Rookery Hall Hotel & Restaurant
 Cheshire 16
Rookery Nook *Dorset* 47
Room With a View *Cumbria* 29
Roots Vegetarian Cafe *Co Kerry* 217
Rosa Villa Guest House *Kent* 68
Rose Cottage *Norfolk* 110
Rosedale B&B *E Yorks* 56
Rossan, The *Kirkcudbrightshire* 198
Roti Restaurant *W Yorks* 156
Roti Roti *London SE24* 91
Round Meadow Barn *Derbys* 34
Rowan House *Warks* 144
Rowan Tree, The *Cumbria* 31
Rowland House *E Sussex* 51
Royal Hotel *N Yorks* 117
Royce Rolls Wholefood *Avon* 12
Roydon Hall *Kent* 229
Royd Well *W Yorks* 153
Rudstone Walk Country Hotel &
 Cottages *E Yorks* 55
Rufford Arms Hotel *Lancs* 73
Russell Hotel, The *Kent* 69
Rye Wholefoods *London EC1* 83
Ryton Organic Gardnes *Warks* 145

Sabras *London NW10* 90
Saffron Vegetarian Bistro *Hants* 62
St Andrews Hotel *Notts* 124
St Ann's Well Cafe *Worcs* 160
St Antoine Guest House *Dorset* 45
St Columba Hotel *Argyllshire* 182
St Judes Guest House *Cornwall* 20
St Martins Tea Rooms *W Sussex* 150

St William's Restaurant *N Yorks* 123
Salad Centre *Dorset* 48
Salamander Restaurant *Notts* 125
Salisbury Healthfoods *Wilts* 159
Sally Lunn's Refreshment House *Avon* 9
Salts Diner *W Yorks* 156
Sanctuary, The *Devon* 38
Sanctuary Cafe *E Sussex* 54
Sandpiper Vegetarian Hotel, The
 Devon 40
San Remo Hotel *Dorset* 45
Sansbury Place Vegetarian Guest House
 N Yorks 118
Santor Maa's Bhel Poori House
 Surrey 141
Saru B&B *Co Sligo* 219
Scaitcliffe Hall *Lancs* 73
Scoffs Wholefood Cafe *Avon* 10
Screes Hotel, The *Cumbria* 29
Seacliffe Hotel *N Yorks* 119
Seagreen Restaurant & Bookshop
 Highlands 195
Seapoint *Somerset* 134
Seashells Hotel *Dorset* 47
Seasons of Lewes *E Sussex* 54
Seasons Restaurant *W Sussex* 150
Seaward Guest House *IOW* 61
Seawind's Guest House *E Yorks* 56
Selbourne Hotel *N Yorks* 118
Serendipity *Avon* 7
Shahanshah Vegetarian Restaurant &
 Indian Sweets *Middlesex* 108
Shahee Belpoori *London SW16* 93
Shambhala Healing Centre
 Somerset 229
Shaw Hill Hotel, Golf & Country Club
 Lancs 71
Shiplake Mountain Hostel *Co Cork* 211
Silverdale, The *E Sussex* 52
Six St Mary's Place Guesthouse
 Edinburgh 186
Skylight Cafe *Warks* 145
Smeare Dubha *Co Kerry* 217
Smollensky's American Bar & Restaurant

THE ANIMAL-FREE SHOPPER

fourth edition
ONLY £4.95

A handy shopping guide
to buying products which are
free of animal ingredients and
involve no animal testing.

Thousands of products listed und
food and drink
toiletries & cosmetics
remedies & supplements
baby & infant care
footwear & clothing
home & office
animal care
garden & leisure

user-friendly
guidance on additives
background information
useful contacts
mail order addresses

INDISPENSABLE!

for your copy
**PHONE THE VEGAN SOCIETY
CREDIT CARD HOTLINE
01424 427393**

or send a cheque/postal order for £5.90 (p&p incl),
payable to 'The Vegan Society', to:

Dept TGP
Donald Watson House
7 Battle Road
St Leonards-on-Sea
East Sussex TN37 7AA

A selection of resources from

THE Vegan SOCIETY

GENERAL

Information Pack
List of Information Sheets/
  Booklets
List of Trade Mark users
Merchandise catalogue
The Vegan magazine
  (subscription £7.80)
The Animal-Free Shopper (£5.90)
Vegan Nutrition (£10.45)

FOR SCHOOLS

Teachers Pack
Vegan Catering booklet

FOR BUSINESSES

Trade Mark Pack
Media Pack
Retail Trade List
Vegan Catering booklet (£1.95)
Vegans Welcome Sticker (£2.20)

FOR HEALTHCARE PROFESSIONALS

Healthcare Information Pack
Vegan Nutrition
Pregnancy & Childcare Pack

All items are free except where indicated ( ). All prices include p&p.

THE Vegan SOCIETY

Dept TG
Donald Watson House
Battle Road
St Leonards-on-Sea
East Sussex TN37 7AA
Tel 01424 427393

THE Vegan SOCIETY

MEMBERSHIP APPLICATION

Promoting ways of living which avoid the use of animal products – for the benefit of people, animals and the environment

☐ Individual £17 ☐ Family/Joint** £23
☐ Unwaged Individual £11 ☐ Unwaged Family/Joint** £15
☐ Junior (under 18) £9 ☐ Life £275

Eire & overseas: all applicants must add £5

Please tick as appropriate:

☐ I adhere to a vegan diet and wish to become a Vegan Society member. I undertake to abide by the Society's *Memorandum amd Articles of Association**

☐ Although not a vegan I support the Society's work and wish to become a supporter member

Membership subscription	£_____
Memo & Arts (£2)	£_____
Donation	£_____
TOTAL	£_____

☐ I enclose a cheque/PO payable to 'The Vegan Society' *(Eire & overseas: payment must be made by sterling International Money Order or sterling cheque drawn on a British bank)*

☐ I would like to pay by standing order. Please send me a form

☐ I am a UK taxpayer and would like to help the Society claim the income tax I have paid by sending me a Deed of Covenant form

☐ Please debit my *(delete not applicable)* Visa/Mastercard/Access/Eurocard/Switch/Visa Delta/Connect card number

☐☐☐☐☐☐☐☐☐☐☐☐☐☐☐☐☐☐☐☐☐☐☐

Name on card _____

Signature _____

Start date ☐☐☐☐   Expiry date ☐☐☐☐

Today's date ☐☐☐☐   Switch issue no. ☐☐

Name _____

Address _____

_____

_____

Post code _____ Tel _____

Skills/Profession _____

_____

Return to: Administration Officer (Membership), The Vegan Society, Dept TGM Donald Watson House, 7 Battle Road, St Leonards-on-Sea, East Sussex TN37 7AA, UK

Tel 01424 427393 Fax 01424 717064

*   £2 – or may be viewed at the Society's office

** All applicants must reside at the same address – please supply names on separate sheet

Membership includes The Vegan *magazine. This form may be photocopied. Please send both parts.*

Vegan Society Founder, Donald Watson, reflecting in 1944–45 on the difficulties facing vegan travellers

There were few vegetarian guest-houses and fewer still adept at providing meals for vegans.

Donald Watson commemorating his 87th birthday by climbing Fleetworth Pike in 1997